THE
COURAGE
TO BE TRUE

The Courage To Be True

First Edition
© Brian Smyth
ISBN: 978-1-7392187-6-8

To discover more about Brian Smyth, visit www.maybe.ie

Publishing information
Design & publishing services provided by JM Agency

www.jm.agency
Kerry, Ireland

THE
COURAGE
TO BE TRUE

A story of one manager's journey to find
a meaningful life...

BRIAN SMYTH

Dedication

In memory of my nephew and friend, Gerard Hayes

This book is dedicated to the memory of my nephew and friend, Gerard Hayes, who believed he could no longer live with the injustice in the world and with his own inability to do much about it. Because of that, he gave his life, but, as he said, he died "happy with the knowledge that some day a better way of life will be brought about for everyone."

(Why?)

"Most of us get by through protecting ourselves from the hardness and cruelty of our world. But this 'protection' is bought at the cost of a certain loss of feeling in the face of the hurt and pain that we inflict on each other in this world.

There are only a very few people who fail to build up the defences that we call necessary; such people are vulnerable to all the pain and all the suffering that an unloving world can inflict on people – they suffer the most.....the only response that will do justice to the gift of God to us that is Gerard is that I will never deny the rightness of his being so sensitive, so vulnerable so truly human.

I want to grow in being all the things he was and for which he paid such a cost. And I want to spend my life trying to make the world whose humanity he knew so well a little more human, a little less cruel, a more suitable place for those who want to love. This is the only way to do him justice."

—Brendan Lovett

The book is my small attempt to do justice to Gerard and to live up to his call to us to make this world a more tolerable and loving place for everyone.

Contents

Preface

Worth Reading?

"I'm glad you asked that question," as politicians say in interviews.

The answer is: It depends!

If you think that everything is fine in the world as it is, including the world of work, then the answer is No! This book will *not* be worth reading. Better things to be done with your time including your reading time.

But, even if, like me, you *don't* believe that everything is hunky dory in the world, you still won't get much from this book if you believe things are, while not great, 'as good as they get'. If this is just how things are, and if they are not going to get much better, then, again, this book will not be worth your while reading.

Still here? Ah good. Let's take it you don't belong or want to belong to either of those clubs. I don't either.

Let's join the ranks of those who are not at all happy with how things are in the world and who want something better.

But, maybe *you* are not sure, not fully sure.

Maybe it is just an inkling you have that, yes, a much better world and way of working is both badly needed and possible but not much more than that.

Maybe you have tried or experienced some things that did not work or didn't work as well as you had hoped.

Maybe this is how you are feeling and you feel tempted to forget those aspirations and dreams and just put your head down and get on with things.

If that is so, then this book is here to grab you and shake you and ask you to pay attention to what you are feeling deep down. The book is imploring you to, with Rumi, 'not to go back to sleep'. Trust those feelings and lovely hopes and dreams. We need you.

We need you to try and take risks and to do things, new things. If the world was replete with innumerable examples of very different kinds of organisations, wildly human and exciting ones, we wouldn't need you. But it's not and we do.

A 'True' Story

So here we are, the two of us, faced with the choice of roads and we look with interest and some trepidation at the one less travelled. Maybe you are still making up your mind and have not chosen one of those roads...yet.

Ok. Well, you have in your hands something that will *help* you to choose.

No, it is not a series of copper-fastened, well-chosen and cleverly tailored and presented arguments based on carefully selected case studies. It is a story, but it is a true story. Not true in the sense that all these things actually happened to our man, Mike, but true in that they did happen in different bits and pieces to many 'Mikes' that I have met and worked with over the years.

The book, your companion down the road less travelled, is not an academic collection of theories, but rather a description of what I saw happen and sometimes helped to make happen. So it is true. It is true in that the stories are the fruit of my own experience, from working in and for many different organisations in different parts of the world. The story is also true, I believe, because everything that happens in Mike's story and that works for Mike and his team does so because it is based fundamentally on the truth of the human, on how I believe people really are. And I, as the story creator, am being true because it is how I try to work and live. Convinced? I hope so.

It is being told as a story because through the story you can get a *feel* for the real personal and emotional challenges involved in choosing the new way of leading, a truly trusting way of leading, a truly new road.

Some things can only be learned by doing, such as learning to swim or ride a bicycle. If we depended on words, theories and explanations alone, lots of people would fall off bicycles or drown. The story is intended to ensure that what is being described and proposed makes sense in the real world with real people. The intention is that you will not only know what you should do, but get a real *feel* for what doing it involves.

Questions:

For this reason, every chapter concludes with questions which are intended to be a message, an invitation, a challenge to you to jump in, take a risk and trust in some aspect of how you manage your people, area or organisation. 'Most of our battle is asking the right questions,' as Donna Goddard put it.

The questions are not intended to be checks on your understanding but, rather, aids to your understanding. They are also invitations for you to explore the implications of your understanding, on your life and work.

When reading a book of this kind, I ask myself two questions:

- What is my understanding of what was said?
- What implications does this have for my life and for what I do?

I hope you find the questions useful for your own reflection on what was covered in the chapter.

But why is this all this so Important or worth going after?

Another good question! But I thought we had answered that. Maybe not. Let's see.

We agree, I think, that you and I, and billions of other human beings, need to enjoy much richer lives.

Many of these hungry-for-life people spend most of their lives at work in different kinds of organisations. Wouldn't it be great if we found the keys that would help enable them to live much richer lives in their work situations or environments?

I wonder if, like me, you ever look at the worried, troubled faces of people on their way to work in the mornings! Ok, it is early morning so maybe it is to be expected.

If I meet a local farmer on my early morning walk I invariably get a big, energetic and enthusiastic wave. No head down on the way to face an ordeal, but someone who can't wait to get going and get big things done. Sometimes we chat for a few minutes, even if I can see that he is anxious to get going, and not to make some official start-time, but to get going on all the important things he wants to do.

I believe work for all of us can be very different, and that it is very important to make it different. I believe it is important for the millions of people themselves, who work in and belong to organisations. Just think of the change we could make to people's lives if we were able to transform the organisations they work for!

And think of the change this would make to society overall if it were made up of people who enjoy what they do instead of resenting it as an interference in their lives, or as a chore they have to go through to earn a living, to 'put bread on the table'.

Our world is not just a mass of individuals however. Individuals, people, belong to and are shaped and identified by organisations of all kinds - companies, clubs, societies, parties, churches and so on,

In order to improve the lives of people at work and in *organisations*, we need to change our organisations. It is this that you are being invited to support and help bring about; a better way to manage and lead our organisations, whatever they are. If together we can improve and transform, organisations the impact it will have on our world will be extraordinary.

In this book, I show how managers and everyone in the workplace can remain faithful to their values and to what is of real importance to them as people in and through their work. How you can do great things in work, not only while being really *yourself* but *by* being really yourself, your true self. If we can do that, work will change for everyone and return to being something enjoyable and fulfilling for everyone. Society will change moreover, as the *raison d'etre* for business in general and for companies in particular changes.

Is this, then, only for Companies and Work? For Business?

No! The kind of shift that needs to be made in how we relate to and manage our people, and our organisations, is not one that is confined to work or even to organisations. It is an essential and core part of *all* of life. When we listen to the great pioneers of religious or spiritual traditions, the message is the same - trust, let go, live and encourage life; the truth will make you free.

What they said, however, is not seen as relevant for vast segments of our lives. We don't see their relevance to how we manage and relate to people in work environments and organisations. We understand that these spiritual and moral values are important, but we also feel that large sections of our society can do fine without adhering to these 'rules for life'. We think we can play by different rules and dance to a different tune. It's like the trick question often put to managers: "Which would you prefer – to be successful or to be happy?" No need to answer this. You will find it in the book.

This book conveys how relevant being truly human is to work and organisations. It also illustrates how the lessons learned from working and living in this way apply to all of our lives. How we can only be really successful if we are true to life and to ourselves. Ready to sign up?

But using the Business World?

Yes. You may not be alone in raising eyebrows at my choice of organisations, specifically business organisations and companies as the way to 'change the world'! Are these not strange bedfellows? Is it not the case, as many understandably claim, that things are the way they are and as bad as they are *because* of companies. Neo-liberal capitalism destroying communities and countries, profits always put before people, unprecedented scales of inequality reached, and our precious world being seen and treated as a mere company resources irrespective of how the very existence of life is in jeopardy. Let's not forget moreover, how wars and conflicts of all kinds are seen as good…good for business. Need I continue?

Yes, it would seem that this would be the last place you would travel to locate a different and better world. Maybe it is a road that should never be travelled. I am frequently challenged on this, on why I spend my time working with the 'enemy', even getting paid by them to help them become better, better at doing more damage! Yes, I know the story well and I *understand* it. And just because I say I understand it, does not mean I have irrefutable answers to the challenge.

My answer is that we are always going to have commerce in the world, and we are always going to have organisations. And if we are going to survive, not to mention thrive, we need to identify healthy, human and honest ways of designing good commercial organisations - 'companies' included. That is what I am about, and that is what this book is about even if it does seem we like are starting from very far back. Far back, maybe so, but I think we can do a lot right now to bring about radically changed and improved companies and business organisations. I believe we can do it, and if we succeed it will go a long way to achieving that very different world. I believe this is a good way to achieve that kind of world. I believe it can work because it will not be reliant on any kind of radical indoctrination of people on a global scale. It can and will happen through the changes of thinking, attitudes, and relationships that people live and experience in their daily lives at work and in organisations. This is my hope: That if we change and enrich the experience of people during eight hours of work, every day, wherever they spend it, this is bound to make an enormous difference to the quality of their lives and to the society of which they are a part.

So, we will learn from Business Organisations from Companies?

Yes we will. Sure, there are many things that are wrong and need to change around business organisations and companies; many things.

But companies and organisations also enjoy unique insights into many things that are critical for a healthy society and world.

We know this because they are very successful in many ways. They have to be doing some things right, things that we can learn from.

Leadership is one of them. I'm not saying that this is handled perfectly in companies, which is one of the main reasons why I have written this book. But one of the reasons why the world of companies is so successful is down to the kind of leadership they practise and enjoy. Here is one area where society can learn from the world of business.

Quite frankly no company would survive for any length of time was it to operate along the lines of the so-called democratic systems followed in most parts of the world, which use voting as a way to reach decisions. Need I give examples of the leaders this disastrous system repeatedly throws up and expects us to heed and follow? Or do we really think that a system or government that most frequently operates with close to 50% of the people against it will work? Would it work for a sports team? To vote on who plays and who doesn't? Or a hospital or orchestra? That we continue to follow this dysfunctional system is down to the illusion of what democracy really means. We equate it with the individual voting system. The choice we need to make is not whether we want to be democratic or autocratic. It is about coming up with and operating a much richer version, in every sense, of what real democracy looks like and how it should operate. By showing how well these would and do work in organisations and companies, the book provides models for how we can handle all kinds of situations in the world at large. You will see and hear how delightfully easy and enormously beneficial - indeed essential - listening to and engaging with people is and so you will see how equally easily and well this can work in society in general.

But these are only thoughts, ideas. Let's see what happens in the real world of Mike and if any of this is true and how it might work. Ok? We can talk afterwards.

Brian Smyth

Chapter 1
The Loneliness of the
Long-distance Commuter

Ever ask: Is this it? All there is? What's it all for?

The traffic was light as Mike drove to work, but his thoughts and mood were anything but light.

"Why am I feeling like this?" he asked. "Everything is going quite well in my life at the moment."

But it was as if he had a foreboding that something bad was going to happen, or was already happening, even if he did not know exactly what it was. Maybe it was because he had mentioned to Joan that he would be late home from work as he had a conference call with his corporate boss that evening? Not that Joan was upset or even surprised. They had had a conversation over breakfast. Yes, he knew that she had problems with the time and attention he was giving to his job and he knew it was not because she was unhappy about her part in looking after the home and family matters. It was a bit more than that.

"You know I'm not complaining," she had said, "it's just that I would like the children to see you more."

"But I do see a lot of them," he replied. "I'm early, or relatively early, most evenings."

"I know that," said Joan, "but sometimes I feel you're not really here. I feel your mind is elsewhere, even though I know you make a big effort to pay attention to us and I know you worry about us and care for us all."

Joan didn't mind taking care of the house and looking after most of the children's needs and issues. She had had this on-going conversation with herself on many occasions.

"It's not that, and I'm not ungrateful for all we have and enjoy thanks to Mike and to his hard work and achievements. I know the pressures that are on him that demand so much of his time and attention. But it's more his attention than his time that worries me. He works hard to spend time with us all, but it can feel that he's not always really with us. We can all feel we're coming second to work and it can be so hard to argue with that. I'm not even sure I know myself what I want or what a way out of this would mean. Is it a golden cage we're all in? Maybe it's as much about me and how I feel!"

What more could one want?

Mike knew much of what Joan said was true. He appreciated all she did and the sacrifice she made by giving up on her own career to be with the children at this critical time. But it was hard to stop worrying about things at work. He knew that Joan realised he was not doing it all for himself. He knew she appreciated their comfortable home, the holidays, the lifestyle, and the security his good job guaranteed them all. Was that not what everybody aspired to – a family, and a job to support that family and give them all a good life and lifestyle? Holding on to that job was essential.

> "I have nothing to say of my working life, only that a tie is a noose, and inverted though it is, it will hang a man nonetheless if he's not careful."
>
> **Yann Martel**

Nothing could be taken for granted. That cosy situation could all come crashing down at any moment as had happened for so many others and it could happen again. Few people were aware of his insecurity because of the tension with his bosses, even if some of that was his own doing. Joan knew of the tension and she understood Mike and why that tension existed. But she was not aware

> "Life is either a daring adventure or nothing."
>
> **Hellen Keller**

of the full implications of this for her and for all of them. She thought it was just another corporate or company spat that would eventually be resolved with some compromise. It had happened before.

That was not how Mike saw it, but he chose not to share all that was on his mind with Joan or anyone else. He had an unclear inkling that this time it was different and that there were some things that would not get resolved – things that he was not prepared to sweep under the carpet. He felt he owed more to the people in the company, to the community and to himself. But then, what about Joan and the children? Would they have to be sacrificed for the sake of his so-called principles? Having to move house, change schools, lose friends, and some of their existing luxuries. Is that what Joan wanted?

Not as it seems on the surface

Joan was right. She carried an unfair portion of responsibility in managing the home, not that she ever complained. She was doing some part-time teaching, filling in for absent teachers which helped her sense of value and dignity. She had her own friends, and he did his best to ensure she had time to spend with them.

"I'm not sure what more I can do," he had told her over breakfast. "It is just that there are always problems and challenges to tackle and it's not easy to just walk away from them. I have to keep on top of things, and that inevitably brings its pressures. Right now, without getting into it, we have a major problem with an important customer, some major internal problems of our own with this new Quantum Logistic System (QLS) which never ceases to present difficulties. I'm sure you are sick hearing of that. And, if that were not enough, I have demands and interference from my boss, Martha, who, as you know, is not happy with my approach. I can't even imagine what her family are saying to *her* about her time!" he said laughing. "I might find out when she calls this evening."

Joan had met Martha a few times on corporate visits. They had chatted over dinners about their respective situations and she was never sure whether Martha pitied her for her lower level career or envied her ability to spend more time with her family and friends. But was all this and the breakfast conversation with Joan the real reason Mike was not feeling good?

"Of course, she's right," he thought "I know I give a lot of time and attention to work. And much seems to fall on Joan's shoulders at home. Somehow, she seems to manage all this and still do a good job.

"If Heather can manage it, why can't you?" Joan had asked.

Mike wanted to promote Heather to Customer Relations Director after her second maternity leave absence, and a long absence for an operation to her foot. While there seemed to be general acceptance of the move from his own team thanks to Teresa, the HR manager, his proposal had met with opposition from Martha and corporate management.

He knew this had not gone away. He also knew that Joan was right. Why was he so indispensable, required every day for eight or ten hours when others, like Heather, could take time off and the show went on as usual? Deep down he knew that she was right about the children too. Why could he not do like Heather had done and give more time to the three children – Harry his 10-year-old son, Rose his 7-year- old daughter and Alex the 14-months-old baby? Yes, they had a very comfortable life and maybe enjoyed more privileges than others, but nothing seemed to make up for real time and presence.

He knew enough very well-off families where the children grew up resentful around their parents, despite their lavish lifestyle. They had wanted more than lifestyle. And that was why he made a big effort to spend time at home and with the children. He knew that Teresa would identify with this. She had two teenage children who seemed to be a constant source of disappointment to her.

Why only me?

Mike's Lexus was on autopilot, like himself. A roadworks traffic light woke him up to where he was on his daily trip. But that awareness did not last long. Joan's words rang in his ears as the light changed to green.

"It's just that everyone else can seem to get the job done and still find time for other things," she said. "Frank has his football team, and we all know how important *that* is and the attention he gives it. (Mike's logistics manager Frank had bravely taken on a men's senior football team that had not won anything for a long time and had been giving it enormous time and attention, with very poor results.) "Bernard has lots of time for his community work which he obviously sees as very important too.

Teresa copes now but only just. Tom works on his golf all the time and you just seem to work on your work. It's as if your work is your hobby as well. It's your life, Mike, apart from us, to be fair."

He knew what she meant. She was not right about Tom, who worried him precisely because of the amount of time and effort he put into everything, without ever seeming to get things done. But he thought about what she said. It all made sense, but he wondered if there might be more to his overall discomfort and anxiety.

Was it that everyone seemed to want more from him? Despite the sacrifices he made for the company, why did nobody seem happy or appreciative? Why did he care so much, taking lots of risks for his

> "To laugh often and much; to win the respect of intelligent people and the affection of children; to earn the appreciation of honest critics and endure the betrayal of false friends; to appreciate beauty, to find the best in others; to leave the world a bit better, whether by a healthy child, a garden patch or a redeemed social condition; to know even one life has breathed easier because you have lived. This is to have succeeded."
>
> **Ralph Waldo Emerson**

people, working hard to protect their jobs and livelihoods but never feel appreciated? People seemed only half engaged and yet what he did, was for *them*! Why, then were they not more concerned and interested and engaged?

Less than a year ago Mike was part of the plan to transfer business to his company from another division that was being closed. He felt it was justified because *he* won out and the other chief executive and company lost out because they were not competitive or good enough. But he knew that those tables could be turned any time and plans could be hatched quietly behind his back to plot the downgrading and demise of his own company, especially in view of the relationship with Martha, his boss, and her boss Brad.

Where would his loyalties lie then – with the corporation and a possible move to another division, or, with his own company and his own people and a possible move to another company and a different life? Like Terry, his Sales and Marketing manager, might do any time soon. He felt that Terry just did not share Mike's loyalty to the company. Terry was about himself, but he was a real achiever. Mike did not think like this and felt a responsibility to the company and to the people.

Not the only one lost it seems

Not that many or any of the workforce appeared to appreciate the risks Mike took, and the efforts he made, he thought to himself, reflecting on his old nagging feeling. It was not that he expected Christmas or "thank you" cards. He expected no messages of gratitude but just that people would cooperate and understand when changes and improvements needed to be made. Everything seemed to be a problem.

People seemed to take everything for granted. "Management will solve it." was the attitude. And, when they did, people were rarely happy with the outcome. A pending difficulty supplying product to one key customer was an example and he dreaded the inevitable haggling about overtime, flexibility and conditions that this would entail.

"They just don't understand," he thought.

But something more was wrong. People were just not happy at work. He could see it on their faces, in their demeanour as they seemed to drag themselves to work. He saw it on their faces at the various town hall meetings like the one he had held the previous week in the canteen. And then there were rumblings about some kind of Staff Committee being formed and meeting regularly. Despite his efforts to be honest and frank with people about the real challenges they faced, he felt they did not believe a word he said. When he invited questions, the very few he got were about whether there would be a bonus this year, the sports and social club and questions about where the company stood on a local issue from a community representative. The rest just sat there looking surly and disinterested. Few on his own senior team could understand him when he spoke about this.

"What do you expect, Mike," they would reply, "work is work and people are the same the world over."

But he did not buy this and could not accept that it had to be like this. He could not explain why he felt this so strongly. People everywhere just did not seem happy... or as happy as they might be.

The Beatles song *Eleanor Rigby* came on the radio as he drove.

Ah, look at all the lonely people
Ah, look at all the lonely people
Eleanor Rigby picks up the rice in the
church where a wedding has been,
Lives in a dream
Waits at the window, wearing the face
that she keeps in a jar by the door
Who is it for?

All the lonely people
Where do they all come from?
All the lonely people
Where do they all belong?

Father McKenzie writing the words
of a sermon that no one will hear
No one comes near.
Look at him working, darning his socks
in the night when there's nobody there
What does he care?

Yes, that was it. A lot of lonely people. Where do they all belong? Certainly not at work, it seemed. And he himself felt like Father McKenzie – no one hearing him. And why should he take on this problem? He was trying to run a business, not change the world. Or was he? Was that not in fact what drove him and what brought many of the problems on to his table or on to his head? Was that what Joan meant by having no other hobby?

A great team and a mixed lot

Even his own team failed to hear him. This did not make things easy either. Teresa, his Human Resources manager, did at least understand his frustration despite her own issues. Her husband had left her two years earlier and they had subsequently been divorced. She had been single since with two teenage children and things were not easy for her. Everyone wished she would meet someone new, and everyone was surprised she had not. She was a very attractive woman, and everyone liked her.

Frank the head of logistics did have some interest when his mind and heart were not on his football team. Bernard in the quality department was also interested, even if he and Frank reported directly to other heads of functions, and seemed to understand what Mike said and was after. Others did not. Terry, his Sales and Marketing executive had little interest or time for such discussions and at times did not seem all that interested in the company. Mike again wondered how long he would stay.

> "It's a funny thing about life; if you refuse to accept anything but the best, you very often get it."
>
> **Somerset Maugham**

Sally, his Head of Finance, just wanted a steady ship with minimal risks. Natalie, the Head of Purchasing did not seem to care either way and Tom, the operations manager, was focused exclusively on getting the job done, whatever that involved - along with his golf.

Not that the job ever really got done. It seemed that there were always problems that kept recurring. Like the one with the Quantum Logistic System, a crucial area that had successfully resisted all efforts to work as it should.

Tony in the engineering department cared, but only that everything was done right. He was quite intolerant of sloppiness or inconsistency, whether that came from his own engineers, other workers, or from members of his own peer group – like Terry for example – with whom there always seemed to be problems. If *he* was unhappy, he knew Tony was even more unhappy. Unhappy with the "flawed" people around him and unhappy with himself. This caused much tension and Mike felt things could snap any time.

And why do I think I am right about my version of life or people? This was a conversation he had had on several occasions with Heather. She had graduated in philosophy and very much retained her interest in philosophy, psychology, and mythology as well as in religion. She and Mike had many enjoyable conversations around Mike's beliefs and values.

"I'm not saying you're an idealist, Mike, but I'm questioning the basis for your infinite belief in the goodness of people," she often joked with him.

Well fed, safe and looked after lion

Well paid, secure and comfortable manager

But everyone is different, aren't they?

"I can't argue this with you, Heather, and you're much more knowledgeable about this than I am. Nor am I saying that people are naturally or innately good. What I'm saying and what I believe is that there is a basic goodness and hunger for life and full living in everybody and that goodness is there to be developed and put to good use. I think that people need meaning in their lives, and hunger for more meaningful lives."

"I agree with that, Mike, but people are different, and it can be a mistake – and a disappointment – to expect too much from them. Apart from original sin, Darwin, Freud, Jung, Nietzsche and others might just question some of your ideas and hopes," she laughed.

"I understand what you say, Heather, and I have no intention of lining up the witnesses for the defence on my side. Let's see what we can do in practice, and you can keep me sensible and sane in the process. And, you're right. I have a strong belief that what I want is achievable and I hope I don't end up disappointed, as you say."

> "The true rebel is motivated by outrage against the diminishing of human life"
>
> **Albert Camus**

A tale of two lives

What a mess. A bit like *A Tale of Two Cities*, it was the best of jobs and the worst of jobs. Maybe a strange thing for the general manager of a vibrant company to say. Maybe a bit ungrateful too. Yes, he had worked hard and earned his various promotions, but he also got some good breaks along the way.

A lot to be thankful for – financial security, a good lifestyle, a rich mix of challenges and opportunities, success in many different hues, considerable influence in and out of work and a long and rich career if he wanted it. Yes, if not the best of jobs, then, a pretty good one. All great but not enough.

There was the shadow side, the other side of the coin. The ongoing, constant struggle to make things happen, the never-ending and never successful effort to really get on top of things, the conflict with head-quarters, the underlying gnawing sense of unresolved tension between his family life and his professional life and all the "lonely people" including himself all hung like dark clouds casting long, unending shadows over everything else.

He wondered if other CEOs and managers felt like him. He often tried to observe them at conferences and gatherings, but they all seemed content. He tried to subtly sound out some of them at times but got no response. They seemed puzzled at what he was trying to say.

"Could it be" he asked himself, "that there must be more than this? Could it be that all this, good as it is, is not enough, not enough to meet the dreams I had as a child and to live up to the desire to make a real difference that I had in college? Is this what Harry, my son, is dreaming of? To end up like me? Or is this why Rose is going to school?

If they asked him if he was fulfilling or realising his dreams, what would he say? Would he tell them that there is little room for dreams in the real world of work and families and responsibilities and business demands? Again, he returned to his question – "what's wrong with this? Nothing! Is it just about me, he asked? He looked around him at people making their way to work. They definitely did not look very happy. Lonely people. Where do they all belong? Where are their hearts?

"Why should they be like this?", he asked himself again. "Are they not pleased and grateful to have a job, and a good job at that? Or maybe having a job and even a good job is not enough for them anymore either, or no more than my job and my success are good enough for me" he pondered. "Is it that they feel they are leaving their real lives to spend time at work? That they are sacrificing their lives for work, for a salary? Why should that bother me? That's not my responsibility. It's my responsibility to manage the business so that they have jobs and can support their families.

And this I do, and do well, not that anybody appreciates that too much. And what about the sacrifices I am making? The ones that Joan talks about? And why worry about all this? It's not as if there is anything I can do about it. I have my responsibilities to Joan, to my family, to the company and to the workers. I cannot walk or run away from them. Nor do I want to. Maybe I am the one being selfish, absorbed in my own world. Can I just settle down and accept things and live a normal life, like so many others do."

Around and around it went in his head as it had done for a long time. He arrived, not at any answers but at the company car park.

Questions for reflection and action

1. Have you ever felt, or do you often feel, somewhat, like Mike?
2. Do you agree with what Heather said to him?
3. Do you have any ideas on what he should do? Continue his search? ... or be "realistic" and settle for what he has?
4. Which of his various issues do you most identify with?
5. What should Joan do... if anything?
6. Is there anything you should do ... or think about, having been with Mike on his drive to work?
7. Do you recognise some of those on Mike's team? Are you one of them?

Chapter 2
A Groundhog Day with Some Differences

A manager who is a problem-solver will have work and problems for life

He shook himself out of his mood and focused on what his day would bring. As always, it would bring lots of problems. He would hear very quickly about these at the 10 o'clock team meeting. He already knew what some of these would be – ever-increasing demands from customers and corresponding problems meeting them, and another update on the Quantum Logistics System He imagined the battles that would ensue and the pressures Tom, his operations manager, would be under. As always, Tom was in the eye of the storm, and may even enjoy being there.

He was still mulling over all of this as he arrived. He saw people with their heads down, making their way into work. A lot of lonely people. He shook himself out of this troubled mindset and geared himself for the tasks on his daily "to do" list.

He asked Anne at reception, how she was and was on the point of asking her how she really was, but stopped himself. Anne, of course, was "great thanks" as always. "Maybe it is just about me", he thought again as he trudged up the stairway to his office. "Maybe everything is fine, and this is how life is ... "as good as it gets" as they say". Maybe I should just put aside those feelings and get on with things like everyone else. None of the other general managers I know seem to be bothered. Yes, maybe it is about me! "Forget about it" he told himself.

That is what he did, and the day followed its usual course. The 10 o'clock meeting was fine. Tom had his usual hard-luck stories from his golf game the previous day and the expected banter from his colleagues.

"Ok, ok," he fought back, "When are we going to have this four-ball? Let's see how good you all are where it matters?"

Bernard and Tony all had excuses for the delay in playing, but assured Tom it would happen soon. Mike wondered what Heather made of it as it was her first team meeting. How did the team view her participation, given her long history of being in and out of the company for parental leave etc. What would she make of it all? There was the usual over-run too, of course. When the meeting finished, people seemed to drag themselves away. He knew before he told him that Frank's football team had lost an important game the previous evening. He knew that Frank's job as Logistics Manager really mattered a lot to him, but he also knew how important his football team was. Bad as it was, Joan would say he at least had a hobby!"

"Another defeat, Frank?" he asked. "Yes, and a bad one too. I don't mind losing so much but when they don't perform or give it their all and don't do justice to themselves, that really annoys me. I put so much into it because I want them to not just win, but be different – a special team. But some of them just don't seem to care. This is just not good enough for anybody and no one is really enjoying it."

"Could I see you for a minute?"

Then a few people wanted to see him. Sally, his Head of Finance wanted him to approve some figures urgently before they were sent off to H.Q.

"Sorry about this, Mike, but I only got to finalise them over the weekend. Some people let me down and, quite frankly, disappointed me. I just don't understand them."

He glanced through the report, knowing that there could be many mistakes or important and hidden details that he did not have the time to look for. He trusted Sally, though at times he wondered if she trusted herself any more or less than she trusted her staff. Still, it was good to have someone safe in Finance. Sally was a worrier, and could spot problems a mile off. But it never ceased to annoy him to have to check everything and sign everything.

"Why am I going through this charade, then, of approving and signing", he asked himself. But he knew there was no choice. That made things worse. He was surprised when Sally told him of a meeting she had had with government officials over their tax situation and tax liabilities.

"I thought that had gone away, Sally, and we had got them to back off?"

"Well, no Mike, we haven't, and I don't think we should".

"But why change what we have always done and what every other company is doing." He was astonished at Sally's position and at Sally herself.

"I know, Mike, but we did say we would look at it and think about it and I still think we should. My meeting was only a preliminary and explorative one, but I would like to continue talking with them. The person from the government agency is very interesting and is making a lot of sense. I would like to continue talking to them. I know that what he is saying is unusual and may not go down well with our corporate people, but I think we should look at it. Did you not say that you want us to be a different kind of company?"

Mike was flabbergasted. And Sally above all people! "I'm a bit surprised, Sally. I agree with you that it's unlikely corporate will have any interest in anything that would negatively affect their profits by paying more tax, but you seem to think it makes some sense. I admire your resolve on this, so why not continue to talk to her and then come back and talk to me again when you're ready."

Sally laughed. "Ok, Mike, I'll do that and I promise I won't do or change anything without telling you," she said and then left.

She had had a meeting with the company's financial advisers and auditors and the issue around paying corporation tax came up. The adviser, Larry, explained that there was a way to avoid paying a considerable amount of tax.

"It's called Section 42." he told her.

"And why are you raising this with me? Won't we avail of this? Isn't this what any company would do and what all companies, in practice are doing?"

"Yes, it is, and you are perfectly entitled to go that route and I can help you with that. But I was just wondering if it was what *you* wanted to do?"

"Why would I not want to do it, Larry?"

Larry laughed. "I don't know. It is just that you always seemed to me to be someone who wanted to do what was right."

"And is this Section 42 not right?"

"Technically it is, but really, it's not. Now everyone – or nearly everyone – gains from it so no one is going to change it. The companies win, of course, and the government is happy to hold on to the companies and so to maintain good relationships with them… and on it goes. The only ones who lose out, the ordinary people for whom there is no money to do more things, are not aware of any of this, so they don't complain. But your not using Section 42 could take up to 100 homeless people off the streets over a few years. Or it could provide for up to 100 social or care workers in the community. That kind of thing. It's is not my job to say all this to you, Sally. It is just that I thought it might be something you might like to think about. I know Bernard and some others might have strong views on it too."

"Never doubt that a small group of committed citizens can change the world. Indeed it is the only thing that ever has."

Margaret Mead

"Really? Can we look at it?"

And they did and they continued to look at it and work on it and eventually began discussions with the relevant government tax authorities.

Oh not that!

"Teresa from HR wanted to talk about a manager, Bobby, who felt unfairly handled in a recent promotion that was made.

"Some people are impossible to satisfy", she said, and he couldn't disagree.

"I went to so much trouble to help him, Mike, and I assure you we were ruthlessly fair. Young people are so difficult to deal with sometimes."

They agreed that Mike would have a word with him even though he resented having to do it.

"What difference will it make to talk to *me*, Teresa? I'm not going to change the decision."

But Teresa felt it would help Bobby to finally accept that he hadn't got the position. There was some sympathy for him from other managers, some of whom had also failed to get the job. There was talk of favouritism, and the system being flawed and unfair and this had garnered support from some others who believed managers had too much power and there was a need for some kind of representative group.

"They are not talking of a union or anything like that, Mike, but more of a committee that would represent people, like this person, and would be the voice of people on other policies and procedures. What annoys them is what they see as inconsistency. They see some people being very well regarded by their managers and others treated harshly. You know how the managers differ in how they rate their people's performance in reviews. Some are golden and others harshly assessed and criticised. Natalie claims she has a team of saints or stars, but Natalie never has problems or conflict of any kind. Tony, on the contrary, is never happy with his people and claims that standards are dropping. You know how he is … such high standards and so principled about everything. People see this discrepancy and resent it. That's why I thought that you having a word with Bobby might nip things in the bud."

> "If there were no unions in B.P. I would introduce them because I don't trust myself"
>
> **Rolf Stomberg,**
> *Former V.P. BP Europe*

34

"Sure I can do that and see where it leads, Teresa. We have to do something about that performance review issue. It's forever causing problems."

"I agree Mike, and I'm working on it and getting some advice on it. I can understand people's annoyance. I think we're very paternalistic in how we handle people. And I really mean "paternalistic."" Mike knew what she was getting at and what she felt, based on her personal experience.

"But the bigger topic of a representative group being formed is an interesting and curious one. I don't want a trade union in this company and it is not because I am against trade unions. Quite the contrary. I remember working for a large European oil company many years ago and, at a meeting of senior managers, people were complaining about the unions once again and the problem they were creating. After a few minutes of this, the senior manager, a vice president of Europe, lost his cool and announced with the greatest seriousness in tones of steel:

"If there were no trade unions in this company, I would introduce them … because I don't trust myself."

"The effect was startling. But I agreed with him. But here it's different because I do trust myself or at least I'm working very hard against some odds to trust myself."

"I think I understand something of what you are saying, Mike, but I would like to understand it better."

"Yes, Teresa, we can do that. It's a big topic and we'll talk about it and do so in the team as well."

Finally, Tom, the Operations Manager, wanted to talk to him about overtime – the old bugbear. It was always the same story – overtime required to fix some issues in order to meet deadlines that nobody was happy with or really believed in. It was the same old problem of the Quantum Logistic System and having to put more and more time and resources into it. But if you waited for things to be perfect you might be waiting forever. Tom wanted to get agreement to put on an extra shift at the weekend to deal with a backlog of supply to an important customer.

Mike didn't like or want this. It created bad habits and went against his principles of taking people away from their families at weekends – a sore point on his own home front. But he knew Tom and failing or not delivering was never a runner for him. Success was his lifeblood. Tom was aware of all the problems with overtime and how it was now at a point of being dangerous, not only financially, but in terms of burn-out of some people. Fifteen minutes later they had agreed what Tom had already decided, on condition that the fundamental problem of overtime would be addressed. And Mike wondered if Tom was marking his card on a bigger issue, the increased demands from another customer which was causing lots of problems and lots of friction.

"You know my views, Mike, that we take on too much and don't know how to say no." Mike didn't want to get into another discussion around Terry and sales.

"Why do I do this?" Mike asked himself, after Tom had left. "What value did I add to Tom and why do we have a backlog in the first place? And will this problem ever get resolved?"

Yes, it was a normal day. Nothing new, really, until the phone call came from his boss, Martha. She called to tell him that the International Operations Director, Brad, wanted to visit the company later in the year. Nothing remarkable or to worry about in that. Corporate visits were plentiful. But it was clear from her tone that this was not a usual or normal visit.

Guess who is coming to visit?

"I think you should know that this is not a routine visit, Mike. He is not on a tour. He specifically wants to visit *you*. I'm sure I don't need to spell it out for you, Mike. And you know it is not just about performance and results. These are always good and as good if not better than any others in the company. He is concerned about the future direction of the company and the direction in which you are taking the company.

He and others want to be confident that you are operating in line with corporate principles and policies. You know what I mean! You know there are several issues that he is not happy about. He is not convinced that you have the interests of the corporation at heart or that they are what most matter to you and what you focus on. It's not the first time we have spoken about this, Mike. He believes you need to decide whose side you're on."

"What do you mean "whose side" Martha?"

"I think you know what I mean, Mike. Brad feels, and I understand him, that you are more loyal to the people there and that you look after *their* interests rather than corporate issues, which is what you are expected to do and paid to do."

"That is not how I see it at all Martha and I have explained my position to you many times."

"Well, whether you have or haven't I think you know Brad is not happy with all that or with the level of control he has and you do know he has to answer to some very anxious and nervous people who do not like vagueness or any weakening of control."

There was little Mike could add or ask or say. Martha was right. They had been over this ground many times. And he had never managed to make sense to them about how he saw things.

"I understand Martha. Maybe it is no harm to get everything out on the table and to do it here where he, and you, can see for yourselves what is going on and what I'm doing and how I am doing it. Believe me it's in the interests and well-being of the corporation that I'm most concerned with, even if that's not always how it's perceived or understood."

"Yes, but it's not clear to Brad, or to me either, that you're exclusively focused on the performance, results and well-being of the company, but we can talk again about it. I just wanted you to know as early as possible about the visit and to make sure you are clear about the nature of the visit. Is that alright?"

"That's fine, Martha. I appreciate that."

Rocks and very hard places

He knew that discussions were taking place about the future of some of the Operations, including his own. This was bound to be on the agenda. He knew he would be on the agenda also! He knew that not everyone was happy with what he was doing and how he was handling things. Martha, his own manager, understood him, even if she did not always agree with everything he did. She took his side and looked after him. Now it sounded different. He picked up that she had run out of explanations. She could cut him no more slack. He was on his own this time. And what would they see on the visit that would impress them? Disgruntled staff, thinking of forming some kind of representative group as if he was on the side of the corporation against them, when in fact

> "The words leadership, vision and common purpose have replaced the words control and authority forever"
>
> **Charles Handy**

he was trying to protect them and the Operation and make it a really good place to work.

He knew he would be alright anyway. He would have a good job or a big settlement, but neither of those things were what he really wanted, deep down. Talk of rocks and hard places!

So despite his best efforts, was he actually achieving anything? As he left for home that evening, he could not help thinking of the people he saw as he locked his car that morning, and the very different faces of the people who closed their briefcases or slung their bags over their shoulders as they left for home and freedom in the evening.

He re-entered the cloud that descended on him in the morning, even darker and closer now than in the morning after the events of the day. He once again ended up asking himself:

"Is this it? Is this all that I studied and prepared for? Is this all there is to life, or to work-life at least?" "Why, after all these years," he asked himself, "do I have to hold meetings, solve problems, keep after people, challenge people, be disappointed with things and go over the same things day in and day out and year in and year out and get no recognition or support for it from any side. So many words! Are they of any use at all, or are they a bit like Fr. McKenzie's sermon never really heard or acted upon – *words … that no one will hear.* And no one seems to hear on *any* side".

Maybe the issues are related; people not being really happy and excited in their work, with the organisation still struggling along and pressures and lack of appreciation on all sides. His worry and annoyance turned to hope and excitement.

"Maybe if I was able to help people to really enjoy their work and feel great about themselves both at and through their work, maybe then our whole performance might change also, and we would get big breakthroughs and achieve fabulous things. Maybe that might even be enough to fight the good fight with Martha and with Brad and the others like Brad. Am I just dreaming?" He laughed to himself as he pulled into the drive at his house. "And maybe that would solve the problem at home, as well, That Joan had spoken about. Just maybe! Worth a try, anyway," he thought, as he locked his car. "Anything would be better than what we have now".

A long shot. A very long shot.

Now he had to empty his head and give attention to the four most important people in his life, even more important than his boss Martha or Brad or his own staff and workforce.

"Remember what Joan had said to him in the morning, to be really present to them … in every way.

Questions for reflection and action

1. How familiar are you with the kinds of people and issues Mike deals with? Do you understand his frustration? Or is that what his job is about? And your own?

2. Do you think Sally was foolish or irresponsible to get into discussions on government taxation with Larry? And what about Larry?
3. What do you think of Mike's attitude to some kind of staff representative group? Why so apparently different from that of Rolf Stomberg? Where do *you* stand? Should people not have a say in what gets done and how?
4. Why do you think Mike has run into problems with corporate? Is he unclear about his loyalties? Can you serve both?
5. What would you do on various fronts if you were Mike? How do you currently see them and handle them? Or do you see and have any similar issues or dilemmas?

Chapter 3
Why Do Some People Never "Work"?

How to transform "work" for yourself and everyone

Dinner was on the table when Mike got in and Joan, Harry, his 14-year-old son and Rose his 6- year-old daughter were ready to eat. He knew he had kept them waiting but they all knew that he would first spend time with Alex, their 18-months-old brother. They were not altogether happy with all this waiting. "Daddy will be a bit late again" was not a message they liked. They knew their mother was not happy with it either and that it was an issue between their parents.

Mike's time with Alex varied depending on how early or late he came home from work but when he finally got Alex settled in his cot he realised his mind was still buzzing with his earlier thoughts. But now it was dinner time, so he abandoned his world of work and worry for the world of his wife and children. He remembered what Joan had said to him about being really there with them and not away somewhere in his head. As he sat down Joan was telling Harry about her Uncle Pat whom she had visited in hospital on her way home from school and about the holidays she had spent on Uncle Pat's farm as a child. He listened while Harry quizzed his mother on Uncle Pat and her life with him.

> "All happiness depends on courage and work"
>
> **Honoré de Balzac**

"But what did he work at?" Harry asked.

"He didn't work as such actually," answered Joan laughing, "he was a farmer."

"But don't farmers work?" Harry persisted.

"They do", Joan replied, "but many don't see it as work. It's just what they do. It's their life, or at least it was at that time. And while it might be hard work and tiring, they enjoyed it."

"And why don't all Daddy's workers enjoy their work?" Harry asked with a grin.

"You'd better ask your Daddy that question", his mother replied, ducking the challenge.

"It was very different then," Mike told his son.

"In what way?" Harry persisted.

"Well, he didn't have the same pressures that we have at work. We have a lot of customers to satisfy and they can be very demanding and it can be difficult to meet those demands. As well as that, we have owners, shareholders, who must be kept satisfied too, and the managers who represent these owners. I work for them and it's not always easy."

Martha and Brad, and Martha's earlier phone, call flashed across Mike's mind, but he quickly got rid of the image and of the frown that had formed on his forehead.

"And did Uncle Pat not have customers and owners?" Harry asked.

"He did, but relationships were different then. There was more trust and Uncle Pat's customers knew him and knew that he wouldn't let them down or cheat or short-change them. He owned his farm or most of it. Some of it probably belonged to some bank who had loaned him money to buy land and machinery. But relationships were different then and people mattered. In a sense, people mattered more than the deal over the sale of a cow or some animal or even if he fell behind in a payment to his bank because of a bad summer or something. So they all believed they were in it together."

"What do you mean that they were all in it together? Did they not all have their own homes and needs and very different jobs and lives like we have?"

"They did," his mother answered, "but there was a sense in which they were all in it together. Even the animals!" She laughed. "They knew and loved their animals. I can remember how sad they were when they were selling a cow and my aunt wouldn't want to be around on that day, knowing what was happening. They cared. They cared for everyone and everything – fields, rivers and neighbours. And the people he sold to, his customers and the people who loaned him money also saw it like that. It was very different, Harry."

"And can you not have the same relationship with your customers and the banks or owners that Uncle Pat had?"

You could trust people back then

"It's not as simple as that, Harry", said Mike. "You see we have to make a profit and watch our costs. We have to watch what we buy and get it as cheaply as possible to be as profitable as possible." He thought of what Sally had spoken to him about earlier. He wondered again if it was prudent.

"But do you not trust these people the same way that Uncle Pat's customers and bank trusted him? Do you not want to have a relationship of trust with them like Uncle Pat's customers had with him? Would that not make things much easier?"

Mike felt a bit uncomfortable. He thought of the current issue with their most important customer which looked like being very serious, miles away from the unreal world Harry was talking about. Yet, strange as it was, what Harry was saying did ring a bell in him. He remembered the look on Sally's face when she talked of the relationship with the government. And he thought of the unrest some of the staff felt and the mistrust they were experiencing. But he put all this aside to keep it simple.

"Business is not as simple as that, unfortunately, anymore, Harry. It's quite a challenging task to make acceptable levels of profit every month and every year."

"What makes it so challenging?", Harry asked.

"Many of the things I mentioned," Mike replied a little impatiently, "such as getting the highest price possible from our customers, keeping our costs down and paying as little as possible to our suppliers, and then, of course, being as adaptive as possible and getting the most out of our workforce."

"Yeah, very different from how Uncle Pat worked," Harry laughed.

"Did Uncle Pat have workers as well?" Rose then chipped in.

"Yes he did, but it varied, depending on the season. In summertime, when he was very busy, he would take on more workers, and people from around would help out too."

"And did those workers not mind when he had no work for them?" Rose asked, with a sad look.

"I'm sure they did mind, but they understood too and they trusted him and knew that he would pay them as much as possible. So, when times were good, he would give them more and, of course, he would help them out if they were in difficulty."

> "This is the real secret of life - to be completely engaged with what you are doing in the here and now. And instead of calling it work, realize it is play"
>
> **Alan Watts**

"Very different from how our workers feel and see things," he thought to himself.

"Yes", Joan interrupted, "if people saw that he needed help because he had hay cut and it was going to rain, then they would arrive on his farm and help him and they would do it for nothing.

"Why would they do it for nothing?" Harry asked.

"Because they were a kind of community and they knew that if or when they needed help, they too would get it from Uncle Pat or from somebody They too trusted him and it worked because other people would give them work too."

"It seems that Uncle Pat had very good relationships with every-body around – his customers, his workers, those who helped and the people who sold him machinery. Can you not do the same in your company, Dad?"

"Things and people were different back then, Harry, as I keep saying. You didn't have to watch or control people. Uncle Pat didn't have to check when people arrived for work, for example."

"So why did he not check when they got to his farm or fields, then?" Harry persisted. "Did workers have to check or sign in on Uncle Pat's farm like they do in your work, Dad?"

"No", Mike laughed, "of course not!"

"Why? Was it not important for them to be on time?"

"Not really. Because there was no need. They wanted to do the work, so they arrived on time and he trusted them to do so. And if they did arrive late, they would stay much later in the evening to make up for it and get what was needed done, so it was never a problem. They knew the job had to be done and that's what mattered. It was the job that mattered more than the time."

"Did he have a supervisor or foreman to watch them like Dad has, Mum?"

"No of course not." Joan answered. "Sometimes they worked on their own and sometimes he was not even there if he had to go to the vet with an animal or something."

"So why did they not take it easy or take time off when he wasn't around like happens in your place, Dad?"

"They would never do that. That would have made no sense to them. They had a job to do and they *wanted* to do it and did it for its own sake."

"And why can't you …"

"That's enough interrogating for one night, young man," Joan intervened, sensing that Mike was getting a little irked, "that was then, now is now. And talking of now, it's time for your bed or you'll be late in the morning and *you*'ll be disciplined!

"Did you find my old football boots?" Harry asked.

"No, I didn't nor am I likely to. They're somewhere out in that garage … or jungle … and I have no intention of getting lost or hurt going in there looking for them at this hour," his mother answered, giving Mike a knowing grin.

Out of the mouths of babes

But when they all left, Mike remained, feeling agitated and wondering why he was not able to answer the children's questions.

"Children have no idea," he consoled himself, "they believe people can come and go as they please and enjoy work. If they had their way, there would be no morning clocking in. They think people will just get the job done without having to be managed. People back then simply saw a need for something to be done and did it. But people are not like that anymore. They need direction, organisation, and motivation.

But everything was different back then and there was great trust with customers, suppliers and banks – the whole working environment. Uncle Pat didn't have a very demanding manager breathing down his neck like I have." He continued to justify things to himself. "Work was not seen as just work or business but as part of society. It was meaningful. It made sense because it was part of a whole way of life for all involved. Because it was meaningful, there was no need for complex structures and agreements. Everyone understood the rules of the game and it made sense. You could trust people back then.

Trust made all the difference. Now you have to manage every-one because you just can't trust." But he wondered why All that the children had said made such sense. Wasn't it just this that was causing him all the wondering and searching he had been recently doing.? In a sense he felt more assured. "Reassured by children who know nothing?" he asked himself. "Out of the mouths of babes and sucklings …" yes… maybe…exactly." He felt a little better, but was still unhappy. Isn't this how everyone around him seemed to feel, despite his best efforts?

Questions for reflection and action

1. Do you understand why Uncle Pat never "worked"?
2. What was so different then?
3. Is that or some of it feasible for you now?
4. Why was there no need for control?
5. Is that same or similar level of trust realistic of feasible now?

Chapter 4
Why Seeking Happiness Doesn't Make You Happy

"Are you ok after all that?" Joan asked later when Harry and Rose had gone to bed. "I know that wasn't at all easy for you given all that has been happening and our own recent conversations. But you seem particularly preoccupied today! What's up?"

"Yes, you are right, it wasn't easy, but I have to say both of them made a lot of sense even if I didn't want to admit it" he laughed. "We have two sharp children and challenging ones. I have to admit I didn't have answers for many of their questions, but they were making a lot of sense."

So he told her of what had been on his mind all day, and about the impression he had that most of the people who worked in the company did not seem happy at work.

"And I don't feel happy for lots of reasons, one of them being that I feel frustration at having to deal with the same things over and over as if I were making no progress. Every day can feel a bit like Groundhog Day. We have ongoing customer problems and, while I'm not involved in it yet, I know I'll end up having to become involved. The same is true with the new Quantum Logistics System. I don't understand why they can't solve it on their own. What complicates it even more is that, unless the customer issue gets resolved quickly, lots of other people will become involved too – like my boss and her boss – which will confirm them in their judgements or prejudices about me."

He then told her about the call from Martha telling him about the visit from Brad, the International Director, and how it was not going to be a routine, cursory visit. Joan sensed that there was something different going on this time. She had had this kind of conversation many times with Mike and was always happy and interested to do so. She knew Martha personally, and she accepted that it was normal that they would spend so much time talking about Mike's world than hers. His was much more interesting and she was accustomed to it. It was what happened in family and social gatherings too. Mike's world of business and work seemed much more interesting than her world of the home and children or the occasional story from school when she was working. It was not that she was competitive or wanted to be centre stage in conversations. She accepted the role of "second fiddle" as how it had to be for a mostly-working-from-home mother. She just swallowed it and played the game as it was.

"But you're doing very well, aren't you, and you always meet your targets. So, what's there to fear?"

"Yes, you are right that we always deliver on our targets and there is no issue around them. What some people don't like is how I handle things. They want more and more information and reports on everything and want more and more detail."

"But why is that a problem? What's wrong with giving them what they are looking for if it leads to a peaceful existence?"

"Well, it's a bit like the two children were saying about how we manage things. They're right; how we manage things makes little sense in lots of ways. If I controlled everything like they want me to do and got into all the detail they want me to get into, it would be an even more difficult place to work for me… and for everyone else too."

He went silent for a while and took a few sips of his tea.

"You know, crazy as it may sound, Harry and Rose are right in a sense about Uncle Pat. Something has to be seriously wrong if people are so unhappy in work. And we try to treat people well, to pay them well, to be fair with them and, in general, we treat them better than many other companies. But it doesn't work. It doesn't seem to make them any happier."

Treat people well

"Well, here's another coincidence for you", Joan said. "The school had one of their "Away Days" last week and I went along as you know, and we discussed this very point. We had a really great presentation from a person on happiness, and the part schools have to play or should play in this. He brought "happiness" back to mean being really human and being true to what being human means. So then we discussed what being human really means and he asked us who we would regard as being good examples of being human."

"Very interesting", Mike remarked. "I'm fascinated. And who did you or he pick?"

"We talked a lot about it and what being human meant. Then he gave us examples of people he thought were real human beings. He mentioned several but focused in on just three – Viktor Frankl, Nelson Mandela and Rosa Parks."

"Really? Three very different and impressive people. And why did he pick those ones?"

"Well, we asked the same question but he made great sense. He said that in each case these people were faced with challenges and difficult situations, and they responded in a really powerful, and human, way. Viktor Frankl showed how you could live a meaningful life even in a place like Auschwitz.

> Viktor Frankl shows that even in the most awful of circumstances a man can still lead a meaningful life.
>
> "When a man finds that it is his destiny to suffer,' he writes, 'he will have to accept his suffering as his task; his single and unique task. He will have to acknowledge the fact that even in suffering he is unique and alone in the universe. His unique opportunity lies in the way in which he bares his burden."
> **Viktor Frankl**

Frankl said that "A person's unique opportunity (to be human) lies in the way in which he bears his burden." And then he went on to Mandela. Yes, Mandela was a nice person but there were lots of nice people around then, like now. But what made him truly human was the stance he took on equal rights for his people at an enormous price – 27 years in prison. Then there was Rosa Parks. She realised on 1 December 1955 that to be true to her humanity, she would not move back down the bus one morning to allow more white people to sit in the reserved front seats. Her little stance – or seat – in a sense, began the whole civil rights movement.

That's why I said that treating people well may not be what it is about but more about treating people in a human way by challenging them to be truly human and giving them the opportunity to be so by responding to their challenges in a really good way. Like these three people did. Not that it has to be that dramatic. What do you think?"

"Goodness. That's a mouthful, Joan. I'm impressed. My own family know much more than I do and are much more aware of what's needed. I have been thinking a lot about this but now I feel I need to think much more, and in particular, about what you are saying. Like most people, I always thought of being human as being nice and soft, and I always heard "treating people in a human way" as about being nice to them. But you're saying something quite different about being human. You're using words like "challenging them" and "inviting them to face up to and address their challenges well". I understand that and we do some of that but still they don't look happy."

Happiness as the goal and George Best

"And this may sound stupid, but why do you want them to be happy?"

"Well, from my viewpoint, or the company's, having people happy is good for business and good for the organisation."

"How?"

"Well, it will lead to people feeling better in general and so making a better contribution. And it's also important so that we get and hold on to good people. We are currently replacing someone who left, which is a lot of trouble, and costly. In the process of replacing her it's important not only to attract the right person but also to be able to hold on to her replacement. And, we now have a silly issue over some promotions. They are causing unrest among some people, and it's not just about Heather. It's hard to hold on to people and to keep them happy these days, be they Millennials or Generation X, Y or Z, believe me. Talk to Teresa about it. Her two have her driven insane. And, even apart from all that, I think people should be happy in life, so it's a goal or end in itself."

"But that's the point I was making. Maybe happiness isn't the goal! Maybe going after happiness is not what brings happiness!" Joan commented with a grin. "Frankl apparently said that happiness is always a by-product of what we do, what *results* from what we do, but is never the goal."

"Now you're going really deep on me. What do you mean? Surely, we all want to be happy and to feel happy?"

"Yes, I'm sure we do but going after it as a goal may not be the best way to get it. If we have to keep checking whether we are happy or not and ensuring that everything we do is making us happy, it may not lead to a very happy life or a really good and true life. This was the understanding we reached

> "Happiness is like a butterfly, the more you chase it, the more it will elude you. But if you turn your attention to other things, it comes in softly sits on your shoulder"
>
> **Nathanial Hawthorne**

on our "Away Day". We concluded that life and feeling fulfilled was not about feeling good or being happy or having a good time. Think of George Best, one person we spoke about."

"What about him? He had a ball – forgive the pun – and had everything he wanted!"

"Yes, he did, and he is dead! But you know the story about the hotel waiter who found him in bed with Miss World."

"No, but it sounds good!"

"Well, this is a story that George himself told. He was in bed with Miss World, drinking champagne and downing caviar and the waiter came in with the rest of their breakfast. He asked, "Where did it all go wrong, George?" Now George told this story against the poor waiter who, according to Best, was missing the point of what was actually going on and how good things really were. Far from things being wrong, he was having a great time and was just enjoying life.

However, it was George who was missing the point because the point was not and never is just about having a good time. Enjoyment is not everything. In reneging on his real calling and innate skills and gifts as a footballer, he was failing to be truly himself. He was failing to be the full person he could have been, failing to be fully human as George Best. So being truly human is more important than being happy or having a good time. I mean, do you think it is the happiness of his footballers that Frank wants? Am I making sense?"

"Yes, I see what you mean. So is happiness the result of doing certain things, of being who you should be and are, rather than it being a goal in itself?"

"Yes, exactly. Frank knows that his players will be happy if they do well but that will be the result of something else, not the goal. Sorry about this and I feel like I'm preaching, but I loved what the presenter showed us."

As Joan said all this, she could not help asking the question of herself: "And what about *you*? How fulfilled are *you* and how good is your response to your situation? Yes, there's no doubt that looking after children and helping to shape young people's lives is as great a thing one could do but it often doesn't feel like that. I feel there should be more or a better way of doing it."

But Mike who had become silent was talking again.

Happiness is the result

"I understand. I hadn't seen it like that before! I wonder what it is we miss out on when we do that. I ask that because I'm wondering if I've been taking the easy route and running things – the same way everyone else does and seeing them as ordinary. It's very different from your three people! It's easier in a sense and involves less hassle."

"I know" said Joan.

"A pretty major penalty I would say."

"Yes, and one that very many people pay, often without even knowing it. They think this is life – "as good as it gets." Now I think that Uncle Pat, Frankl, Mandela and Rosa Parks, not to mention George Best, are enough for one night. Forget them for now and enjoy your cup of tea."

"Ok, I will, but I learned a lot in that chat Joan. I see that maybe I need to go after something very different in how I manage people. And I see that pleasing them and just giving them what they want is not necessarily the right thing. Even if it were feasible. They need and deserve much more than that. They need challenges, as you say, that will bring out the best in them and develop them as human beings.

"Eckhart Tolle would say you miss out on life. He describes sin as 'missing the mark' like the bull's eye in life, so the penalty is missing out on real life and real living"

This will make it possible for them to give much more and to be much more. The company needs much more from them than it's currently getting. I think I see how I might have been letting both down. And I see how these two things go hand in hand. And they will have their effects on me as a person and how I am here at home and with everyone. They are all tied up together. Thanks for that lesson, Joan. Do you want a job?

No thanks Mr. General Manager. I have one thanks ... or several jobs or bits of jobs. But now that you mention it, why don't you have another chat with Brendan? You always found that useful in the past." Brendan was Joan's brother and she and he had many conversations about these things. He himself had been the managing director of a company for many years but had resigned to devote himself to finding better ways to manage and lead and was working on very different ways of running organisations.

"Well, it's an idea. I don't like to bother him again. I would like to work it out for myself if I can."

"I know. I'm sure you'll work it out but the view of an outsider like Brendan can often be very helpful. He knows the company, which is a help. And it seems too important not to. I already suggested to Teresa that she might talk to him about her situation with the children."

"And what did she say?"

She said it might be a good idea and that she would think about it.

"That's good. But all you have been saying makes a lot of sense and I need to think a lot about it. I feel that if I don't make this happen, I'll fail not only as a manager but as a person, as a human being. Yes, you're right, it is the most important thing of all."

"And, talking of jobs, you still have that job to do on the garage or more properly the jungle out there ... ok?"

"Yes, I know. I keep putting it off but I will get to it. I promise".

Questions for reflection and action

1. What do you see that the three – Frankl, Mandela, Parks – had in common? What do you most admire in them or in any one of them? And its significance for you?

2. Do you agree that "happiness" should not be the goal? Why is this important?

3. What is this saying that people really need to feel "happy" or fulfilled as human beings? What are the implications of this for you and how you manage and lead?

4. Why is it absolutely true that you have a unique and wonderful opportunity as a manager or leader to help people enjoy wonderful lives as rich human beings?

5. Mike has some thinking to do after his chat with Joan, what thinking might you want and need to do?

Chapter 5
Turning the Interview and the World on its Head

Deciding who comes first – the company or the employee?

Next morning when Mike awoke, his thoughts turned to the day ahead. It was to be a normal one, with the exception of a meeting Teresa, his HR manager, had asked him to have with a candidate for a project engineering position. He had not really agreed to meet the candidate, Albert, and he wanted to ask Teresa why he had to be involved. Yet he trusted her, because she genuinely cared for people and for their welfare, in spite of her own personal challenges. She truly believed in the potential of people to be great.

Paradoxically, Mike knew that she was not too happy with her own children, Jenny and Robert for those very reasons. Jenny had tried several things but stuck with none of them. Robert, it seemed, was very gifted but repeatedly missed out on opportunities. Teresa was handling all of this on her own. Mike wondered if she was projecting some of her own concerns on to Albert. On the other hand, it could well be that she was only concerned about hiring the right person.

Intriguing, yes, but that was for later. Right now, his intrigue remained around Joan's comments of the night before about treating people well and what that meant. Could that be what he and the others were getting wrong? They had a job to do, a business to run, and at the same time, tried to treat people as well as they could so that they would be happy at work. Yet it seemed that neither goal was being achieved or achieved well enough.

The business was just trundling along and people were also trundling along with their lives. It was like they were falling between two stools, but it did not seem right to just focus on the business and forget about the people and their happiness. It certainly did not seem right to only focus on making people happy if that was not what they were about, especially in light of all Joan had said last night.

There was something in what Joan said that he liked and could identify with. Mandela, Frankl and Parks all seemed to hit on happiness without going after it directly. He thought of the fundamental principle that it is how we handle our situations that ultimately matters. We all face reality and similar situations, but what really matters is what we do with them, *how we handle them* and whether we make the very most of them. Maybe that was what Joan meant by being human?

That is what made Mandela, Rosa Parks and Viktor Frankl so great. And maybe it is what makes all of us human at the end of the day. They came up with and gave wonderful responses to their different realities. They knew what being truly human meant!

Maybe that is what Joan meant by challenging people to do this very thing at work. Maybe that is what we and our managers never or very rarely do with other "human beings". We are not inviting them, challenging them to see their situations, their reality, their lives, as equally being full of challenges and beautiful possibilities. We are letting them down too. And we do this because we do all the managing of things and decide or control and direct how they respond and behave for them. Little did he know that he would come up against these same topics a short time later in his meeting with the potential new recruit.

> "Finding the very best and richest way to handle our different situations, whatever they are"
>
> **Anonymous**

No fear or ambition?

He barely noticed that he had arrived at the car park, so engrossed was he in his search for the connection between work and being truly human, whatever that meant.

Teresa was waiting for him when he arrived at his office as agreed.

She was anxious for Mike to spend some time with this man because, while she felt positive about him and his track record was very good, she was worried that he was too idealistic, not grounded enough and a little too cocky or arrogant ... or something like that. She was worried about his commitment and whether he was suitable in the longer term. He had already left a few companies. She knew people like that, two of them very well, unfortunately!

"He's strange, Mike. He doesn't seem to be too worried about his level in the organisation or the salary on offer. I wonder and worry about his drive and ambition. Will he stay? He is really well qualified and has ideal experience for what we want, but I wonder if we are taking on trouble or someone who will be gone again in a year? He reminds me of my own two children in ways. They don't know what they want and won't stick at anything."

The situation was puzzling to Teresa, and Mike knew how shrewd a judge of people she was, but in this case she was unsure, and everything did not seem to add up.

He decided to meet Albert in the canteen rather than in the formal environment of his office. Albert seemed to have no problem with this. Casually dressed, relaxed and friendly, he struck Mike as somebody with unbounded energy and some strange sense of strength and confidence. He spent little time on Albert's history as this had been well covered already and all seemed fine,

> "You can't build a forever restless, opportunity-seeing company unless you're willing to hire forever restless, opportunity-seeking individuals"
>
> **Ken Lay Enron**

so he quickly got into what Albert offered and wanted to contribute to the company. But he was a bit taken aback with Albert's answer.

Make a difference

"I want to make a difference through my work Mike, and I'm looking for the opportunity to do something great here. That's why I want to join or at least why I think I would like to join. I want the opportunity to do justice to myself and, in doing that, make a serious contribution to your company."

Mike was both excited and troubled at what he heard. He now understood why Teresa was concerned.

"And what would that opportunity need to be, Albert?"

"I don't know, but I got the impression from Teresa and the other people I met that there are possibilities here to do great things. As you can see from my CV, I have worked previously with two other companies and, I believe, done very well in them. I don't think I get bored easily but I'm looking for something special, a place where I can make a difference and test and stretch my abilities, yet be myself in the process. I got the impression from Teresa and others that this might be so in your company, but I'm not sure."

Mike began to wonder who was interviewing whom. Who was trying to decide on whom?

"Well, I'm glad they gave you that impression and I hope they're right. That's another day's work." Mike smiled. "But why is this so important to you – seemingly more important than other more fundamental business matters? I find this a bit unusual. We are a business, after all. Do you know what I mean?"

"Yes, I do, or I think I do. I've thought about it and for me the most fundamental thing of all is making a difference, making a real difference and being challenged and tested to be the best I can be and to do justice to myself. I believe that if I do this then I'll be doing what is good and best for me, for other people and for the business. Otherwise, I can't see how I can add value to your business, Mike. I've had a few jobs and have been successful in them. And yet, it seemed and felt like there was always something missing."

Realistic or idealistic?

Alarm bells and reminder bells rang in Mike's head. He could hear Teresa's stories about her two children ... word for word. Now he understood her concern. And Joan's three heroes from last night's conversation flashed into his mind.

"Are you not being a bit idealistic or unrealistic, Albert? What did you feel was missing if you had a good job and were successful?"

"Well, I look around me at successful people and I am not thrilled at what I see. I look at my own parents and they have done very well and been good parents who provided for my sister and myself. That's all fine, but I ask myself if this is all there is? You join an organisation, you go after success, you progress and are successful but then you wonder what it was all about – at least I do. Of course, I want a job and to earn a livelihood and enjoy the things that a good job provides, but I feel as if I would be sacrificing my life for this, if this was *all* there is. I feel that is too high a price to pay. Does this make any sense to you, Mike?"

It was making too much sense! It was sounding like an echo. Mike's thoughts that morning on the way to work came back to him, and he smiled.

"Believe me, I do understand what you're saying, Albert, but, tell me a bit more about how that circle could be squared, or maybe how the square of a company could be circled? What would that mean in practice for you? We're not a club or social group, you know!"

"Well, I may not be able to explain it very well but when I was younger, I loved music and played the violin. I was quite good at it but wondered if that was what I would do with my life – playing in an orchestra or in chamber groups. But in the end, I chose not to. There were many people willing to advise me about the risks of a career in music. It might have been tough, and it may not have worked out. But I know that if I had followed that path, I would at least have been doing what I really wanted."

"But do you think it is realistic to go after what we really want?" Mike asked mischievously. "Do you really think that's possible? How many people are doing what they really want? Belonging to a company means serving that company and doing what *it* wants and needs, not what each individual wants. Is it not?"

I want to do what I want

"I understand what you are saying, Mike, and you are right about not too many people doing what they really want or even giving any consideration to that as an option or goal. But it is what I want, and

> "So we have to be idealists in a way, because then we wind up as the true, the real realists"
>
> **Viktor Frankl**

I believe it is possible, even if that might sound like a dream. If you think it's a dream and if it makes no sense to you in this company, or what it would mean here, then I can finish my coffee and just leave. And I don't want to appear in any way ungrateful or disrespectful in saying that," he laughed.

Mike laughed too. "No, you're right, Albert. You have a good nose for things! You make good common sense. No, I don't think it's nonsense even if I'm not fully sure what it would mean or how it would work in practice. But tell me, are you sure that you're right in being this demanding around work and what you do?"

"Yes, Mike I do, and I have thought about it. The most important thing in life, I think, is "meaning". In order to be happy, we have to be human and that, to me, means being faithful to what makes sense and to what is right and good. I believe that if I fail to do that or if what I am doing is not meaningful, it doesn't make sense and won't be any good. So, no matter how well I do and no matter how successful I am, I will not be happy. I see so many people who have to find meaning and interest outside of work – in sports, hobbies, travel and the like. That's fine, but not if it compensates or makes up for what they do all day. That's why I said that my music career might not have brought me great wealth or renowned success, but it would have brought me meaning."

Mike now understood why Teresa was concerned and now he was too.

Meaningful work

"And what do you think that would be like in practice and what do you mean by meaningful work, Albert? What would work need to be and how would a company like ours need to be in order for it to be meaningful for you?"

"The company would have to be such that what I would be doing would be what everyone else was doing and would make sense and that I would understand the value it would add. And because it did add value, then I would really want to do the work. Surely that's possible Mike? Is it possible to design and shape work so that what everyone does makes sense, and they understand that and so they want to do it? As I keep saying, work cannot be just a means to an end. Life can't be a means to an end. I also think a company does not or should not exist in isolation or in a vacuum. It must be part of the community or society where it is situated. It cannot be a monstrosity, cut off from everything and everyone around it, only serving some people thousands of miles away. Surely that makes sense?"

It did, and more sense than Mike chose to share with Albert, even if he still did not know exactly what it would mean in practice. He thought of Bernard and the drum he was forever beating on this topic. Albert is right on this and so is Bernard, he thought.

"I understand that. But what else would a job have to be, or would we have to be to make work meaningful for you?"

"I want to work in a place where I'm trusted and relied on. I have had some nice jobs, but I was doing what I was told or what was expected from me and answering to others. I want to be trusted and let get on with things so I can do what I think is right and best. I was a child for long enough and yet I see many people in work situations who are still being treated like children, who then behave like children and who are never happy as a result. I don't think this is good for anyone or for the organisation. It means we are not getting the best from people."

Again, Mike thought of his conversations with Joan and with his own children and of his differences with Martha and Brad. But, hearing it from someone else like Albert worried him a bit. He wondered how a Terry or Tom could deal with and handle someone like this – Terry with his single-minded ambition and Tom with his driven approach.

> "Don't blame us, Brian, if we behave irresponsibly sometimes, like children. We are treated like irresponsible children all the time"
>
> **Union Representative in Rhone-Poulenc**

Like being managed?

"So you don't like being managed, then, or having a manager?"

"No, I do. I think it's important that there be managers or leaders. People, groups, teams, organisations need them but the right kinds of managers or leaders. By that I mean managers or leaders who know how to get the best out of people and make the most of them. That means letting go and trusting and allowing and enabling people to use their heads and everything to get the job done. It may be different for you, Mike, at your level, where you are not controlled and are free to do things as you want and see best, but it is very different when you are not allowed or trusted or helped to do this."

If he only knew, Mike thought to himself. But, again, he decided to keep his thoughts to himself, though he was getting more and more interested in Albert and, at the same time, more and more apprehensive about taking someone like him into the company.

"And do you think you might do all that better here than somewhere else?"

"I'm not sure that I will, and that's why I'm making up my own mind as well here in this chat. And I don't want to come across as disrespectful or ungrateful as I mentioned earlier. As I said, it's good to have a good job and a good salary and security and all that, but it's not everything to me. I have had all that. I got the impression from all I have heard here that I might feel happy in myself and, above all, feel that I am making a difference and making the most of my life and being trusted and relied on. And I believe that the better I do that, the better I'll be for your company if you take me on."

"But would that not put a huge onus on us to ensure that we're playing our part in being the kind of company that meets your needs? Is this not the tail wagging the dog? And please don't think I'm being disrespectful now."

"I don't think so and I don't see it like that. I'd like to make it clear again that I am not just talking about myself here. I will not be the right person for you if the company is not the right company for me. And, for that, it has to be a place where I enjoy what I do and where I feel I'm making a real difference and doing justice to myself. But I believe that if I think and work in this way, I'll have a very good career because I'll  be making a big contribution wherever I am. I feel a bit like Michelangelo when he said he was not making angels out of stone but *releasing the angel* that was already in the stone.

I too believe that there are angels or really great possibilities that are waiting to be released or realised in every situation and challenge. Now I know that may sound too much like apple pie, but it happens to be what I believe and what I want."

"I don't hear it like that, Albert. It reminds me of something I heard once about Japanese sculptors. Apparently, they take a block of wood or something and ask it: "What do you want to be?" I think you are saying something similar and asking what our company or situation wants to be. And that's a question I'm asking myself in these times too. I admire all you are saying but it still comes across to me as, forgive me for saying it, idealistic or very spiritual." Tony would love it, he felt and Natalie too with her spiritual values, but what about Teresa and what he would say to her? He felt Albert would confirm Teresa's worst fears around her own two children.

"I'm not saying that we should not be idealistic but there is a balance that we have to find. We have to be practical or pragmatic too. Do you think you are, Albert?". Mike knew he was on shaky ground as he would be unable to answer his own question.

Being a responsible adult and parent

"It's a pity that you see it or hear it in that way, Mike. I think you know that I'm married and that we have a young child. My wife is not working at present and may not do so for some time. We're both very conscious of our responsibility to our child and to make sure that these very important years in her life are well handled. We're not too happy about handing that responsibility over to a childcare facility or person. We do have support from our parents and friends, even if many of them don't really understand me, but we don't want our child to take second place to other needs or things in our lives. For that reason, I'll have to carry the main burden of income for the immediate future, but I still believe that I'll be a better and more responsible parent if I'm being myself.

And I also believe, coincidentally, that if I'm myself, I'll be more successful in whatever I do. So, maybe I am being idealistic, but I also think I'm being responsible and realistic but maybe I'm wrong and if you think I am being unrealistic in what I am looking for, then I don't think this will work out. I had hoped that this company was different, which is why I'm here, but if you believe that what I'm after doesn't make real sense, then I think we should acknowledge that and not waste any more of our time. Does that make sense and is it fair?"

"Yes, it does make sense to me and I do think it's fair. I happen to think that you're being idealistic. I also think that you're right to be so. Some of the questions I asked you were to find out how realistic you were being in being idealistic, if you know what I mean. It seems to me that you are being very realistic."

"Thanks for that, Mike and ..."

"Sorry Albert, but may I add one or two more things please? In what I was saying to you I was also being very honest in wanting to represent the reality of my own situation and our own situation in this company. I didn't want and I don't want to give you a glossy cover picture of how things are here. While I share most of your views and values, I cannot guarantee you that I can deliver on all of those. I'm being perfectly, and maybe overly, honest with you in telling you that not everybody thinks like I do or sees things the way that you and I may see them. I don't want you to join our company under any false illusions. There are people who don't believe that what I want is realistic either. Some think I'm living in the clouds. They question how feasible it all is and some don't agree with my version of how people really are. There are times when I ask myself the same question. On what basis do I believe that a very different kind of organisation with people behaving in a very different way is possible?"

"I appreciate that and, to be honest, I'm not very surprised. I am intrigued by it. I like a challenge. Can you give me some idea of what's happening and where you see the main challenges?"

Sharing the challenge

"I'm very glad to hear that you're ready for a challenge, Albert, and you will find plenty of them here." Mike laughed. "First of all, yes, we're doing quite well and maybe very well in some senses, but, that said, I am not at all happy that we are achieving or being all we can be. There is something missing. I can't really put my finger on it. I don't know if we're different from many other companies, but I suspect we aren't, or not different enough. We've the usual issues.

> "Only those who dare to fail greatly can ever achieve greatly"
>
> **Robert F. Kennedy**

It takes so long – too long in my opinion –to get things done. I don't understand why things don't just happen automatically and easily and I'm working on that and some of the things you were saying are in line with that. I know it's normal and natural that people differ and can't agree on things, but I'd like us to be able to manage differences in a much better way. I have big differences with some people that I need to deal with. I know there are some issues that are just so complex that they need meetings, but we have too many of them.

While I hope this doesn't cause you to abandon the thought of joining us, I wonder if, deep down, these people are all that happy, even if they see what's going on as normal. That's why I like what you're saying. I was telling my wife last night that not only was I not happy with how things were, but that I didn't think anybody else around here is all that happy either. She made the point that maybe it was not about making people happy but about challenging them and inviting them to go after great things and make a difference. That happiness is what comes from doing that, rather than being the goal you go after."

"Thanks for your honesty and I'm glad to hear you think like that, because it's how I see most companies too. And I'm very glad to hear what your wife says and that meaning and making a difference are what make us more human and so more fulfilled as people rather than all happy, as I keep saying. That's why I said I would welcome the challenge to play a part in bringing about the change that you want. I have some friends in the arts.

Some are actors and some of my friends are, of course, musicians. I never cease to be amazed at the lives they lead. Such insecurity and risk, but they love the challenge and the joy of doing what they do and enjoying doing it better and better. It's like as if they are prepared to sacrifice security for challenge. This is why I want to make sure I'm doing the right thing and making the right decision this time. Before I have at times played it too carefully, probably out of insecurity.

But can I ask you, Mike, how you see this part of your job compared to your responsibility to strengthen and grow the business? I know you're part of a larger corporation, but I'm sure that doesn't protect you from threats. I'm not being cheeky or disrespectful, Mike, but I know of so many managers who talk impressively about their values and their culture but, when the pressure comes on, the culture and the values all disappear off the screen."

Risk!

"No, I don't think you're being disrespectful, Albert, and you're right – that's the reality and is the real challenge. Believe me, most people around here think like you do, but when I talk about how I would like the company to be, they only half-believe me and few of them believe that it's realistic to think like this in a business environment like ours. Which is why I asked you about being realistic. And as for corporate management, well that's a whole other story, and I don't want to go into it but you can imagine how it might be."

"I think I can, and I understand why it would not be appropriate to get into all that here."

"Thanks Albert and I only want to repeat that I cannot guarantee that we will live up to all that you want. There is a risk in joining our company that you will be disappointed, and  I can't pretend that I can remove that risk. Just like we would be taking a risk in taking you on too."

"I understand that and I do believe the line that says: "Risk and reward ride together. Avoid one and the other passes you by." I suppose we both have to weigh up the risks."

Mike again thought of Teresa and whatever he would say to her and how he would convince Tom.

"I agree Albert. Can we both take a little time to reflect on this exchange and talk again in a day or so? If it's ok with you, I'll ask Teresa to get in touch with you to find out how we both feel. Would that be ok?"

"Yes, that would be fine Mike and thanks for being so open and honest."

"And the same to you too Albert. I really enjoyed our conversation. It's important that we're each happy because, as you yourself said, a bad decision for you will be a bad decision for us and vice versa".

"Now I have to leave you as I have a team meeting in ten minutes, and I need to get ready. I will ask Teresa to pick you up and look after you while you are waiting and thanks for the chat and for your honesty. I hope we get to talk more and maybe to tilt at those windmills together."

While Mike was somewhat perturbed by all the points and issues Albert raised, he also felt heartened that there was someone who saw the world as he saw it and as he wanted it to be.

But then there was Teresa, and how to handle the conversation with her, as well as agreeing for whom Albert would work if he joined the company. Who would benefit most from working with him and with whom would he work best? It all depended on if he and Teresa agreed to employ him.

Questions for reflection and action

1. Why do you think Mike was letting Albert interview HIM?
2. Do you think Albert is being too idealistic and not realistic enough?
3. How much of Albert's wishes or vision for work do you share?
4. Do you agree that a life of work without meaning is not really worth it? If you do, what implications does it have for you?
5. Do you now have a greater feel for the enormous responsibility and power you have to enrich people's lives?

Chapter 6

Back to Reality...but Which Reality? Sisyphus?

Getting away from the "same old, same old" problem solving

Mike needed the ten minutes to prepare for the meeting. But, before he could do that, he had a call from Terry, the Sales and Marketing Manager who wanted to meet him urgently, to which he agreed.

Terry was worried and very frustrated. Something had happened! He lived in a well-off suburb quite removed from the company, so his daily commute was a long one. He normally listened to news programmes on the way to work or to motivational talks he had downloaded. However, his rosy world was suddenly spoiled that morning by a call from, Sharon, the Logistics Manager in their main client, Key Services Limited. Apparently, there was a mix-up over an order and right now, their customer was in serious trouble, or would be very soon.

"Just now, I am not too interested who is at fault, Terry," she barked. "We don't have product that you were supposed to deliver. We're in trouble and, therefore, so are you, and that's all I want to communicate at this time. Do you hear me?"

This kind of language and tone was very unusual for Sharon, so it had to be serious. He tried to get Mike and Tom on the phone but failed. He could not get to work quickly enough. At times he wondered if it was all worth it. There were so many problems. With Tom in Operations, who always seemed to be under pressure. With Tony in Engineering, who always wanted things done *his* way and was so critical and inflexible. Maybe it was time for a move to fresh pastures?

He had lots of options both within and without the company. In just the last few weeks he had calls from four agencies with appetising opportunities. Maybe ... but right now he had to get this resolved and get Mike to make it clear to Tom what needed to happen. He couldn't get to Mike early enough to ensure his support.

Mike had barely checked his mails, when Terry, and Tom, the Operations Manager in tow, knocked on his door and asked to see him. Terry explained the problem with the customer. Apparently, there was some disagreement about the size of the last order and, whoever was right or wrong about that, the fact was that they now needed to bring forward the delivery date of the existing order by two weeks, as well as catching up on the alleged shortfall. Tom was not in a mood to be very helpful or conciliatory. He saw it as being Terry's problem and he did not want to let him off the hook so easily.

He had followed the schedule he had been given and had jumped through hoops to deliver on it. On top of that it could not have come at a worse time because some key people were scheduled to take overdue and much-needed holidays. The two of them stood there empty-handed and at loggerheads. There were implications for other functions like the Materials, Shipping and Engineering departments, so they agreed to deal with the problem at the 10 o'clock meeting.

When they had left his office Mike felt quite down. This was not so much because of the customer problem, because he knew they would eventually find a solution; they always had in the past. What was even more worrying was his increasing loss of confidence in the ability of his people to independently and creatively deal with problems like these. It cannot and should not be that difficult. Both Tom and Terry were great performers, but the antagonism between them was wearing. He thought of what Albert had said about the importance of being a united team. "Let's see how united we are", he said to himself. He decided this time he would sit back at the meeting and observe for a change. He would watch the different people and how they behaved and responded.

The rock and the hard place

At the 10-o'clock meeting, Terry explained what had happened and recounted the phone call from Sharon of that morning.

"We have no choice here, Mike, we just have to get them what they want and get it to them as, like yesterday."

Mike remained quiet. Everyone else did too. Everyone knew that Tom would break that silence. They needed to do nothing. They had not long to wait.

"Ok, so we satisfy her, the squeaky wheel, and let other better and at least equally important customers down. Is that it?" Tom retorted.

"You can say what you like, but we simply cannot let Key Services down. It would be suicide. Grossly irresponsible. Not on?" Terry barked back.

"But whose fault is it that we are in this? It always comes back to *us*. Always comes back to the Operations Department picking up the pieces.

"We need to spend our time resolving the problem rather than blaming people, Tom. That will get us nowhere. Have you ever heard of something called "flexibility" or of putting the customer first?"

"I resent that. And you know that resolving the problem means just one thing – the Operations Department jump through hoops as always to satisfy you and cover up your mistakes. We can't do that to people. You know, Mike, how we are struggling with the new system. There is only so much they can take, and we have to think of people as well and take them into account. It can't only be about the business and the company. People have lives as well or are supposed to have them. Their lives have been non-existent in the past few months because of so much overtime and they can't take any more. And I can

> "Part of customer service is knowing you cannot make some people happy, no matter what you do"
>
> **Steven Magee**

tell you, they won't. You can trot out all the flexibility and customer jibes you like but it won't wash with people."

"Well, they'll have lives and no company if we don't look after our customers, Tom," Heather the customer relations director interjected. "Customers are our life-blood."

Mike was surprised at the strength of Heather's comment given her short time as a member of the team. No apologising for her existence here!

"They certainly are our life-blood and never more than now," Sally from Finance added. "We can't afford to have any slip-up or problem in this quarter. I would need to know for definite what is going to happen as I will have to report any change to our forecast. You know how they are about these things, Mike? And, at the end of the day, you know that only one thing matters which is the bottom line – figures, meeting targets and projections, return on investment, share price etc. Once it gets known that there'll be a drop in forecasts, everyone will want to be involved as you well know, Mike."

Mike knew very well and he thought of the phone call from Martha the previous evening. The same old issue. More grist for the mill. More rods to beat his back. But he still said nothing.

Battle lines

"We have a problem too.", Tony, head of Engineering added, "We need to do some critical system maintenance checks next weekend so we simply cannot let anything get in the way of that. We have this in the plan for over months now. You all know that don't you? And I made this very clear to you when we agreed it, Terry, And are you telling me that now you are going to renege on that and scupper our plans? It's ok to beat us up with talk of how important customers are as if we were little children. But we all have responsibilities, and we have to understand that and help each other rather than doing what suits us best."

Mike caught Teresa's eye. They were not surprised to see these two combatants slug it out.

"That's very unfair, Tony, but thanks for the lecture." Terry replied. "The fact of the matter is that our customer has a problem, and it's not one that I created. We have to solve it. This isn't just *my* problem. The hole

isn't only at my end of the boat. Surely we all agree we are only here to serve customers. If we fail to do that, we may have a very effective and well-maintained system, Tony, and comfortable people, Tom, but without a business. Is that what we want?"

"Hold on," Teresa intervened. "We have to resolve this. Mike, you know that if we mishandle this it will undo all the hard work we've put into our employee relations. This could reopen a whole Pandora's box of complaints and grievances about overtime, pay and conditions, work-life balance and consultation. We would have to consult people and representatives if we were to put on a new shift for example. Are you all aware of the rumblings that are going on? We could lose all control and all over just one mishandled situation. I have to be honest and say that I'm worried about all of this and what it might lead to within our whole workforce. I don't know if any of you have heard but I understand that there is a small group of people who have formed or are talking of forming some kind of committee, a works or staff committee!"

"What?" Tom interrupted! "A works committee, like a union?"

"Oh, not that", Tony said. "That's ridiculous. It seems you can't say boo to people any more or they complain."

"Maybe it is," Teresa replied, "and I don't know much about it."

"But why?" Tom asked.

"I understand," Teresa answered, "that they feel they have no say in things and that we as managers decide everything and they are expected to roll over and go along with everything. I don't think it is a trade union, at least not yet, but they want to represent the people and have a say in things."

"Well, let's not get caught up in all that now. We have a different problem to solve; this one with our important customer. What do you think Natalie?" Mike asked, "you have been quiet?"

"I don't know Mike really. It doesn't affect me directly and I can see we have major differences of opinion. Joe told me yesterday that he could see this coming as he met someone from the purchasing department in Key Services who said there was a problem. But he only told me this yesterday."

"A pity he didn't warn us earlier. That would have helped. And you, Bernard? It's not like you to be quiet either!"

"I know Mike. I think we're in a bind and it's not easy to get out of it. We seem to be caught between several rocks and hard places – customers and people needs, ourselves and the corporation, Terry and Tom. I don't see a way out of it and I'm afraid you may have to make the call."

"Yes, I think so too," Frank said, "no one has mentioned the Logistics Department in all of this, and we are right in the middle of it and caught at both ends. We will be involved and affected whichever way this goes. But, as always, we get taken for granted and are expected to jump through whatever hoops people give us. Never any shortage of flexibility in Logistics for sure."

> "Work is about a search for daily meaning as well as daily bread, for recognition as well as cash, for astonishment rather than torpor; in short, for a sort of life rather than a Monday through Friday sort of dying"
>
> **Studs Terkel**

"Well, I agree with Bernard and I think you have to make the call here, Mike," Terry came back in, "there is only one way to go on this. The implications from not meeting this important customer's requirement will be devastating on a whole range of fronts. It's as simple as that to me."

"When did you say you would get back to her, Terry?" Mike asked.

"I didn't say but I know I'll have to get back to her before close of business tomorrow at the latest. And, by "getting back" I mean confirming that we will deliver."

"That's not fair," Tom muscled in, "that's putting a gun to our heads and to yours too, Mike. It's not fair ..."

"Ok, Tom. I hear you. We're not going to decide what to do now but I want you all to think about it and we'll meet in the morning first thing to deal with it. Is that ok?"

Everyone mumbled and everyone knew it was far from ok.

Those millennials or generation whatever – never happy

Mike knew it was not ok also, but he needed time to think and he needed to put an end to the pitched battle that was the meeting. He felt he needed help. He finished the meeting and phoned Joan on her mobile and caught her on a break.

"Sorry for taking you away from the children but I believe I have bigger issues with my own children here. Any chance that brother of yours might be around? I could do with that chat with him that you suggested."

"I'm sure he is. I know he was in China a few weeks ago but he's long back from there. Give him a call. He'd be delighted to talk to you. He always enjoys it, he says. Keeps him fresh and on his toes. And you know he's interested in the company for lots of reasons"

Mike wasn't sure what Joan meant, but he let it go. "Well, we have an issue now that might knock him back on his heels. Thanks Joan. I'll see if he's free."

Brendan was free and Mike agreed to leave work early to meet him.

But before leaving he had to meet Teresa to agree what to do about Albert.

Mike told Teresa that he was going to meet with Brendan. "You know Brendan?"

"Yes, I do. Joan suggested I meet with him to discuss some of my issues with him, and we have met once or twice."

She looked a little nervous about this, probably, Mike thought, because of family connection with Brendan. So Mike told her he thought this was a very good idea and that he thought Brendan could be a big help to her.

Mike then told her about his meeting with Albert. Teresa looked a bit anxious or upset. Maybe, Mike thought, it was a follow-on from her upset at the previous meeting and he asked her this.

"Not at all, Mike, this has nothing to do with our meeting. It's just that I see Albert as a photocopy of my own two. I agree with you about how experienced he is and how apparently honourable he is. But I know, like my own two, he will be gone inside a year. I would bet half my salary on it."

"Only half? That doesn't sound too bad. But, maybe you're right and Albert is like Jenny and Robert and for the same reasons. I know that you think they can't stick at

> "The point is, there is no feasible excuse for what we are, for what we have made of ourselves. We have chosen to put profits before people, money before morality, dividends before decency, fanaticism before fairness and our own trivial comforts before the unspeakable agonies of others"
>
> **Iain Banks**

anything, but could it be that, like Albert, they have never found anything or any organisation in which they really believed and that would have encouraged them to stay?"

"I don't think they ever will. They're not living in the real world. Their only loyalty is to themselves. Not to any organisation or company to which they belong."

"And the more I hear from you, Teresa, talking about your two children, the more I can hear Albert talking. Let me ask you about loyalty. How loyal are *we* or our company to our people? Do you think that if it suited us to move somewhere else and close down this company that we wouldn't do so?

> "Peace does not mean an absence of conflicts; differences will always be there. Peace means solving these differences through peaceful means; through dialogue, education, knowledge; and through humane ways"
>
> **Dalai Lama XIV**

Do you think that, even for one minute, it would cross our minds to ask about our loyalty to our people? Do you think it would cross any manager's head to consider the damage this 'good business decision' would do to people's lives? Forever, in some cases. Not just a loss of a job and income but the loss of dignity, respect, livelihood and the awful loss of confidence. And we can do all this without batting an eyelid because we deem it 'good management'.

Doing what is good management or apparently good for business justifies the most awful of actions. It allows us as managers to cease seeing people as flesh and blood human beings.

Remember what Tolstoy said: "(managers) accept as a law something which is not a law, and they do not acknowledge the eternal, immutable, pressing law that God himself has written in man's heart. ... And indeed they are terrible people - more terrible than brigands. A brigand might, after all, feel pity, but not these men: they are insured against pity as these stones are from vegetation. That is what makes them so terrible."

Do you not think that people see this and know that, despite our lovely words, that ultimately, they are expendable? They know that we know we will be alright no matter what happens to this company. We'll be looked after. Why would they be or how could they be loyal? When I talk to people, I know they don't believe what I am saying.

They think I am only thinking of myself and of the overall company and my own welfare. I can see it on their faces at our canteen meetings! And this is so because it's all they have ever known, and they have never known or worked for a company that saw them as important and that would be loyal to them. They have no idea, nor could they have any idea of the tension and pressure somebody in my position has to deal with in terms of being loyal. Being loyal to the company or institution is risk-free at one level but is enormously risky and damaging at a deeper level."

"I hear what you're saying, Mike, and maybe you're right. I have some idea of those pressures you talk about. So, I take it you want me to offer Albert the position?"

"I would like you to but only if it makes sense to you and you think it might work."

"Well, I am far from convinced but I'm prepared to work to make it happen even if it costs me quarter of my salary!"

Mike laughed. "Well done, Teresa. Thanks for your confidence and trust. I will be equally prepared to eat lots of humble pie if it doesn't turn out well as I hope it will do. There's one little thing I would mention and it's around your phrase of "offering Albert the position". I think that's fine, but you might need to include it in a longer conversation which would include seeing if *he* is open to offering us his time and effort and life. It's a two-way thing. Do you agree?"

"Yes, Mike, I understand. That makes a lot of sense to me. Now, if only I could find a person or a manager like you that would take on Jenny and Robert," she laughed.

Help from outside the hole

Brendan was familiar with the situation in Mike's company and with the different players. Mike told him he was delighted he was helping Teresa, his human Resources Manager. Mike, then, brought him up to speed with the latest saga.

"You know yourself, Mike, there are many aspects and angles to this issue. There's a clash between looking after customers and looking after your people. There are internal clashes between people and functions – Tom and Terry in particular this time. There's the usual dilemma of what or who is more important – the company or the people. There's the risk of doing something in the short term that will do more damage in the longer term, like continuing to pour on overtime and get Tom to roll over. There are other players who are watching on and want to see if pragmatism will rule again this time, irrespective of whether it's the right thing to do or not. And then you have the constant threat in the background from corporate management who, if they hear about it, will simply take the reins from you and decide. Do you know what I'm saying, Mike?"

"Oh, I do Brendan. You are being very helpful! All that makes me feel just great! Glad I came to talk to you ha ha.

"I understand how you feel Mike. You're a bit stuck, and being stuck is like someone caught or stuck down a hole. You need help to get out of it and that help has to come from outside the hole, which is what we will look at later."

"Well, yes, I am stuck and, there is one other shining star in my firmament that you should know about." And Mike went on to tell him about the phone call from Martha and the ominous visit in a few months of Brad, the Vice President and Head of International Operations.

"Amazing, so they are really turning up the heat. We should talk about all that if you wish. But for now, I would prefer not to do that but to focus on how you're going to decide how to deal with this issue, irrespective of the actual decision itself."

"That might be interesting, Brendan, but we – and Terry in particular – have to give the customer a clear answer by tomorrow afternoon. It is that – the actual decision – that I need help on, rather than on how we might reach that decision. Do you understand? I am all for learning, but right now I just want to resolve this problem."

"Oh, yes I do, Mike, and I know what I am suggesting might seem unhelpful and you could hear it as avoiding or delaying the decision. But I hope that's not the case and will not be the case. Do you have a good answer for what to do on this thorny issue or dilemma?"

"No, I don't. If I had I would have told them, given it to them and I wouldn't be here bothering you. I'm down a hole. Remember?"

"Ok, and even if you had the answer, telling them what it is might not have been the right thing to do, but I understand.

"What do you mean "not the right thing to do"? If I had the answer, it would be the right thing and so would be what we should do. Surely?"

"Well, I understand, but forgive me for this, but could it possibly be that your answer – if you had one - *might* not be the right thing to do? Just possibly?"

Being certain can be dangerous ... especially when you are the boss!

"Yes, of course ... but unlikely to be wrong if I'm certain that it is the right one. I've been around here and this kind of thing for some time, as you know. That's why I have my job and is what people expect from me."

"Maybe! But being certain and being right don't always go hand-in-hand and are not synonymous. Does that make sense? Your manager in the corporation – do you think he's right about you and what you are doing, even if he's certain he is right?"

"No, not at all. I think he's not understanding at all and is seriously mistaken because …"

"Fine, I understand. The only point I'm making is that even if you had the right answer, meaning that you are certain it's the right answer and will work, you could still be wrong."

"So, what are you saying to me then? That I should do nothing because I might be wrong?"

"No, I'm only defending or explaining what I said earlier about the wisdom of you coming up with the right answer or solution for this problem and giving it or announcing it to your team. And that's why I said at the outset of this conversation that I would prefer to talk to you about *how* you're going to decide this, rather than the actual decision, especially given that you feel down a hole. I'm only saying that your coming up with the right decision and announcing it to your people might have some flaws in it because it might not be the right or best decision. That's all."

> "If you think you are right about everything, you need to talk with God"
>
> **Paulo Coelho**

"So, you're saying that I should make sure that my decision is the right one, and be very sure of it, before I tell the group what my decision is. It that it?"

"Yes, that's a lot of it, but, even if you were absolutely certain that you were right, why might it – and I stress *might* – still not be the best thing to do, to simply tell them your decision?"

"I'm not sure. You're probably thinking that I would be making the decision for them and that they might simply go along with it, even if they didn't fully understand it or agree with it. Is that what you mean?"

"Yes, that's a lot of it. That's exactly what might happen and some of them, particularly those who don't agree with your line of thinking, might hope that it doesn't work out. Even if this would be bad for everybody. Can you imagine that happening?"

"Yes, unfortunately I can. I have seen this happen very often. Last year, Terry, our sales manager, went after some new business against the wishes of people in the team. They didn't think it was good business for us but it became a point of conflict between different people. In fact it would have been good if we had got that business.

But, I can remember very clearly the looks on different people's faces when they learned that we hadn't got the business. They found it hard to hide their smiles. So, yes, I do understand what you're saying."

"Good and, even though I don't know your people or most of them, it may be that some people are just inviting you to walk into this one, take no responsibility themselves for what the outcome might be but enjoy the whole drama and excitement that might ensue. Nothing like a bit of excitement in life, especially when someone is bored."

"You're right, and I can see that happening already."

"I'm sure it is. It happens all the time. But, the good news, Mike, is that you are not going to make that mistake this time!"

"Why do you say that?"

"Because you *don't know* what to do and you're not certain about what the right thing to do is, so there is little chance of your dumping your decision on them," Brendan said, laughing.

"Ha-ha you're right. Not that that is of much help to me, or that you are much help to me for that matter."

"Maybe not, or maybe I am. Tell me, Mike, how does it feel not to have the answer for once?"

"Not good at all. I don't like it. It doesn't feel at all comfortable."

"I understand and I can see that but that may not be a bad thing."

"Well, it doesn't feel good. And I can't see how not knowing what to do can be a good thing. It's my job to know what to do. It is what's expected of me as a manager as I said."

"In every situation? Always?"

"Yes. That's what's expected of managers and what's expected of me."

"Great, so you're expected to always have all the answers for whatever situation arises, for whatever problem? Sounds kind of godlike, don't you think? Is it not asking a bit much of you, great as you are?" Brendan laughed.

"I hadn't seen it like that before. It's how I have always behaved. And it's always worked out ok. I believe."

"Good, and glad to hear that but maybe sometimes you did come up with answers that were good but may not have been the very best ones. I don't know. I say that because, quite apart from the points I made earlier about people not taking responsibility, it can be good to admit that you don't have answers sometimes … when you know you don't have them. As managers we want to stay on top of things, remain in control but sometimes that's just not possible. We can get stuck, feel lost, and uncomfortable as this may be, and inappropriate as you may feel it is for you, it can be the right thing to do as a manager.

"How can that be?"

"Well, first of all, just for sheer honesty. If you don't know and you're lost, then admitting it is a pretty honest and admirable thing to do. And, when you do that, you're showing respect for the situation, for the reality, And when you do this, you may eventually get a breakthrough. Just staying with it will allow the solution to emerge. If we rush in with our answer, we are preventing that from happening. It is our old model of the Person and the Situation or World. It's a partnership between us and the world or what the situation or reality is. And when we respect both sides -the Person and the Situation -good solutions emerge. We

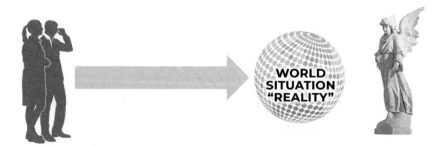

must trust that it will happen. It's not comfortable, but it's being honest and trusting yourself and the world."

"I understand but, I assure you, it's not comfortable."

"I know that, and I'm sorry, but we'll get there. But before that I think it would be good if you were able to take advantage of this situation to learn how well this works, and to do that you'll need to deal with this issue of decision-making with your team once and for all. You remember the four decision-making styles we talked about once?"

"Yes, I do, though I haven't looked at them in a while."

"Well, I think you should, and I think you should talk to your team about them so that you and they are clear. That won't resolve this situation, but it will help deal with other ones and prevent people looking for you or others to make decisions and topics where they are accountable."

"I understand and I think you're right, but what about this particular issue – the one I came to talk to you about."

"Ah yes, that one, I forgot about it," Brendan said laughing. "This won't be easy, but I think it will work, even if it's risky."

He and Mike talked for twenty minutes about how Mike might handle the meeting the following morning and what to do regarding the dilemma about the customer.

"So, are you ok Mike?"

"Well, I still have no idea what to do about this situation but I have some idea on what I might do at tomorrow morning's meeting."

"I'm sure that's not an entirely comfortable place to be for you, no?"

"Definitely not," Mike laughed, "It's most uncomfortable. I always know what to do and, what's more, my team expect me to know."

"Good and "comfort", is not a valid reason on its own for doing things. But, for once at least, you can live with some discomfort for now?"

"Yes, Brendan, I can."

Questions for reflection and action

1. Do you recognise situations like this with demanding customers and the conflict between Terry and Tom ... and others? Who do you think is right? Know what you would do?
2. Do you understand Teresa and the risks she sees around Albert? Think she will lose half her salary?
3. What do you think of Brendan's views on Mike's role around decision-making? What is he saying?
4. What is so wrong or dangerous about being certain? Especially when you are a manager who decides?
5. How do you feel when you just do not know what to do? How do you handle those kinds of situations? Do you ever admit it?

Chapter 7
Up Against It ... Be It a Rock or a Hard Place

The skill of watching, allowing and helping a solution to emerge

Everybody was on time, and seemed anxious and apprehensive in the early morning meeting the following day. Mike got down to business.

"No need to go over the details of what this meeting is about. And, I'm sure, there's little or no need to explain why it's so vital a situation and important that we resolve it. We have one big problem, namely that a client requires a service from us and is making it very clear that they will not settle for anything else.

Unfortunately, if this is the rock, the hard place is that providing the client with what they need will cause us serious problems, and possibly long-term damage. We're not sure that we can get our workforce to actually get the work done or do so without risking damage to our people and to staff relationships. Getting the work done will mean seriously endangering our capacity to deliver on this and other work because we will, once again, fail to do some critical maintenance that will come back to bite us sooner or later. Nor are we sure that we have the engineering support to get this work done. And, if that were not enough, not giving the client what they need will get us into trouble in terms of our performance and results in this quarter. And, if even that is not enough, all of this will get us into another kind of trouble with our bosses in corporate management. Is that more or less the situation?"

There was a general and sullen mumbling of agreement.

"Anybody want to say something or add anything or maybe give us a effective solution that you have come up with overnight?"

"I don't have any solution, Mike," Terry said, "but I got a further call last night from Sharon enquiring as to when they would receive the product. I told her we were working on it, but she didn't seem to like that piece of information. I won't go into everything she said again."

"I had nothing to do with this," Tony added, "but there was a meeting of the downtime maintenance crew yesterday evening to ensure everything was in place for the refurbishing programme. I didn't interfere or give them any indication that it might not happen, and I had no ulterior motives for doing so. I'm just hoping it won't come to that. Some of them have cancelled weekend trips they had planned, and one is missing out on an important match he has to play at the weekend. I think this is a crazy mess we have got ourselves into, quite honestly. I don't know how we let this happen" he said, glancing at Terry.

> "Sometimes life knocks you on your ass ... get up, get up, get up!!! Happiness is not the absence of problems, it's the ability to deal with them"
>
> **Steve Maraboli**

"I have nothing to add, Mike, I'm sorry." Tom said. "I thought about it and I still can't see any way out of it. People just won't, or indeed, can't, find the time for it. It's as simple as that. Even if we were to force them to do it, I think we'd get a formal complaint, and not from individuals but from the group or from some representatives of the group. And as I said yesterday, I can't blame them. They've had enough of this kind of thing and of the assurances we have given them. They're right that it's a management problem. We just should not let ourselves get into these kinds of messes."

"I've nothing to add either, Mike," Sally said, "I will, as you know, have to submit an update of our monthly and quarterly projections this week so they will be affected by this particular situation. That may grab some attention, depending on what happens."

"Anybody else got some good news for me?" Mike joked, "It looks like we've got it all tidied up!"

Everyone laughed, half-heartedly, nervously, and people avoided making eye contact.

Facing the monster: or circling the wagons

"What I want to say is that we, we in this room, are going to resolve this issue today", said Mike. "And I mean "we". Not myself or not just Terry, nor Tom, but all of us. I know you might wonder why I'm saying that, given the complexities and impasses we have already come up against, none of which we have been able to resolve. But I'm telling you that we are going to resolve it today for two very good reasons:

One. is that it is our obligation and responsibility to do so – *all* our responsibility. It's what we're expected to do, what we're contracted to do and what each and every one of us agreed to do when we accepted the leadership positions we have. Is that very clear and does it make sense?"

Everyone nodded in agreement, albeit not very enthusiastically or confidently.

"The second reason why we are going to resolve this," Mike resumed, "is that we're capable of doing so. There's ample talent in this room, around this table to resolve this issue and even much bigger ones. And that talent isn't only the individual talent of Terry, Tom, Bernard, Heather etcetera, but is also the enormous talent and power we have as a group to resolve this. I could make the call on what to do, but I don't want to do that.

I don't want to do it because, clever as I am, it might not be the right call. And I don't want to do it because if I did, then it would be *my* call, my decision, and not yours. I want it to

"It is not because things are difficult that we do not dare ... It is because we do not dare that they are difficult"

Seneca

be ours. That way what we come up with is agreed by everybody and supported by everybody. Is that clear?"

Everyone nodded and mumbled yes. There was a small but growing confidence and commitment in the group.

"I think we are all clear about what a good decision needs to be. What do you all think it needs to be. Bernard, you're good at these things and making summaries?"

"Well, I think we are all clear. We have a customer who has a need that we have to meet but we need to find a way to do this which we currently don't have and whatever solution we come up with will have to deal with the serious knock-on effects for the operations department for Engineering maintenance, corporate budgetary obligations and some other things. Is that it?"

"Anybody got anything else to add?" Mike asked.

Teresa came in, "Well, there are some longer-term implications from whichever way we jump that we'll also need to be aware of. What I mean is that we could come up with a solution for this, this week, but end up paying a higher price down the line for the repercussions of our decision. Do you know what I mean?"

Mike and everyone agreed.

"Okay, let's square the circle or maybe better, circle the square of these four different and vying needs. You all know what they are and how apparently unresolvable they are. What I would like you to do is to work in pairs or small groups to come up with a solution for the issue. Teresa, I'd like you to work with Terry and Heather and help them to come up with some way in which this can be handled so that the customer is kept happy in a way that is practical and doable from Tom's and Tony's viewpoints.

I want you, Bernard, to work with Tom to find a way in which the customer can be satisfied but in a way that's feasible for the people involved and doesn't do longer-term damage. I would like you, Frank, to work with Tony and see how his very important maintenance work doesn't suffer in all of this. And, finally, Natalie, I would like you to

work with Sally and help her to handle the outcome of this, whatever
it is, in a way that doesn't get us into big or bigger trouble. Is that okay?
I know you have no idea how this will work or if it will work, but I want
you to take At least a half-hour to come back with ideas, or solutions, or
recommendations that will break this impasse. Is that alright, everyone?

They all agreed and slowly got into their groupings, sceptically
but humorously. Most left the room and headed off to their own and
others' offices.

Bits and pieces but not enough by any means!

Some of the smaller groups were back within the half-hour but
some, not surprisingly, like Tom's and Terry's needed and requested
more time.

When they were all back, Mike went straight to the key players,
Terry and Tom.

"I'm not sure we have solved anything, Mike," Terry said, "but believe
me, we did our best and Teresa was very helpful – if that's the right
word to use! I have to admit that I'm almost afraid or completely afraid
to go back to Sharon but, under pressure from Teresa, I agreed that
I could ask her about deadlines and if there's any room for manoeuvre.
I do think she will throw me out or throw something at me. And I'm
not sure that it would help, Tom, but I'm wondering if it would ease
some of the pressure. That's as far as we got." Terry was visibly upset.
"This could be the straw that breaks this camel's back," he thought to
himself, "I don't need this kind of pressure. I have had enough of it."

"Okay, thanks Terry and Teresa. We will come back to that. How
about you, Tom? How did you and Bernard get on?"

"Well, we don't have any solution either but, as you all know, we in
the Production Department never give up trying to help and make
things happen Ha! Ha! Jumping through hoops is what we do well. It
comes with practice! What we said we could try is to talk to our people

and simply ask them if they would be willing to do the extra hours and explain the need to them etcetera. I know it's far from perfect, and I don't believe it will work but it would, at least, prevent the whole thing from going sour and doing long-term damage. If they did agree, that would resolve the issue, at least in the short term. If not, we'll have to try something else. That's the best that we could think of."

"Tony, how did you get on, with Frank on your planned maintenance problem?"

"We didn't solve it either, I'm sorry to say, but what we came up with was a bit like what Tom and Bernard said. We talked also of going to our engineers and asking them if they would be willing to accommodate us and postpone or park all the plans they have in place, including the work schedules and times that they have agreed with people, while explaining why. They mightn't like it or mightn't even agree to it, but we could at least give them the chance by making them aware of what is happening or might happen."

"That's good, Tony. I won't ask you, Sally, and Natalie, what you came up with because we may not need to go there if we can resolve this, and I still believe we can. I hope you all do too for the reasons I mentioned earlier, namely that we need to and that we're able to. So let's keep working on it and do things in this same spirit. What else can we do that might help resolve this?"

"As I was listening to what Terry and Tom were saying," Frank said, "I was wondering if, instead of asking her to compromise and delay the delivery, what if we asked her to stagger the delivery? I'm pretty sure that not everything or all of what she is asking for is immediately needed or critical. I think we could give her, or propose to her, a schedule of delivery over a few days that would ease the burden and possibly make it much more doable for Tom and with far less disruption."

"I'm not so sure that she would agree to that," Terry objected.

"I know she may not like it, or say that she does," Frank said, "but it would be a good, respectful and healthy way to go. And an honest one. She knows deep down that this was not all our fault and she might acknowledge that."

"I believe this is a good and healthy way to deal with clients anyway," Bernard added. "I agree with Tom that we also need to be strong with our customers and work in an adult way, and that's no reflection on you, at all, Terry. I think intelligently pointing out a good solution for her and one that will work for us will actually earn us more respect in her eyes."

"I like that too," Sally said, "but what I was a bit worried about was Tom's plan of asking people to work extra, requesting them to do so. It kind of gives them a veto and could establish a dangerous precedent. What if they say no? Then we have nowhere to go. I think we have the right to ask people to work and we should not forfeit that right. But we could lose a lot of our power if we did that."

"I understand, Sally," Tony came in, "but what if we handled it slightly differently. What if Tom explained the situation to them and the options facing us and them, and told them what we want to do and believe we need to do and check with them if that makes sense? Let them know that it is what we – and Tom – believe is the right thing to do in this situation and hope that they will agree, because it makes sense. Maybe we have to trust that it will make sense to them. I think that's always a good way to go, just stick with what is right."

"I like that too," Bernard said, "because it's not so much asking their permission but explaining to them what we believe is the right thing to do. It shows that we respect them and that we trust them. I really like that."

"But what if they say No?" Sally came back, "What do we do then? "

"Maybe we have to trust them and that they won't say No!" Bernard said. "Maybe if we are open with them, make sense to them and demonstrate that we genuinely believe this is the right and best thing to do, maybe if we do all that, they will see the sense of it and not say No. I use this all the time with groups in the community who are angry or upset about something. I never try to manipulate them or to get leaders or groups from within to work on them. And it works. I can't even explain why, but trust and respect do work. That's why I say: Why not trust them?"

"Yes, and maybe our very respect for them and trust in them is what will make the difference. I really like that." Natalie said. "I think it might avoid getting into differences with them and a whole lot of trouble as well."

Trusting others and ourselves

"It could be, Sally," Mike commented, "that the only precedent we would be setting if we did that would be the precedent that we will always do what we think is right and best and that we will very often check that with people to make sure that we're getting it right. And, even if they did happen to say "No", we might still need to press on, explain to them why we are doing it and ask them to go along with it. How does all that sound, Sally?"

"That sounds fine, Mike. I see what you are getting at. That way we don't really lose our right to make the call or take decisions. It actually helps it."

"All that sounds fine to me too," Terry said, "But what happens if Sharon doesn't accept my approach or my request? I can see how Tom might be able to persuade his people even if they weren't fully in agreement with his request for them to work extra hours, but I don't have that same kind of power with the customer that he has. She might just refuse and feel perfectly entitled to do so. What do we do then?"

"Either we have hope within us or we don't; it is a dimension of the soul and it's not essentially dependent on some particular observation of the world or estimate of the situation ... It is an orientation of the spirit, and orientation of the heart"

Victor Havel

"Do you mean," Teresa asked, "that you don't have the same kind of power that Tom has? What kind of power do you think Tom would be using in this case?"

"Well, his power as the manager, surely?"

"But that is not the kind of power that Bernard was suggesting Tom would use, I think," Teresa answered. "I think that what was meant was that he would rely on what made sense to them, what was best, what was the right way to go on this. Tom wouldn't be pulling rank on them. He would only be explaining the situation to them, suggesting to them – and even strongly recommending to them – that this would be the best way to go and trusting that it would make sense to them too. I see you being able to do the very same with her."

"I can see that, but I think it's a bit different in my case. She might very well turn around and say no."

"Yes, she might," Bernard said, "but maybe she won't. Maybe what you're saying and how you are saying it to her will also make sense to her! Sure, there's a risk but there will always be risk as long as we respect people's right to do what they believe is best for them. It just means that you'll have to trust her and, like Tom, trust the wisdom and reasonableness of what you are proposing."

"I understand that, Bernard," Heather said, "but I agree with Terry that this is a dangerous way to go. They are such an important customer and if we lose them, all hell will break loose. And it will break loose for you too, Mike, as Sally well knows. No, I wouldn't be in favour of approaching her in that way. It's just too risky. I know Sharon!"

"I think I agree with you too," Sally added, "if it works, great, but what if it doesn't? What will we do then? And, if it goes wrong, we will be asked why we didn't let corporate management know in advance."

"What if Tom tried talking to his people first of all?" Frank said, "if that worked, then we would have no problem. How about that?"

"Okay." Mike came in. "It seems that there are different ways we can handle this, and we are not all in agreement about which is the best one. What I would like us to do is the following: You go ahead and talk to Sharon, Terry, and see if you can reach agreement on that way we talked about of satisfying their immediate needs so that we're able to do so without causing serious damage to Tom and his people, and to Tony and his Engineering staff, as well as to the long-term health and welfare of the operation.

At the same time, Tom you will talk to your people, as we said, and hopefully secure their understanding and commitment to delivering what's essential for the customer, whatever that turns out to be after Terry has spoken with Sharon. And, as you said, Tony, you will check in with your people and, hopefully, come up with an alternative maintenance plan that will work for everybody. That's what I would like us to do. Is that alright?"

Overall, there was general agreement.

A square nearly circled. Or who decided?

"Now, I know this is not your preferred way to go, Terry, but I think it's the right and best one. I understand what you are saying. This is a very important customer and customers are our lifeblood. I agree with you that we have to find a way to meet our customer's needs. I understand and agree with all that, but I am asking you to talk to Sharon along the lines I described. I think this is the best way to go and I'd like you to believe that it is and commit to it, really commit to it and not just do it because I am saying so. Because I think it's the best way to go I would love if you were able to agree to that and give it your full support. Can you do that? I really do not want you to do this unless you are both willing and able to do so. Can you do that in this case, Terry?"

Terry felt trapped. Now he regretted not having gone after some of the positions and opportunities in other companies. But there was something about Mike and his tone that felt different. For some reason he heard himself answering:

"Yes, I can, Mike, and I will even if it's not what I personally would like to do."

"You see, I think Bernard is right," Mike said. "I'm not coming the heavy with you but isn't this skill, this ability, this responsibility the very reasons why you have your job, your important job as a manager and leader? Otherwise, we could put anybody into your position, and they would be able to carry it out purely because that was their position. You have your important role because of the skills and attributes and gifts that you have as Terry, and it's these attributes that you can bring to influence this situation. Does that make sense? Is that fair, Terry?"

> "Some might say: 'That's impossible. Keep your feet on the ground. Get your head out of the clouds. But I say: Keep your head high in the clouds because up there the view and the air is clear"
>
> **Mary Lawlor**

"Yes, it does. And I will give it my best shot. I don't mean by that that I will simply try to make it happen. I'll *make* it happen."

"Great," Mike said, "well done, isn't that good everybody?"

Everyone nodded and agreed and looked very pleased.

"So, what about you Sally? You and Natalie got off the hook. Hopefully we won't need a plan from you for how to handle our masters or gods in corporate management. What were you thinking we should do if we haven't or didn't find a solution for this?"

"I think you'll like what we concluded," Sally said. "We agreed that we were going to recommend that we would not and should not report or say anything about this problem until we came up with what *we* believe is the best solution. We thought that we shouldn't go with a problem but go with a solution, a way forward, what we as a group believe is right. It's up to us to give leadership, and if we leave the space vacant, meaning unresolved or up in the air, all kinds of people will fill it and will crawl all over us. It would make finding a solution even more difficult. So, while we didn't find an answer to the problem, we were clear about how we should handle it, whatever we decided. Isn't that right Natalie"?

"Yes, Sally, and we were thinking and saying that it might be easy for Tom or Terry to use you, Mike, to resolve this and work on you to try and get the best solution for them as individuals. In fact, that is very often what we do when we disagree, isn't it?"

Everyone nodded in agreement.

"But what has that to do with how we might handle our corporate bosses?" Mike asked smiling.

"It's just that we could make the same mistake," Natalie said, "and renege on our own responsibility, hoping that somebody else will make the decision for us. I've seen that happen, not only here, but in other places where I have worked. And it's a mistake I can make sometimes too, because I don't like hassle. I've seen people play political games, and use these kinds of situations to impress others and win favour. Isn't that often true?"

Everyone again nodded in agreement.

"I really like what you're saying, Natalie and Sally. I think it's very important. Thanks. How does all this fit with you and your plans, Tony?"

"We intended talking to our people and we'll still do that, based on what we're agreeing here. But, we'll do it now in a different way, in a respectful, engaging way, making sure that it makes sense to them, to the engineers etcetera. I'm not very comfortable handling it in this way, but who knows, they may have other and better ways to deal with how we handle the required maintenance. Isn't that so, Frank?"

> "When you are about to climb mountains the demeanour of the group leader is half of the battle"
>
> **Tom Humphries**

"Yes, Tony, that's how I see it too and I think it will make sense to people and they'll be fine with it. And, if it doesn't, we'll will cross that bridge then."

"Good, that's great." Mike concluded. "We're all clear and in agreement about what to do. Let's go off and do it and I trust that you will all do it very well. Can we take it and agree that we believe this will work and we will only reconvene if something serious doesn't work? Is that okay?"

Everyone wholeheartedly agreed.

"One last thing before we finish, a question. It's around decision-making. Are you all happy that this decision is a really good one? By that I mean that it will deliver what we and our customer want, and is feasible. What do you think?"

They all agreed quickly and strongly that they were happy that it was a very good decision.

"Good, and tell me, who made the decision?"

"We did," many said in unison.

"You did." Others said. "You made the final call and got us all, including Terry and Heather, in agreement."

"Okay," Mike said, "I want us to come back and talk about all of this at our next meeting. We'll tag on an hour to the meeting to just discuss this. I think it's important for us as a group but also important for you with your own people and groups. Okay?"

They all agreed enthusiastically.

"Ha ha it went great," Mike told Brendan on the phone, "and, as you said, I did very little talking. To be honest, I can't pinpoint where the full solution came from. It just came out, it emerged."

"Delighted to hear that Mike. I was talking to Teresa about something else and I picked up from her that it had gone well. As I said, it is about trusting the wisdom and goodness in people and especially of people in groups or teams. When we do this, as you have done, we actually create a new and very different kind of intelligence and a much more powerful one. It's a completely different view of the world from the normal one. But, tell me, who actually made the final decision – you or them?"

"Ha ha – that's a good question, Brendan. In fact I did, but how I did it made sense to them so that they were in agreement with it, even those who originally weren't fully happy with it."

"I understand, Mike, and I think what you have to do with them now is to clarify some things around decision-making – some of those things we have spoken about."

"Yes, I understand. I think it will be important to do that and I said that to them already. Thanks again, Brendan, and I know we'll talk soon."

Questions for reflection and action

1. Do you think this could really happen? It does, you know! And it will!
2. Why do you think a solution or way forward emerged?
3. What did this call for from Mike? And from the others?
4. Did you feel that Terry was coerced … or bullied into talking to Sharon?
5. Think you could play the same role that Mike did?

Chapter 8
Don't be an "Idiot" - (literally a "Private Person"). Make Good Decisions

Develop your decision-making styles

Strangely, at the next meeting, not much time was spent on the issue, nor was it necessary. Everything had gone very well and, in fact, better than anyone had expected.

Terry had met Sharon, the client representative, and it was a great meeting.

"I actually asked to *meet* her rather than talk on the phone and she agreed and was very pleased with the whole thing." Terry said. "I assured her at the outset that we wouldn't let her down and were committed to doing that. I left her under no illusions. But, when I explained our plan to her – and Heather was a great help with this, as was Tom and his people – it made a lot of sense to her. She admitted that she had panicked because she knew that her own people were much to blame for the problem. She even put forward some ways to make it easier for us to meet her requirements. I spotted some ways we could work better together so this doesn't happen again and she was in full agreement. So, you were right Mike to put that pressure on me. I think I was being too soft with them and a bit too soft on myself and our team". Terry seemed delighted – a new man.

"Why might you have got it wrong around Sharon, if you hadn't taken that risk and handled it as well as you did?"

"Yes, I have thought about that and my wife asked me the same question. She asked me if Sharon was a bit of a Jekyll and Hyde character, that maybe she could be a demon or an angel."

"And what did you tell her?" Mike laughed.

"Well, I thought about it a bit before I answered her. Then I told her we are all Jekyll and Hyde and we can be or become one or the other. But, we can also "make" people into one or the other by how *we* are and how we treat *them*. I think that if I'd handled Sharon differently, I would

> "Courage is not simply one of the virtues, but the form of every virtue at its testing point"
>
> **C.S. Lewis**

have brought out the Jekyll in her. But, because of how I approached it, honestly and fairly and respectfully, I brought out the Ms Hyde in her. People are not just as they are but as how we make them by our relationship with them. Do you know what I mean?"

"I do indeed Terry and I find it very powerful. Thanks for that, Terry," Mike answered. "And I hear you got on very well too, Tom?"

The power of helping people to be responsible through trust

"Yes, I did", said Tom, "and I have to say I was even surprised at the response. I agree completely with what Terry has just said. My people also turned out to be how they were based on *how I was* and how I related to them. Not only did they not have any problems, but they were very willing to make things work and they had lots of other ideas too. What made the difference, I think, was the fact that I asked for their help. As you all know, normally we would decide on something and then put it to them as a decision with which they had to comply. When we do this, they feel cornered, obliged to do what we ask, and they feel disrespected, taken for granted."

"Remember I asked you, Tom, what would happen if they said "No"? What would you have done?" Sally asked.

"The straight answer is, I don't know! I just trusted that it would make sense to them because it actually made sense. I put all my faith in that. I think I would have kept at it until we made sense to each other."

"And I think you would, Tom," Bernard said, "the way I see it is that by refraining from using your power as a manager or boss, you were putting all your trust in it making sense to them *because* you believe it makes sense. After all, don't we only want them to do things that make sense? Of course there's a risk, but taking risks is part of managing and part of life.

You know what we have often said; "Risk and Reward ride side by side. Avoid one and the other passes you by." Too often we want to avoid risk at all costs and so try to manage everything and control everything and everyone and this actually becomes counter-productive."

"Yes Tom, I understand that. You made the request or proposal to them as the person responsible for this, but you did it in a personal and human way." said Mike.

"Yes, that's completely true. I was very honest and authentic with them. I was myself. And, Sally, I think this actually established a good precedent for the future. It established that it's what makes sense that governs and that it is my responsibility, to come up with what I think makes sense for everybody. It also means that we have to subscribe to that and obey that "commandment" to make sense. Sometimes what we come up may not be what makes sense or makes most sense and we have to be open to that. How often have we done just that, listened to them and changed our minds because of something they said? Never, I would say. Do you know what I mean?"

"Yes, I do," Sally replied.

"And I understand you got on very well too, Tony?"

"Absolutely, it matches exactly what Tom said and will help us in the future. I went to them honestly and respectfully and they were willing to adjust and make things work whatever happened. Magic!"

"I'll believe it when I see it. Rather: I'll see it when I believe it"

From the Caterpillar Doesn't Know

"Before leaving this," said Mike, "I think it would be good to spend some time understanding why this works well and why you all succeeded. What made such a difference in a very short time? Don't forget that just last week we were all stuck on this issue, and now we've agreed a solution that has improved everything. I'm not looking for any kudos here, but what happened does seem a bit miraculous or magic, don't you agree? Why this enormous change and wonderful result?"

"For me," Tom said, "what made a difference was that we each took responsibility or ownership for the problem. You left it with us and up to us and we were invited, and maybe obliged, to do what was required, and I think everybody played their part and took ownership for their bit of the problem. That made all the difference."

"I agree, Tom," Terry said, "and, in my case what inspired me was how you challenged me, Mike. You made me go after something that, initially, I didn't want to do and didn't believe would work. I don't believe I would have done what I did had you not challenged me and explained the importance of facing up to that challenge. I think it's something we don't do often enough, and, if we do it, we handle it badly in a telling, hierarchical way. Had you not done that, I would not have done justice to myself and to everyone else. Does that make sense?"

"I think it does," Frank said, "but I don't think it would have worked if Mike had simply thrown out the challenge and didn't himself, believe it would work. I think he was confident it would. So I imagine you did too."

"You're absolutely right, Frank, I felt Mike's confidence and his belief in me, even if he had to push me a little on it." Terry laughed. "All kinds of things were going on in my head when Mike challenged me. I'd be afraid to tell you, he laughed.

"One thing that was different," Teresa said, "was that you left it up to us. I think very often we can slip into believing that *you*'ll find a solution, Mike, that, at the end of the day, you'll pull some rabbits from the hat and so *we* don't take real responsibility. We behave a little like children. It was different this time because you treated us like responsible adults and left it up to us. At least that's how I felt. Not that it felt comfortable or easy."

They all agreed.

"One thing that struck me," Tony came in, "was that this was probably the first time that we went to people without a solution in our heads or in our back pockets. Maybe we had some proposals, but we were genuinely open around them, and I think this made a big difference to them. What I felt was that, because we didn't have a plan or an answer or, as usual, a decision that we wanted them to follow, people were able to see the situation for themselves and so felt free to respond to it as they saw fit."

> "Twenty years from now you will be more disappointed by the things you didn't do than by the ones you did. So, throw off the bowlines, sail away from the safe harbour. Catch the trade winds in your sails. Explore. Dream"
>
> **Mark Twain**

"I think that is important." Frank said. "One big change that I've made with our team is to ask the players what they think. They've been used to being told what to do and to follow our instructions. Now we're being much more honest in admitting that we do not have all the answers. They seem to appreciate that more and they are much clearer about what we need to do. They still know who is in charge but it's as if they now respect us even more from listening to them. I know it's a different world, but some things carry over."

"I agree, Frank," Bernard said, "not going with an answer or decision allowed them to see things for themselves and so they were free to respond as they saw fit. I think there are big learnings to be had from this."

Good decision-making is everything

"That's great and well done everyone. Lots of good things here that we will come back to and talk about again." Mike said. "Now I want to return to what I mentioned at the last meeting about decision-making and how we make decisions. I'd like to do this, not only for ourselves, which is very important, but also for all of you so that you can work in the same way with your own people and take good decisions with them. Before getting into that and agreeing what we mean by a good decision, what are the different ways we, or any group might make decisions? Do you mind if I ask, how you take decisions in your own teams? I mean, do you decide, or does the team decide? Which of these is better or the right way? So how should we make decisions here?"

"Well, I think it's important to listen to people," Teresa said, "and to involve them as much as possible. That's what you did, at that last and wonderful meeting, Mike"

"I agree," Tony said, "but sometimes you can't do that. *You* have to decide. The buck stops with us, as they say. It's our job to make sure that the right decisions are taken, rather than throw it open to everybody. And, in a sense that's what you did too in that last meeting, Mike; you decided," he laughed.

"I hear what you're saying Tony, but I agree with Teresa," Bernard said, "so sometimes even though I know what is the right or the best thing to do, I involve and ask the group, because it makes them feel committed and valuable. I nearly always know what I'm going to do anyway but I think it's good and important to involve people! We got a new system from the Quality Department a few months ago and I wanted the team to follow my version of it. I could have told them what I wanted but, instead I got them involved and listened to them and led them along until they finally agreed to go with it. I knew who the important people to get on board would be and who

> "We often trick ourselves into thinking that we possess enough knowledge or control over any given situation to make correct choices. Maybe that is why we hold on to the decisions we make so dearly even when we know we are wrong"
>
> **Spencer Fraseur**

might be difficult and I worked on both groups. Don't you do that with us too, Mike?" he laughed.

Mike said nothing.

"Sometimes," Sally said, "I take the decision but I check out some aspects of it with the team. For example, for very good reasons, I switched the roles of two people in the department last month, but I left the precise timing of the change and some other details around responsibilities up to them. You did that too with Terry at the last meeting, Mike. I think you were quite adamant that he should approach the client, but you left it up to him *how* he did it."

There have been a lot of different ideas on how to take decisions and, in some cases, apparently contradictory ones. Let me check this with you. Would you agree that you have named or described four different ways in which you decide things, or ways in which we should decide things, as follows", said Mike.

- "Some of you believe it's right and best to include and involve your people and get their opinions and input etcetera. Right Teresa?
- Some think that you have to make the call yourself sometimes. Ok Tony?
- Some have their minds made up or pretty close to it, and still involve their people to make them feel good or whatever or get their buy-in. Bernard?
- And some of you make the decision but leave aspects of it open for people to decide themselves. You do that Sally.

So which of these do you think is the right or best one?"

"I believe with Bernard, that the more you involve people, the more commitment and buy-in you get from them" Natalie said. "And, that way, you can get consensus and avoid differences and conflict."

"I agree with you Heather," Tony said, "but there are times you just can't do that. If something is right, then, you have to insist on that and stick with it."

Okay, okay," Mike said, "what's happening here and who do you think is right?

"Ha ha, maybe we all think we're right." Tom said.

Yeah and maybe we are all right in some way… we all have bits of what is really right."

"I agree", Mike said, "and I want to come back to that later and find out what to do about all these differences so we don't end up endlessly arguing, or with winners and losers. That can happen, can't it?" he asked, laughing.

All joined in laughter.

"I take it that what we want is to come up with and agree the way that will deliver the best decisions. And, in doing that, we're all seeing it a bit differently. But what should a good decision be, so it's seen as and actually *is* a good decision?"

"It should be the best way to deal with some situation or solve some problem obviously," Tom said. "the one that gives the best results."

"Yes, and it should be feasible, workable, practical, and so should have as much support and commitment from people as possible. That's what Bernard has been saying, isn't it?" Natalie added.

"Great," Mike said, "so what we want in any decision, then, is the decision or way forward that will best deliver the results we want and, secondly, that it is practical, feasible, doable. We'll come back to those two criteria. But now let's list the four different ways of making decisions you mentioned here on the flipchart.

I'm going to list them across the flipchart for reasons I'll explain later.

1. The first one is I decide. Full stop. Ok? That's what you said, Tony.
2. The second one is the one that Sally mentioned, I decide but I'm open to looking at different ways of making it happen that may make it easier for people or that will resolve some issues for them. If I can.

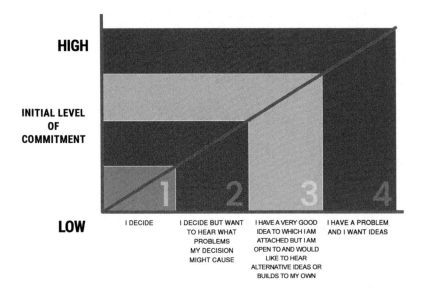

3. The third one is when you've a really good or strong idea that you think will work and believe is the right one, a bit like Bernard said, and so you involve the group but not in the way that Bernard said he sometimes likes to do," he said laughingly.
4. "And the fourth one is to consult, involve, listen to your team or the group etcetera, that you mentioned, Teresa."

Now, if I put here on the vertical X axis the level of support for a decision, I think you can see that the more I go towards number four, the more support and buy-in I am likely to have, as Teresa has been saying. Alright? So if that is the case, why would we not use number four *all* the time, and why would we ever use number one?

"Because," Tony said, "there are some decisions that cannot and should not be shared in the group, as I have been saying. For example, Mike, if you wanted to reduce the size of your team by one or two people, I imagine you wouldn't involve us in deciding who the one or two to go should be! So there are some tough, unpopular decisions that a manager has to take and, it would be wrong to ask or consult people on them."

"It's not so much that," Terry disagreed, "it's more that there are times when I have to take some very quick decisions, sometimes on things that are not of critical importance, and it would be a waste of time to involve my team in making them."

> "'Idiot' originally in Greek meant a private person - someone who is unable to learn from others"

> **Flow**

"Yes, but do you not agree there will always or often be hard decisions to be taken and that we as managers have to take them?" Tony replied.

"I agree with Terry," Tom said, "the buck stops with me or with us. I know it's a trivial example but it's like our famous game of golf that never happens. No one is taking the decision and leaving it to everyone else."

"Ok Tom but who's right here,?" Mike asked. "Tony or Terry?"

"They both are," several people replied.

"Yes, and, as I said earlier, I want to come back to this. But does what they're saying make sense? Mike asked. Because at times we'll have to take tough decisions, as Tony said, and because as Terry said, there will be times when we need to take quick decisions where there's simply no time to consult or involve. In all these cases we can and should use this one, decision- making style number 1.

"Yes," Frank added, "and there'll be some obvious or minor decisions that don't merit discussion, like what time our coffee break will be, which unfortunately you'll take it on yourself to decide Mike.. eventually?" he laughed. "If I want to win a match, then, I have to pick the best team and I have to decide that. I can't try to get everybody to agree to the team that I think is best, especially those who haven't been chosen."

"Yes, very good. And the coffee is on its way, Frank. Don't panic. That's another case where we would just decide as in decision-making style number 1. And I take it you can see the value of what Sally described where – if there is room for it – you can make a decision easier for people by changing some aspect of it or letting the people involved do so. That would be decision- making style number 2, Sally."

"Yes I see that and it makes sense to me." Sally answered.

Ensuring commitment to decisions

"So far so good. Now, what about Bernard's situation, where he feels quite certain that his decision is the right and best one and yet he wants the involvement and support of his people and so he asks their opinion, even though he knows already what he is going to do and what should be done?"

"No, I get what you are saying Mike," Bernard said, "I can see that it's really a form of manipulation and I don't like it and I know my people don't like it either. But it's hard to know what to do when you are fairly certain that your solution is the right and best one. I mentioned before how I am often in this position in the community, and it can be very tempting to manipulate people. Do you know what I mean?"

"Yes, I do very well, Bernard, but if it is ok, I would like to leave it for later or for another day if we run out of time. Is that agreed? Let's keep going and move on."

(Mike had seen a message from his personal assistant saying that Martha was looking for a meeting with him "first thing" – for her – and he had agreed to call her at 5 p.m.)

It was agreed with everyone.

"That can easily happen," Sally said, "and it's often the case that people may want something that's good for them, but that we don't agree with. What would we do in that case?"

Mike thought of his own situation and of the scheduled call with Martha for later

"It is only through relationships that we exist in the universe"

Xenophanes

that evening. He hoped he wasn't being dishonest with his team or misleading them on the tough realities of business life. He did not feel that it was the time to get into that, even if he had a full answer for Sally

"Yes, I know what you mean Sally. Very well. You're asking, I believe, what we should do when what we want is not what people want, what our employees or staff want. That's a bigger issue that I want to leave for now and come back to. And it's a very important issue."

"Yes," Sally answered, "that's fine."

"Thanks Sally", Mike said. So I take it we are fairly clear and comfortable with decision-making style number 4? But let's come back and have a chat about style number 1 – what do you think about this one?" Mike asked.

Just decide or involve

"Well, as we said," Heather commented, "there are times when this is the correct style to use, even if it can appear autocratic."

"What do you think makes people feel that a manager is being autocratic, what would help reduce that feeling when you are going with decision style number one Heather?" Mike asked.

"Well," Heather said, "it would help if you gave the reasons for your decision."

"But would that not give people the impression that they can argue and even challenge the decision?" Tony asked.

"I think it could," Natalie said, "but I still think this is the right thing to do because it gives the person the chance to understand the rationale for the decision, as well as giving them a message that they are respected. And I think you can be firm about your decision and, at an appropriate time, let the person know you don't want to continue talking about it anymore, and move on. I'm not saying this is something I do all that often, but I would like to operate like that and I think it works."

"I think that's very important," Mike said. "I can remember in a company I worked in once where people received letters on Friday about a layoff on the basis that they wouldn't have a chance to talk about it or complain about it, and it was that which caused more problems than the actual decision itself. So I think Natalie is right that we should have the courage to tell people, when it is appropriate, the reasons for our decisions, so they can understand them. They may still not agree with them but it will help them to come to terms with those decisions. I would also add that if you are making a decision in this way, on your own, then be sure you can carry it off and make it happen. And, be confident that it is the right or best decision."

"What you have just said," Teresa commented, "might seem blindingly obvious but I believe, that it's key. Unless the decision itself is a good one, no amount of process skills or techniques will work. People will see flaws or weaknesses in it because they are there. So we have to take the trouble to make sure that our decisions are good ones and not simply presume that they are because we have taken them. I hope that makes sense."

"It does to me, Teresa and it's a strange thing," Bernard said, "but, in a sense the more involving and listening we are as managers – using style number four – the better we will be when we use style number one and go it alone.

"Why do you say that,?" Tom asked.

For two reasons," Bernard said, "one is that you'll probably make better decisions if you're normally in touch with people and listen to them, while involving them. This always works for me both in work and in the community. And secondly, I believe that you'll have more credibility with people when you have to go it alone and take a decision yourself, because people will know that you normally involve others and that you have good reasons for not doing so on occasions. Does that make sense, Tom?"

"Well said," Mike interrupted. "I couldn't agree more. So the more we are a "four", the better we will be a "one"! So, while we all agree that there will be times when we have to use style number one, we believe that the more we go towards four, the better our decisions will be and the more credibility and support we'll have from people when we take them using style number 1.

"Teresa agreed and added: "I think it's really important that in every situation or as often as we can, we give reasons for our decisions. Even if people don't like them or are resisting them, giving them the rationale and why it makes sense, nearly always works and will ensure that we are asking people, as we said earlier, to do things not just because we say so, but because they're the right and most meaningful things to do.

I think that's core to our being a truly intelligent organisation, because it'll mean that we're appealing to what makes sense always and using that as a justification for asking or getting people to do things, and not just because *we* have the authority from the positions we hold. I think every time we take an arbitrary decision without getting an understanding of it, buy-in to it, or at least explaining the rationale for that decision, we are giving people a message that what they think or what's right and best doesn't matter so much.

And I think we inadvertently do that all the time. We can give them a message that what gets done is because *we* say it and not because it makes sense or is the right and best thing to do. In effect, this changes the "rules" or culture in the company and people learn to act to please us or their manager rather than working out for themselves what they should do. Am I making sense?"

Mike thought of his own current situation and his relationship with Martha and Brad. He wondered what she wanted to talk about, even if he could guess. He put that out of his mind and came back to this meeting.

Decision-making can be a form of bullying

"Yes you are, Teresa" Mike answered. "Lots of it. That's why I'm never surprised when I hear or read of cases of bullying in organisations. If managers don't give reasons for their decisions or don't take decisions on the basis of what's right and best but rather just "order "or "instruct" people to do things, then this, to me, is bullying. It's what we spoke about some time ago on the amazing statement by St. Thomas Aquinas: "Obedience is always wrong, even if it is to God!" But, as well as that, I believe that, far from losing power when we decide in this way, we are actually far more powerful. Now am I making sense?"

"Nothing in life can match the fulfilment of knowing you've done what you truly believe is the right thing"

Anthony Robbins

As he said this, he wondered if he would have the courage to disobey Martha and Brad when that time came!

"Yes you are," Sally answered, "but I have one further question, if you don't mind. Suppose you have someone in your team, and you have really tried hard to explain your reasons to them. And suppose you have really listened to their side of things but, having done all that, the person is still not convinced. Surely, in that case you have to take the decision and "order" or "instruct " that person to do what you have decided and want? In those cases you're going against what St. Thomas whatever his name was said?"

"I know exactly what you mean, Sally," Mike answered, "and I've been on both ends of this one and maybe I still am to some extent. But I think there's a good answer to it. I think it's still not only possible but important to handle these situations in a respectful and intelligent or rational way. If I were in a situation like that with you, for example, I think I would say something like: 'We have talked a lot about this issue, Sally, and about what to do and we have not been able to reach an agreement on it, nor have I been able to convince you, and I understand that and understand what you are saying and why you are saying it. The

117

way we, and indeed most organisations are set up and run is that in situations like this, I, or the higher-level person decides, makes the call. That's the system that operates here and one that I bought into when I joined the organisation and the one that I believe you also bought into. I'm not saying that I am right on this, even though I believe I am, but I do have a higher-level view of things and, because of that, it is my responsibility to break the impasse and make the call. Is that ok and do you accept it?' How does that sound, Sally?"

"It sounds good," Sally answered, "but is that not ordering and commanding and instructing, albeit in a nice way?"

"No, I don't think so," Mike answered. "What I would be doing is appealing to a different level of reason or rationale, namely the "rules of the game" that the person openly subscribed to when they joined the organisation. It's not blind obedience but a willing and clear and conscious agreement to operate in a particular way. Just like Frank's players go along with decisions referees make even if they don't always agree with them…or at least I hope they do, Frank. And, for this reason, I would be quite strong on this and, in a nice and friendly and respectful way, make it clear to them that they need to follow and operate and communicate the decision as *theirs* and not present it as something they were told to do. Of course, if it's a matter or principle for them, then they won't be able to do this, but such cases will be very rare. Need I say that the skilful and respectful handling of these situations is very important. Just like you all did in your various meetings. This kind of handling is a long way removed from bullying. Are you agreeable with that Sally?"

"Yes, I'm fine with that. I see what you're saying, that the manager, even in this way, when they decide, is still doing so on the grounds of what is reasonable and rational. Yes, I think it's very helpful."

"I hope all of this has been useful?" Mike asked.

"Very", they all chorused and several of them commented on how important it was to get this part of their managing and leading right in order to become a different kind of company and the one they all wanted it to be.

"That's great and I think we did very good work today and I would like you all to really take on board all these learnings and use them. I would like us to continually check on how we are doing in terms of working in this way."

All agreed.

"Good. Now the question arose earlier about what to do if there is no agreement in the group or team over a decision or direction. Remember we touched on this earlier and how we were not all in agreement about the best way to make decisions?

They all did and nodded.

"And I'm sure you also remember our meeting on the customer problem and how there was no consensus on what to do. Remember?

"Very well," Terry answered laughing.

"Yes, I do too" Heather added.

"So, let's come back to that another day, at our next meeting. I think we have done enough for one day and I have a call to take at five o'clock which I have to prepare for. I'm sure you would all like a break and get that coffee for Frank, or get back to other things you have on."

There was no disagreement.

Questions for reflection and action

1. Do you believe this kind of result or response can happen? Does happen? Will happen?
2. What did it require from Mike to make it happen? What qualities? What skills?
3. Which of the four decision-making skills do you mostly use?
4. Can you think of situations where you could use each of them?
5. Why is this approach absolutely fundamental for good leadership and a healthy and respectful culture?

Chapter 9
Ensuring the "Buck" is Good Before It Stops with You

Experience the power and skill of decision-making in groups and teams

Mike was getting ready for his team meeting. He half regretted having put the question of taking decisions on the agenda for the team meeting in the light of the conversation he had had that evening with Martha. He wasn't sure where it left him or how the conversation fitted in with what they were working on around decision-making.

"I understand how you feel, Mike, but there's a bigger picture here and you have to understand that you're part of it." She had said.

This was part of a long and difficult conversation with Martha later that evening. Mike had felt good after the success of the team meeting, and the clarity they had reached and agreed around decision-making. And now this!

It was not her doing or her plan, she had explained, but part of a corporate strategy to centralise and cut costs. The proposal was to transfer responsibility for everything around Human Resources to a central source. Some of this made sense in terms of simplifying aspects of the bureaucracy around policies and procedures and corporate guidelines. But some of it Mike saw as dangerous.

"I'm thinking of the bigger picture, Martha. I don't think it's wise or healthy to track and hold information and take decisions on individuals in some central place, removed from the operation and the world of the individuals themselves, particularly when that information is based on what I regard as a very flawed Performance Review System."

"Well, I'm not sure what you mean by our Performance Review System. I think it's pretty good and we've put a lot of work into it. But, that aside, this is a corporate strategy and one that we want to follow. And that's why it's not helpful when you are awkward about these things, Mike. Do you know what I mean?"

> "There are no solo high performers. The best support teams are tight open and honest, they have learned that agreement is not a priority but understanding the truth is"
>
> **Richard Young**

Mike wondered where this conversation lay on the four decision-making styles described earlier. He could only keep going in order to find out.

"I'm not trying to be awkward, Martha, but rather trying to make sense of things and to do what's right and best for everybody. I don't think that the strategy is right for us or right and good for the corporation either, for that matter."

"You're quite entitled to that opinion, Mike, but you have an obligation to go along with what the corporation decides. I hope you understand that!"

There it was again. It sounded like decision-making style number 1 was in operation. He decided for now to act as it were not number 1.

"Of course I do, Martha, but I also have an obligation to my own people to say and do what I think is right and best for them and what I believe is right and best for everybody, including the corporation."

"We've been here very often before, Mike, as you well know, and it has got us nowhere. You realise this is part of the bigger issue, so I would like you to think about it. It's important and serious."

"I have thought a lot about it Martha."

"Well, Mike, I would suggest that you have some more thinking to do, for your own sake."

He felt some relief that, at least, it still remained open and that he had made it clear that he wanted it to remain open.

But he felt angry after the call. He felt cornered, trapped, and he didn't know what to do.

He knew he had to perform well and there was no major issue on that front, apart from the usual and the annoyingly repetitive managerial issues, such as the recent incident with the customer supply problem. But although he did want to improve performance and how they got things done, this conflict with the corporation was a different one. Even if he did get things working really well, it seemed there would still be a problem at that level. Yes, he recognised that things could be better with customers than they were at present, as Terry would endorse. And he definitely wanted things to be much better on the personnel front, not only with the workforce but with his own managers and management team. But, even if these two were greatly improved, the problem with the corporation would still remain. Indeed, trying to keep the corporation happy could, in fact, damage both of these. He believed it would. What he wanted to do ran a major risk of getting him into more trouble with corporate management.

Deciding in groups and who decides?

Even if he was not entirely clear about his situation regarding the corporation, he knew he had to come back to the unfinished business around decision-making with his team and so he raised it again at the end of the team meeting. This was about the topic of taking or reaching decisions in a good way with one's group or team. This had worked really well at their last meeting but there were still some issues that Bernard had raised about what happens if you can't reach consensus in a group on something. The team had also requested the opportunity to discuss why their meeting on reaching a decision had worked so well, so that they could handle similar situations in

> "It's a funny thing about life; if you refuse to accept anything but the best, you very often get it"
>
> **Somerset Maugham**

an equally effective way, both at their own team level and with their own teams.

"I want to come back to our decision-making capabilities, which we worked on at our last meeting We looked at the four decision-making styles, and numbers 1 and 2 where the manager decides, don't need much work, I take it? Nor is there much problem with number 4 and working with groups to reach a new and agreed way forward on something using the wisdom and contribution of everyone."

They all agreed. Mike was still not so sure about where he stood with Martha and Brad on these issues, but he could find that out some other time.

"What we weren't clear about and what we are not good at was summed up in the question that Bernard had about how to reach or make decisions in a team or group, especially when there isn't overall agreement. We want input and consensus, and, at the same time, we have to reach a decision. How do we square that circle or circle that square as I keep saying? We want people to be happy and on-board with a specific direction we are taking and yet we can't spend inordinate time trying to reach consensus. Nor will we always succeed in making everybody happy. Isn't this what we need to look at?"

"Yes," Tom answered, "and apart from the group being happy with the decision, I as the manager or leader need to be happy also. We could go with what everybody likes and is comfortable with, but not be convinced or happy with it ourselves and this is not right."

"I agree," Sally commented, "and it can be easy to slip into that course of action. We want good relationships and cooperation and so we want people on our side. In order to achieve that, we could err on the side of going with what everybody likes. That might not be the best way to go. And, we might need to be prepared to be unpopular sometimes for the sake of doing what's right. I face this very issue with some corporate people, as Mike knows, and it's so easy to give in for the sake of peace and an easy life. Am I making sense?"

Several people nodded.

"I think you're making great sense, Sally," Mike answered, "and I think what you're saying is hitting the nail on the head. The question is how can we achieve this? How can we get everybody on board with a decision or direction and, at the same time, be sure that we as leaders are completely happy with it too? Isn't that what we're after?"

They all agreed.

"Well, the good news is," Mike added, "is that we know how to do it because we have just done it! Isn't that exactly what we achieved in our meeting about Sharon, our unhappy customer?"

Again, they all agreed.

"So, let's find out how we did it. Let's retrace the steps and see if we can come up with a good approach or process that will work every time in similar situations in the future. Because it is probably these situations that are most important and most common. What would the first step be, or what was the first step?"

"Name or identify the problem, or the challenge, or the decision that's required," Terry answered. "In our case it was to find a way and agree a decision that would satisfy the customer and do so in a way that was acceptable and feasible for Tom and for all of us."

"Great," Mike answered, "so that's the first step. What did we do, then, to try to find that solution and agree what would be a good decision?"

Passing the buck

"Well, you got us thinking and asked us for our ideas on what to do," Frank said, "isn't that right? You passed the buck, in a sense," he laughed

"Yes, I think I did, Frank," Mike said, "and why did I do that, do you think?"

"I was going to ask that, too!" Tony came in. "Is it not your job and the job of a manager or leader to give answers, to have answers, especially if we're stuck or divided?"

"Maybe, but let's explore and hear some more."

"Probably you did it because you wanted to hear our ideas," Frank answered.

"And why did I want those ideas? Why do we normally involve people and ask them for their ideas? Am I not supposed to have the answers, as Tony was just saying?"

"I was going to say," Teresa answered, "that involving people and hearing their ideas makes them feel included and so gets their buy-in or commitment to whatever the ultimate decision eventually is. But, in fact, I'm not sure that this was so in this case. I think you actually *needed* people's ideas. It was more than just an exercise in motivation," she laughed.

"You're absolutely right, Teresa. I was stuck, I didn't have an answer and so I wanted and needed everyone's ideas in order to find one. Whether I should have had or not, Tony, I don't know but I didn't have the answer, ok. And I do believe that will happen to all of us. So that was straightforward in this case. But, suppose that I *did* have or do have an answer, why might it still be a good idea to consult and involve people, apart from making them feel good or included?"

"Because, as we said earlier," Heather answered, "good as your answer or solution might be, it might not be the best one, even if you are certain or convinced that it is."

"Well remembered and well said, Heather. The US Secretary of State during the Vietnam War was recognised for his capacity for decision-making. His staff once calculated that he made 629 major decisions in a single month. The

> "I like the scientific spirit—the holding off, the being sure but not too sure, the willingness to surrender ideas when the evidence is against them: this is ultimately fine – it always keeps the way beyond open – always gives life, thought, affection, the whole man, a chance to try over again after a mistake – after a wrong guess"
>
> **Walt Whitman**

125

fact that he never seemed to worry about the possibility of a mistake and never looked back afterwards at his decisions was also regarded as a virtue. They subsequently revised this opinion, as you can imagine. So, let's agree this second step then and why we are doing it. It is basically that we ask for and get people's ideas in order to help us and ensure that we're making a good decision. In this case I had no choice. But very often I will have a choice because I think or believe that I have an answer. Bernard referred to this some meetings back, remember? Is that clear to everybody?" They all agreed that it was.

"So what will or might happen then, having done that?"

"Well, hopefully, the ideas you get may give you the answer and solution and the decision you need to get the job done." Natalie offered.

"Providing, of course," Bernard said, "that that answer is really a good one and that you're happy with it too as the manager or leader. Isn't that what we just said a few minutes ago?

"Yes, it is and it's great if that happens and it very often will happen and you'll get an answer or a solution to an issue that may or will be better than what you yourself had in mind or thought was a good solution. So far so good. But is that what happened at our meeting?"

"No, it wasn't," Tom said, "because several of us were not in agreement and there was considerable disagreement between us."

"So how did we resolve that disagreement? Or how could I have resolved it?"

> "Whoever sets himself up as a judge in the field of truth and knowledge is shipwrecked by the laughter of the gods"
>
> **Einstein**

The dangers of "democracy"

"You could have gone with the majority view especially if it agreed with your own. I think you and Heather might have lost that vote, Terry", Sally laughed.

"What would be so wrong with that apart from being very unfair and violent to poor Terry and Heather? What's so wrong with taking a vote on things?"

"Well, it will lead to winners and losers," Bernard said, "and those who are not in agreement and who have lost will be very much against the direction that was chosen. This is deadly for me in community meetings, which can be very political. I know that I could win many battles with a simple vote, but I also know it will come back to haunt me. The losers will wait for and find their day and get their way. And, consciously or unconsciously they will work to scupper the plan with which they are not in favour and where they lose out on in the vote."

"Yes, I agree," Terry added, "and there is no guarantee that it is necessarily the best decision just because the majority support it. I am not being defensive," he laughed. "Of course, it can be an easy way out for you as the manager or leader, but it would be a way out, and a copout. You would be handing over the responsibility to others, to the group, rather than you holding onto the responsibility which always has to be yours."

"I think that's very good, Terry," Tom said, "and I have known managers who have done that. On top of that it would only encourage divisiveness and add to people lobbying and trying to convince others to agree with their stance. No, I think that would be very dangerous."

"I see that all the time at community and council meetings I attend," Bernard said, "When there's a difficult decision to be made, different people lobby and get as many people as possible to agree with their position."

"And what's so wrong with that?" Natalie asked. "Will it not lead to good meetings and avoid conflict and differences."

"Yes, it can do," Bernard answered, "but it creates huge suspicion and mistrust. People know or sense they are being manipulated and resent being set up. We talked about this last time, and I learned a lot from that."

"Yes, I've seen that too," Frank said, "and while the decision might go through as arranged, it may well be that it's not the best decision as it hasn't had the benefit of everyone's thinking."

"I can see that, it is great" Natalie answered, "so, on top of all that and it not being the best decision, it may also lack support and the cooperation that is needed to make it work. Yes, I can see that very clearly."

"I'm delighted to hear that from you all," Mike added, and I agree with you. So, if I didn't take and rely on a vote, what did we all do?"

Emerging clarity and wisdom

"We continued to think and talk it through until you saw one seemingly agreed and good way forward was found or emerged," Tony said.

"Great, Tony," Mike said, "and I like that word you used –"emerged" – because that's what will happen, most times at least, if we genuinely look for a good decision. It will *emerge*. And how did that happen at our meeting, do you remember?"

"You summarised it, Mike, you pulled the various bits together," Natalie said, "and played it back to us or proposed it to us as the decision, the way forward. Indeed, it was your decision. What you put to us was your decision and what you strongly recommended we should accept and run with was your decision, But it was not because it was your idea or that we should accept it just because it was your idea, but more because it seemed, and you believed it was, the best way to handle the situation."

"Very good, Natalie," Mike said, "and why is what Natalie said so important? Think about it."

"Is it," Bernard suggested, "because you were proposing or suggesting or deciding this as being the best way

"The meeting of preparation with opportunity generates the offspring we call luck"

Anthony Robbins

forward, not by virtue of it being your decision as the boss, but because you believed it's the one that made most sense? The subtle difference, as I see it, is around the kind of power that you're using."

"What do you mean?" Tony asked.

"What I mean is that Mike was relying on the validity and the sense of what he was proposing, its value as a way forward, as being the reason for going with that option, rather than because it was his decision as the manager. In other words, the reason for going this route was not because Mike was saying it, but because it made most sense."

"I see that," Tony replied, but why is that important to you, Bernard? Surely as managers we are entitled to decide things. People expect that from us, do they not?"

"I see it as extremely important to handle it in this way, Tony. What it's saying and doing is that it's what is right and best that rules here and decides what we do, rather than hierarchical or positional power. Isn't that what worked for you in your conversation with the engineers, Tony? And what worked for Tom with his people and what worked for Terry with the customer?"

"Yes, I see that." Tony answered somewhat reluctantly.

"Well said, Bernard," Mike said, "I think that's hugely important too and it's important also in terms of us all reaching an agreement. How is that so?"

"Because" Teresa answered, "the better the idea and the more sense it makes, the better chance we will agree with it. Isn't that so?"

What to do when some people don't agree?

"Yes, I think it is," Mike answered. "But, notwithstanding all that and even though I had clarified what I believed was the best way forward, not everybody agreed. I mean Terry and Heather, isn't that right?"

"Yes, that's how it was," Terry answered for everybody.

"So, what do we do in that case? Or what did I do?" Mike asked.

"Well, you explained your decision to Heather and me," Terry answered, "and you explained your reasons for taking that decision."

"Yes," Heather added, "that was helpful and what was equally helpful was your acknowledgement of our reasons for wanting to go a different way."

"I agree," Terry added, "and you went further. You even said that you didn't want to go ahead or want us to go ahead with this approach unless we were happy to do so. In other words, if we had principled or very major objections to following your decision, we felt – or I, at least, felt – that you wouldn't force us to do so. I may be wrong but that's what I felt, and I found it very helpful."

"I did too." Heather said.

"What do you all think of that? Was it not foolish of me to give Terry a kind of veto? Suppose that he had said "no" and that he didn't want to talk like I said to the customer, what then?"

"I agree it might or could have happened," Teresa said, "but I think it was

> "One person with a belief is equal to a force of ninety-nine who have only interests"
>
> **John Stuart Mill**

very unlikely that it would, or that they would use the so-called veto after the respect that you were showing them. I think it's a risk well worth taking and is the right thing to do."

"Well, that's what happened too with the people I spoke to." Tom said. They, too, might have said no."

"And the same with my engineers." Tony added.

"I'm glad to hear you all say that" Mike answered, "and, yes, there may be some risk in showing that kind of respect for the person or persons who have problems with the decision, but it's a risk well worth taking for the sake of respect for people and it's one that I've never seen backfire on me. That's not to say that I'm playing games or being manipulative. There's a process around people who have objections or problems with decisions that I like. Objections can fall into one of three categories:

A. It is just an **OPINION** of mine, how I see things.
B. I think it is **IMPORTANT** and I see it as important.
C. For me it is **CRITICAL** and I couldn't accept or live with it.

Do you understand? Most times, nearly always, objections and objectors will fall into categories A or B and this is what happened with Terry and Heather. Does all that make sense?"

They all agreed that it did.

So they are the steps that we followed and that worked very well and will, I believe, always work. Can you please go through them for me, Sally?"

"I'll try".

1. Firstly, explain or clarify the decision that is to be made so that everybody understands it.
2. Get and hear people's different perspectives and ideas or possible solutions.
3. Work on these until they become a possible way forward or decision.
4. If no clear or unanimous way forward has been reached and agreed, the manager or leader explains what they believe is the best way forward based on what they have heard combined with their own thinking.
5. Share this proposed way forward or decision with the group, explain your reasons and check that it makes sense.
6. If there are people who are in disagreement with the decision, eplain your reasons to them, acknowledge their thinking or reasons and ask them to go along with the decision if they can because you want their support and want them to be happy with it. Is that it? How did I do?"

"Very well, I think." Mike said, "What do you all think?"

Just a form of manipulation!

"Yes, I think she did extremely well," Frank said, "but I have one question, Mike. Is it not a bit manipulative and unfair to ask people for their opinions and suggestions and then you just go along and decide? I don't think that people will feel very happy with that. I see that all the time. Looks of cynicism on people's faces if they suspect it's just a game and that I know what to do anyway. This happens when we invite them to comment and then ignore or don't take into account their comments."

"But that's not exactly what happened, Frank," Bernard interjected, "he heard people's comments, and took them into account, and used them to come up with the way forward and his decision. Isn't that fair?"

"Yes, I think it is, Bernard," Mike said, "but what Frank is saying is important. It might be beneficial Sally and Frank, to explain the decision-making process at the outset, along the lines that hopefully we'll agree and reach a decision, but in the event of our failing to do so, I as a manager, will make the decision. Don't you think that's important and helpful to people?"

They all did.

"Good, so I hope everybody is clear about how powerful that approach is and how it allows you to involve and get people's opinions without it appearing like some kind of false democracy. It will actually add to your strength as a leader and make you a more powerful one. May I ask you again how this would make you more powerful?"

"Because it would help us as managers to make better decisions – ones that work because they enjoy the thinking and contribution of others and that will also work because they will enjoy the support of people," Teresa explained.

"Yes, and decisions that seem to work for everybody," Tom said, "after all, everybody ended up a winner in this situation – the customer, our own people, and the whole company itself. Not bad?"

"Great," Mike said, "We now have a group of truly powerful managers who know how to make better decisions and do so in a way that gets and enjoys the support of their people. Well done."

"This makes a lot of sense, Mike," Sally came in, "but I wonder if it will work as well in practice? I'm not saying it won't, but it would be good to see an example of where it's working."

"I understand, Sally, but sometimes we have to pioneer things and be the first. Otherwise, nothing will change. Trying things and taking risks are very important and I hope we can all be a bit adventurous and try some new things. I'm not sure either myself, but I believe there have to be better ways of doing things. I am forever on the look-out for them. Maybe we can look at some one of these days to give us all heart and more confidence. But what do you think, Bernard, you who raised this question?"

> "Sometimes, but not often, I am thoroughly convinced that the decision I have made is the right one, even though it differs from the others, and I will exercise my authority to approve or reject a decision against their wishes. In most cases, though, if we can't agree on something, a better idea is to table the decision rather than to exercise the power"
>
> **S. Truett**

"Yes, this all makes sense to me. What I was thinking and saying was around what to do when I am certain I'm right about something and still want to get people on board with my decision.

I can now see that, even if I'm certain, it could also be the case that they, whoever they are, might also be right ... or have some other angles on it or even better ideas. Brilliant as I am, I'm sure there will be times when the other eight or nine people in my team may be able to contribute some small improvement," Bernard joked at himself.

"So, in that case," Heather asked, "would you go with what they're saying or proposing because it makes sense and is even better than what you had in mind, even if you believe that what you were thinking and certain about was very good?"

Yes, exactly," Bernard answered, "or what will most often happen is that it'll be a combination of what I've been thinking and want to do and what they think and how they see things."

Stupid, irresponsible and traditional management

"Wouldn't it have been a big mistake," Mike came in, "not to have got these better or additional ideas? Think of the loss that this would be or the potential damage that could be caused by doing something that could be flawed or is missing out on something important. It would seem to me to be nothing less than irresponsible. And yet, we, as managers, do this all the time. Why?"

"Probably as we don't feel the need to ask people because we know ourselves," Tony said, a little sheepishly. "We're certain. And we don't want our preferred way interfered with. Know what I mean?

"Yes," Teresa answered for the group, "it certainly does and it brings to mind a course I was on once on a topic like this around managers. We were talking and then a person announced to the group: 'A manager doesn't have the right to take decisions.' Everyone sat up in astonishment. Then he added: 'A manager only has the right to take *good* decisions. I agree with what he said and that's why what you are saying here Mike is so important. We have to make sure, do our utmost to ensure our decisions are good decisions."

"I think this is huge," Tom added. I must admit that I rarely involve or ask my people because I don't see the necessity to do so. I *know* what to do. Okay, there are some relatively minor areas where they are directly involved, and I might ask what they think, but generally I don't. I can see how wrong and stupid this is now."

"Yes," Tom came in, "when you think of it what happens mostly is that we reach a decision, decide on something and then go to our people with that decision. Having taken the decision, especially if we have all agreed it, it can be very difficult and almost impossible to change or even amend that decision.

And yet, that's the way we normally operate. We see it as the prerogative and even the responsibility of management to operate in this way. And, if some oppose it or challenge it, we regard them as awkward or negative. We have to fundamentally and radically change this, I believe."

"That's good to hear, Tom," Mike said, "but what if I asked you what you would do if what they came up with was very stupid or very wrong etcetera?," he said laughing."

"I get it," Frank came in, "they won't! Or, it's very unlikely that they'll come up with something very stupid or very wrong. Why would they? What are they missing that would make us think that what they would come up with would be silly ideas or proposals?"

"Great," Mike said. "I hope you all get that. It's very easy for us to think that we have all the wisdom on our side. And, even if they did come up with something that didn't make sense to us and that we didn't genuinely believe was the right thing to do, then, we have lost nothing and

> "I don't think you really know for sure what you'll do until it comes down to the moment when you have to make that decision for real"
>
> **J.W. Lynne**

we can still decide, and should still decide, what is the right thing to do. I say that just to deal with the possibility that this could arise. It could be because there's a clash of interests between what they, people, regard as important and good and what we, managers, regard as important, good, and right. Are you still ok with all this, Sally?"

"Yes, I am, thanks. I understand what you're saying, Mike and that's fair, but you know me and how I like to be certain," she laughed.

The meeting finished and Mike felt very good about it but Tom's final comments about everyone being a winner reminded him of his earlier conversation with Martha. He still didn't feel good about his conversation. Nor did he believe he knew how to keep everybody happy, try as he might, even if, as Tom had said, everyone ended up a winner. Was what he was saying just a lovely theory? What about this situation now? How would it all work with Martha and Brad?

But that was only one of many problems he had. He seemed to be surrounded by them. Yes, things had worked out well on this issue and that was great, but that was often the case with a crisis. How could he make that the norm, and do so easily and naturally and without all the effort and discussions they had had to resolve this one. For that matter, how could he transform his own team so that they were able to resolve issues easily on their own? He hoped that the meeting they had just had would be a big help to them doing that.

And then there was the bigger issue of how to transform the whole company, so that it became the kind of place that Albert, the new recruit, had spoken about so that work became something different – fun, enjoyable, fulfilling. That seemed an enormous mountain to climb and now one that he felt he had the resources to resolve. Was it all worthwhile? Was it even possible? Was he in Quixotic fashion merely tilting at windmills? But he refused to give up. There has to be a way. There is a way and he just had to find it.

Questions for reflection and action

1. How frequently are you likely to be in situations like this where there is no clear way forward but lots of different ideas? Seldom? Occasionally? Often? Very often? And not only in work situations?
2. Do you believe this approach will work? How will you know or find out? Like how you learned to ride a bicycle?

3. Why is this so important for your power and influence as a leader? What gives you that special power that they spoke of here? Do you think it will weaken or strengthen you as a manager or leader in people's eyes?

4. Do you see what they are saying about how stupid and responsible we can be as managers? And how much we need to change?

5. What does this approach require? What might be difficult or challenging for you in working in this way?

Chapter 10

"Senior Teams are the Worst Performing Teams in Any Organisation"

Getting in touch with the power of meetings and teams

Mike felt very trapped. On the one hand he wanted to radically change things in the company for all kinds of good reasons, and on the other, he was running into head-on problems with his own corporate bosses who were strongly opposed to those very changes and to his way of managing. Something had to give. And, yet, Mike did not feel like giving in on his goal to transform the company. He met Brendan again.

"The way I see it, Mike, is that you need to strengthen and unite your own team. I see this as being necessary to manage both fronts."

They spent some time talking over what this would involve and about the challenges different team members and relationships posed.

"You seem to be talking a lot about meetings and our meetings, Brendan. Is that not a bit much? People are fed up of meetings."

"Yes, and that's why, or one of the reasons for focusing on meetings. But, there's another, Mike, and it's that you're never more powerful than when you are together in meetings. We are all social and so we are more human and more ourselves and more powerful when we

> "Good timber does not grow with ease; the stronger the wind, the stronger the trees"
>
> **J. Willard Marriott**

are together in groups than when we are alone. For that reason, you need to get them right. If you don't, you'll achieve nothing. If you do, there's no end to what you can achieve. You have seen some of that already with that meeting on the KEY Services issue, haven't you? And doing this will help you to not only deal with those two big issues you are tackling but actually use one to help the other."

They continued to talk about this and to plan what Mike might and should do.

At the next Senior Team meeting, when they had dealt with all of the topics on the agenda, Mike said: "I was talking to a friend recently, a very experienced friend, who said to me that, in his opinion, senior teams are the worst performing group in any organisation!"

Everyone looked up in astonishment.

"Yes, that's what he said, and he seemed very convinced that he was right. What do you all think?"

"I'm not sure what he could have meant." Tony came in, "that's a bit hard to believe because in theory, at least, senior teams are made up of bright and successful people. Usually the best in an organisation. Not saying that *we* are, of course." he laughed.

"I also find it very strange," Heather said ". "This is my first senior team so I don't have much experience, but I don't understand why that would be so, I mean generally."

"I don't think it's true of us, Terry said, "I think we're a good team and do a good job. I know things could be better but, in general, we do pretty well."

Mike came in again. "If you were to assume for the moment that this guy is no fool, and has worked with a great number of companies throughout the world, how might it be the case that he's right and that senior teams generally perform very poorly? We can include or exclude ourselves in that as we see fit."

"I was thinking," Teresa said, "about what Tony said and wonder if it could be a factor that senior teams are very often made up of very successful but also, equally, of very competitive people? This could make for competition and possible conflict and damage good team working. Know what I mean?"

"I was thinking the same or along similar lines," Bernard said, "when you think of it, we're all bosses in our own right, heads of our functions, and this could mean that we might be more loyal to our own function than to this team. And that could contribute to that competitiveness that you talked about, Teresa. If we were honest, we know, we do have our clashes and issues."

Let's be honest and accurate

"I don't think we are a poorly-performing team" Tom said, "I think that we play as a team and Mike is a good strong coach or captain or manager or whatever he is."

"I understand what you're saying, Tom" Sally said, "but, to be honest, sometimes I'm afraid to raise some things because they will make somebody look bad and will cause defensiveness. I'm only being honest. I have information on you all," she laughed.

"I understand that, Sally" Natalie said, "and I do the same sometimes too. It becomes like a golden rule not to step on people's toes, and we do it with the best of intentions. We believe it makes for good teamwork. I certainly operate like that."

"I see that too," Frank said, "and sometimes I feel that we talk about safe topics and avoid delicate ones because we are afraid of offending or ruffling feathers or creating conflict. We get on well because we avoid the issues that might pit us against each other."

More and more people in the room were becoming obviously nervous.

"I can't see that at all," Tom came back in, "I always say what's on my mind and I think we have to behave like big boys and girls in here and not dance around things."

There was silence and some people smiled and some glanced at other team members, catching their eyes.

Eventually Bernard came back in. "I think we spend a lot of time talking about things that are far from being of most importance. We spent many hours and several weeks talking about the new office layout, didn't we? And it took us several meetings to decide on the Christmas or end-of-year shutdown. We spent hours on it and seemed to love it," he laughed.

> "If you had to identify, in one word, the reason why the human race has not achieved, and never will achieve, its full potential, that word would be 'meetings'"
>
> **Dave Barry**

"Well, it's up to people to watch what they put on the agenda, isn't it?" Tom answered.

"I would agree," Terry said, that we can spend a lot of time on some topics, and I often wonder how much of that is really necessary."

"Well, I think people need to take more individual responsibility for things and not dump them on this team or on our meetings," Tony replied. "I wonder how truly supportive we are of each other or are we just heads of functions who meet or have to meet to organise and plan things? I would like more from our meetings and from this group than that."

"What do you mean, Tony?" Heather asked.

"I'm not even sure. Maybe I was being a bit negative and going against what I said earlier! It's just that I do belong to other groups, outside of here, as most of you know, and I get great support from them. I would love to get that same support here. After all, we spend a lot of time together and it would be great if we made the most of that time."

"Yes," Sally said, "and our meetings take a lot of time and very often run over. Maybe that's part of what your friend was alluding to, Mike."

"I agree", Natalie said, "but the biggest problem I have is that, as I said, I don't dare bring up problems in our meetings. I'm afraid that, if I do, I'll get inundated with advice and be virtually told what to do.

Maybe it's because I'm new but I don't think it is. Anyway, most times, I keep my problems to myself and I'm very happy to get involved in any discussion on any other topic. In that sense, I feel we don't get the benefits of real teamworking.

"I feel a bit like that too" Bernard said. "It's not easy to have to listen to and be pressurised into doing things you don't think will work. I watch what I raise here", he said laughing.

"Any more confessions?" Mike asked. "This is all very revealing and very sad", he laughed.

"It seems we also might be one of those worst performing teams after all," Teresa laughed. "I have to admit I recognise much of what people have been saying. One thing I think we get wrong is around problems and discussions. We slip into them and a discussion on anything can go on forever or as long as it takes, irrespective of how really important it is. Even this very discussion is dragging on and aren't we going over the same ground and repeating the same things?

The plague and malaise of meetings

"Yes, I agree Teresa," Frank said, "or sometimes, because we run out of time, we end up rushing decisions on important topics at the end of a meeting."

"Yes, I recognise that too." Sally said, "I need to be somewhere else and yet what is being spoken about is very important and will have big effects. It's an awful feeling."

"So, it seems," Mike said, "that we might be the worst performing team in this company after all?"

"I think we're being too hard on ourselves. I think all this is fairly normal." Terry replied.

"Well," Tony answered strongly, "even if it is normal, it's far from good and far from good enough in my opinion. It certainly could be a great deal better."

"I agree and I think it's more serious than just wasting time," Bernard said, "I believe our meetings can often do more harm than good. Not just our own ones, even if as is obvious, we need to improve these anyway."

"Why do you say that they can do more harm than good, Bernard", Terry asked, "I don't see how we could manage a business without meetings."

"I agree," Tom said, "I think we're very careful about the number of meetings we have and we have reduced them greatly. I can't think of any meetings that I hold that are unnecessary. Mike and I have talked about this too and I am much more careful now than I was."

> "We learned not to meet anymore, We don't raise our eyes to one another, But we ourselves won't guarantee What could happen to us in an hour"
>
> **Anna Akhmatova**

"I'm not sure," Tony said. "What I feel is that I and my people are invited to so many meetings and I'm not at all sure that it's time well spent."

"Surely it's about how well they're run," Heather added. "I don't think it's so much about the number of them as much as it is about quality."

"I don't know," Frank came in, "there are some days when I spend all my time at meetings, and I have to get my work done when I go home. Just look at my calendar schedule for this week. Virtually every slot is taken up with a meeting of one sort or another."

"But maybe you don't have to go to all those meetings," Terry said. "You can send some of your people."

"And I do, Frank replied, "but if you ask them, they'll tell you the same story I'm telling, that they spend all their time at meetings."

And on it went.

"Okay okay," Mike said. "Let's pause this. For a start, how's this meeting and what's going on at it?"

"We're doing what we so often criticise and have spoken about so often, we are differing," Teresa said.

"And who do you think is right, Teresa?", Mike asked.

"Yes, I know what you'll say, it's the elephant story again, we are behaving like those blind men, each thinking that their version is the right and only one. One thinks it's a pipe because water comes out of it. Another at the far end thinks the tail is a rope. The person who climbed up on top believes he's on a hill and the one underneath disagrees and says it's a cave. And the one feeling the leg is convinced it is a tree and so on. We're the same. We all have our own experiences and perspectives and believe we're right".

"Yes, and, as Heather said earlier, this is what so often happens and it can go on and on with no winners or losers, a lot of time lost, and a few relationships damaged in the process. Is that fair?"

They all agreed that it was what happens all the time, both in and out of work.

Elephantine thinking and working

"So what should we do, then?" Mike asked.

Bernard answered, "It's all about sharing and hearing points of view, listening to them and hearing them and, then, working to marry and amalgamate them all until a much bigger and better truth emerges like an elephant. Isn't that it?"

"Yes, it is, Bernard, and it's one of the greatest truths in life and applies everywhere. So, you can see from this huge message that one thing we definitely need to get right is how we run our meetings, and that means we have to make sure that they're well led and managed, which involves ensuring we work in an elephantine way – sharing, listening, respecting and amalgamating views and opinions. And we know how to do that – we have spoken about it very often. You know what I'm referring to, don't you?" Mike asked.

"Yes," Sally said, "it's about facilitative leadership. That there's somebody who's both facilitating the meeting and the thinking and contribution of people and who will ultimately bring things to a close and conclusion. A bit like you're doing now, Mike," she laughed.

"But we can see how easy it is for us to slip back into our bad behaviours," Teresa added. "And if we do that you can imagine how others will do the same. I mean reverting to being the boss or like the chairperson."

"Thanks Teresa". Mike said, "Bernard can I ask you to explain again why you think meetings can do more harm than good, first of all, and then we'll talk about why you believe we have too many of them."

"Sure, Mike. I think it comes down to ownership. Meetings can do enormous damage to one's sense of ownership. This can be hard to explain or understand, but if I expect my people to do something, then, when I call a meeting to see or review what they have been doing, I could be giving a message to them that I don't really trust them. That unless I call a meeting to check up, things won't get done. And, then, at the meeting, they will try to satisfy me, rather than focusing on the job. We can forget that we're undermining people's confidence, their ownership, their accountability by not trusting them to get the job done on their own. While we have often spoken about this before, I think we need to live up to what we have so often said and agreed. But we continue to slip into or stay in the same pattern of having meetings for everything."

"What do you suggest, Bernard, and what do other people think?"

"I think Bernard is absolutely right," Tom answered, "both in terms of what we need to do and the fact that we are not doing it. I am doing it in one area, and I was more or less forced into it, I have to admit. It was the new project leader, Albert, who challenged me on the meetings we were having. I was quite taken aback at first. He put it to me very bluntly – "Either you trust me to do the job or not" he told me. "If you give me a job to do or we agree what's to be done, I'll do it and I'll keep you informed. And, if I run into problems that I can't solve, then I'll come to you. But, until then, trust and believe that things are okay and under control."

"And do you not want and, indeed, need any feedback from me?" I asked Albert."

"Yes, I'd like to get feedback from you regularly to make sure I'm not missing out on something, and I'd like you to feel free to talk to me or challenge me

"We must be the change we seek to create"

Gandhi

on anything. I would welcome it if you were in touch with what's happening in my area and with my people, but that you do so from a place of trust and confidence in me. But, other than that, trust me that I'll do what I said I would do. And that was the end of the daily and regular meetings in his area," Tom laughed.

"And I take it it's working well?", Mike asked.

"Yes, very well, the performance and results are excellent and there's a new energy, a new sense of commitment, and overall a much better atmosphere. I'm trying to extend this to the other areas and slowly educate people about their real area responsibilities and gradually but quickly discontinue most of the meetings we have been holding. Believe me it's not easy to change habits of a lifetime. I hope I'm changing but I can't be sure"

"One thing I think we need to get clear about," Teresa came in, "is when we should and should not have meetings, and for that we need to be clear about why we need to have a meeting in the first place. I think that if we got that clear it would put an end to the enormous pressure there is to get a meeting room. This has become a task on its own," she laughed. "I have a person who just manages that one task and that takes a lot of her time."

"Good," Mike said, "so I wonder if it would be possible for us to agree what the value and justifiable reasons for holding a meeting are? Suppose we're able to come up with five, and no more than five, valid reasons for meeting, what would they be? Maybe there aren't even five!"

"I think one justifiable reason," Bernard began, "is when some relatively serious problem arises, and it can't be handled through the normal systems and ways of working. It calls for a different way of working and meeting and it can't be left unattended. A bit like the issue with Sharon in KEY Services. Should that be one?"

"I think it should, Bernard," Terry said, "and I also believe there are situations that are not problematic, but which require a different way of working. Like sessions to create new products or services or even a new strategy. Unless we've agreed meetings and methodologies to deal with these they won't happen and as you say Bernard, developing new products or services, even ways of doing things

> "You need long meetings only when you don't trust your team, or are less experienced than your players and want to learn from them"
>
> **Vineet Raj Kapoor**

better will not happen by default. They require a very different way of working. This is also an area that can't be left unattended. I think we have to do more and formalise our approaches and our meetings to continually search for new ideas, new products and services."

"You're doing great," Mike said, "have we two or three more?"

"This may sound a little similar," Tom said "but at times you run into problems, get stuck and need help. Don't look so surprised. I often ask for help! Yes, we can solve most problems on our own through the normal way of working, but sometimes we can't, and we have to admit that and give them special attention. I think showstoppers or roadblocks like this would justify holding a meeting ple. What do you think?"

"I agree, Tom," Heather said, "and this may sound a bit similar too but when we are developing our strategy, whether that be in our own areas or overall, I think that's better done together with the attendance and contribution of different people. To develop a strategy, you need different inputs and so I think that strategic meetings are special and justified."

"Very good, you're doing very well," Mike said, "any more suggestions?"

"This may sound a little bit like how we normally work," Sally said, "but I think that it's important and right to regularly check how we're doing and review our progress. I'm not saying that we review everything or get back into checking up on people and making sure that things have happened, like your man was saying Mike. I'm just saying that I think it's healthy for us to regularly take stock and check that we're on course. What I mean is simply to ask or invite people to share ideas that they have or concerns or issues that they have spotted. These will probably become new areas for development or new projects, but I think it's always healthy to have sessions or meetings to openly, honestly and courageously check how we are doing. Does that make sense?"

"That's good work, I think." Mike said. "Maybe there are more or even less. but suppose that we accepted and agreed that these are the only five reasons or justifications for holding a meeting? And we also agree we will only hold these kinds of meetings and we'll stop all other ones? We might need to talk a little about some meetings we are currently holding and see what to do about them, but I think it might be better to do that practically about each meeting or situation rather than trying to agree some general solution. How does that sound?"

They all agreed to go that route and to see what problems it gave rise to.

What's the point?

"I have no doubt that many of us are going to feel very uncomfortable with this," Teresa said, "but we should be prepared. Comfort is not a good criterion for doing or deciding what one does, I believe."

"I agree, Teresa, Mike said. And, to do that, think it would be a good idea if for every meeting we hold or attend, we ask and follow what the point of the meeting is. This is something I learned from Brendan, the man I sometimes use as a coach. So before calling any meeting we must find out what the point of the meeting is. By this I mean:

P   What's the **Purpose** of the meeting – one that makes real sense?

O   What is the **Objective** of the meeting and what Outcomes do we want?

I   Why are these **Important** and why is the meeting Important?

N   What **Need** will the meeting address or what New result would we really like?

T   How will we make the group a **Team** if they are not already a team? And if they are, how will we remind them of this and revitalise them as a Team?

This would mean then that we never call a meeting without having checked the five **POINT** principles and, if we are unable to answer them positively, then we simply should not hold that meeting. It will add no value, will waste a lot of time, and ultimately do more harm than good, as Bernard told us. What do you all think?"

"I really like that," Bernard said. "It makes great sense, it's practical and a very good test."

"I agree." Natalie said, "but I take it that we wouldn't only use it to prepare for meetings, would we? I think we should use it during meetings and check with people at the beginning of a meeting that the meeting will meet all five criteria. Don't you think?"

"Absolutely," Mike said, "this is what should happen and it would be a good check for everybody at every meeting. If they can't answer the five points positively, then they should not be there, and we're wasting people's time by having them there. Isn't that fair?"

Everybody vehemently agreed.

"I believe," Terry said, that we should practise what we preach here. We should only discuss things that are of real importance. That's not to say that you put trivial items on the agenda, Mike," he laughed.

"No, but you're right Terry. We need to look at all items on the agenda and make sure they're worthwhile topics. But don't you think we need to look at some other things too?"

"Definitely," Frank said, "we need to look at the time we spend at meetings. We spend far too much time, in my opinion, and things go all over the place. We all said that earlier."

"I agree," Heather said, "we begin talking about something and then find ourselves going all over the place, often despite your best efforts, Mike."

"That's because we all get involved in everything," Tony said. "Sometimes I'm afraid to even mention some things, bits of information, because everybody jumps in, everybody has an opinion, and then I feel under pressure. If I try to explain something, it comes across as if I'm being defensive."

"Not that you would ever be defensive," Heather said, "but I know what you mean. I often feel the same too. And sometimes a small piece of information turns into a major discussion and debate and problem-solving in the meeting. As you said, Frank, we go all over the place."

"I understand everything you are saying."

Making every meeting a dynamic event

Mike came in, saying. "We're going over the same old ground we covered a few minutes ago about our own meetings. Let me try this and see what you think.

Firstly, we agree the topics for the meeting and only put items on the agenda that are of real importance. We will use **POINT** for that and I will be the ultimate arbiter on that for our meetings, if that's okay.

TOPIC	CLIENT	PURPOSE OF TOPIC (*)	REQUIRED TIME	ACTUAL TIME

- IG: Information Giving
- IS: Information Seeking
- PS: Problem Solving
- DM: Decision Making

But in order to deal with Tony's problem about everybody getting involved, for each topic, we identify who the Owner or Client is and put their name beside the topic. Okay? So it's this person who has the responsibility and who we have to make happy at the end of the meeting so they can go away and do what they now think is best. That will safeguard the ownership and accountability you talked about earlier, Bernard."

They were all happy.

"Next, to deal with Heather's problem, we decide what Kind of item each agenda Topic is. As she said, someone may only be sharing a piece of information like some customer change that Heather knows about. Or, it could be that Sally wants to hear or give some information on some new reporting procedure. Or it could be that there is a sticky problem that we need to talk about and problem-solve. Or, similarly, we might need to make a decision or help Terry or Heather make some decision around taking on some new business. So every topic will have a description of what kind of item it is – Information giving, Information seeking, Problem Solving, Decision-Making. Do you know what I mean and why that would help?"

"Yes," Bernard came in, "it would help us to stop treating everything as if it was an item for discussion or problem-solving when it might only be somebody needing or giving some information. Without that, we can turn everything into an interesting topic for discussion, knowing us. This would educate us on how to react and behave when we see an item."

"That would mean," Sally said, "that some items, like Information Sharing or Information Seeking might require and take only a little time, rather than spending endless time on them? No?"

"But, some items like Problem-Solving ones," Tom said, "might take or require a lot of time, maybe even more time than we have allotted for the meeting. Is that not so? Especially when it's some very serious topic."

"Yes, Tom," Mike said, "you're right and sometimes we might have to fix a different time to work on some problem because, as you say, Tom, it will take so much time or because it might require some different people to be present."

"I think that's true," Teresa said, "because sometimes I sit through some topics where I really have very little to add and so it would make sense to make sure that the right people are present for those problem-solving topics. Yes, I agree."

"And then there's the question of Times," Mike said, "so we would allocate time for each topic, the time that we estimate it will take and then, beside it, the actual time. That way we could see whether the time we have allotted for the meeting and the different topics is realistic or not. If we see that there isn't enough time, then we could either extend the meeting, remove some items from the agenda for this particular meeting and deal with them some other day. Does that also make sense?"

"Yes, it does, lots of it," Bernard said, "how often do we run out of time at meetings and end up frustrated as the meeting goes over the planned time and we're under pressure to go somewhere else, probably to another meeting! All that stuff we said earlier," he laughed.

"Exactly Bernard," Terry said, "or we end up rushing some things through at the end of the meeting and not giving them nearly enough time and attention. I think this is great and actually seeing the time, the estimated time or expected time, will help to keep us all on track so that we manage ourselves better. You know, we could become one of those good Senior Teams this way" he laughed.

"I agree with all this, and I think it's great," Tom said, "and I don't want to complicate it anymore, but I think there should be some place where whoever has put an item on the agenda, explains briefly, why it's important, how it will contribute to what we want to achieve, in other words, why it's worth spending time on. I think it's easy for us to take this for granted but I'm afraid that, with the best will in the world, we'll slip into letting things get on the agenda that shouldn't be there if we're not careful and watchful. What do you think?"

"Yes, I hear what you're saying and I think it should be included and it's certainly something that whoever is leading and facilitating the meeting should always check." Mike commented. "I agree with you that it's easy to drift into talking about all kinds of interesting and intriguing things but which are not adding much value. Okay? So, do we all agree that we'll follow this approach?"

All agreed and Tony said: "I think it's great and I certainly intend to use it in all of my own meetings. I think it'll make a great difference."

All agreed that they would comply with this.

> "Never doubt that a small group of committed citizens can change the world. Indeed it is the only thing that ever has"
>
> **Margaret Mead**

Releasing the power in meetings

"Doing this will be fine and following the schema will make a great difference," Mike said, "but, on its own it won't really work? Why? What else is required, critical in fact?"

"Oh, I bet you're back to Facilitative Leadership?"

"Ha ha. You're right, Bernard, I am, and I won't go over all the same ground again but why do I bring it up again? What might go wrong, even if this format is used and stuck to?"

"The usual thing, Mike," Natalie came in, "differences. People will differ and these need to be managed."

"And how do I know you understand how to do this, Natalie?"

"I hope I do and it's something I need to get better at. It's about the elephant and people around the elephant, each believing they're right. So, it's about letting them know that they're right but that there are other people who also think *they* are right and so maybe – while they are right – it's probably not the full or total picture. So, as the facilitative leader, I would ensure all the different perspectives are shared and heard. Just like the blind people around the elephant all had a perspective but it was the combination of all of the perspectives that led them to the discovery it was an elephant. How did I do?"

"Brilliant description, Natalie."

"Thanks. It's *doing* it that matters and that I will have to become better at."

"Well I need to be better at it too," Teresa said, "but I think that what will make it easier for Natalie and for all of us is having a shared goal that we all believe in. Having this will make it easy that an elephant or angel will emerge to mix my metaphors. This will mean that each person is after something different and greater and not just their own piece or being right. So, for that reason, what we talked about earlier around POINT will be very helpful here too. Like Michelangelo looking at the stone or marble, when we look at an issue or any situation with people, we will be inviting them to see more possibilities in it, to expect to find and release an angel. I think we have to have this attitude in every meeting and to expect surprises and breakthroughs to happen any time."

"I think that's great," Frank said, "and I think it's right to actually expect surprises and angels and breakthroughs when we work in this way as a team. Don't forget what we said about the power of teams. Remember the descriptions we went over about how powerful a team is compared to individuals working or groups of individuals working together? I can vouch for that from my own experience and results."

> "Great achievers know that one person alone, no matter how brilliant, will find it very difficult to match the collaborative talents of an effective team"
>
> **Anthony Robbins**

"Well, I think we just have to develop the power that is available to us." Teresa said. "We saw what we achieved on the customer issue without even trying. What might, or rather *will* we achieve when we work as one team and get and enable others to be equally powerful? On we go! Let's make sure we're not only not the worst performing team in the company but the best."

"Exactly Teresa," Tony said, "and we actually need to be so and give that example to others. Yes, on we go."

"That's great." Mike came in, "I think that if we get this right, we'll do great things together. These may appear small things but if they help us to become united and working really well together, not as heads of functions in a group, but as a team of people that wants to work together to achieve something great, then it'll be truly worthwhile. But it will involve consistently following what we have agreed and covered here. I hope we can all do that. Yes, Teresa, on we go."

Mike felt pleased with the meeting when the last person had left the room. He had done what he had agreed with Brendan and it seemed to have gone well. But, will they do what they said? And, even if they do, will it make the difference he wanted, he asked himself. And, even if it does, what difference will it make to Brad and Martha and corporate management? "This is no way to keep thinking," he told himself, "and no way to keep living for that matter. But who knows what may happen? Lots of things can change and may change," he told himself. He closed his briefcase and headed for his car, looking forward to being home with Joan and the children. He remembered he would be on his own with the children that evening and looked forward to it. It was always enjoyable and always brought a surprise or two.

Questions for reflection and action

1. What truth do you see in senior teams being the worst performers? Don't be offended. I led one for a few years!
2. Why is it so important to get this right? For the team itself? For performance? For the rest of the organisation?
3. Happy with **POINT**? Does it all make sense? Plan how you will use them both to prepare for meetings and at meetings.
4. Are you clear and convinced about all five features in making all meetings good ones?
5. Convinced about the enormous latent power in your meetings that you can tap into and release?

Chapter 11
We are Born Creative

Trust and get in touch with the innate and powerful creativity in people

"How was your day" Joan shouted to Mike after he had dumped his briefcase and hugged the children when he arrived home that evening.

Mike laughed, "Eventful and I'm glad you're rushing out to your theatre, Joan. I'll tell you later but it was probably a bit more problematic than yours."

"Okay. I look forward to hearing that, even if it sounds ominous. I have to rush because tonight we're going to hear about and plan our activities for the year. It will be good for you to have some time on your own with the three, anyway."

Mike was delighted that Joan was going to her theatre group. She always seemed enlivened on these evenings. She changed and didn't seem to be the same person. Or, he wondered, if, in fact, she became *more* herself."

"Yes, go and I'll have a nice cup of tea ready for you when you get in."

He only had an hour with Alex, so Harry and Rose finished their dinner and began their homework. Rose asked him if he could help her later on with something. He agreed, even though he felt that most times she knew the answers herself.

There was some minor protest from Alex when he took him down to his cot but Mike knew it wouldn't last long. He asked Harry how he was getting on and, predictably, his answer was more about football than the academic.

"Oh Dad, I need to find those old football boots. I need them for training so that my good ones are in excellent shape for the matches that are coming up. I know you put them away somewhere in the garage but I have no idea where they are."

"I know, I know, I'll have to sort that place out sometime soon and I'll find them for you."

Rose's problem wasn't about her lessons at all but about a boy in her class whom she felt was being bullied by other boys and girls.

"I don't think it's right or fair and, at the same time, I don't want to go to the teacher and report on them. They might, then turn on *me* and regard me as a squealer. What do you think I should do, Dad?

"Well, first of all, I'm delighted that you're doing this and proud of you. I think it's great that you are able to see that this is wrong and that you want to do something about it. So, well done."

"Thanks, but what do you think I should do?"

"So do I understand you want to do something about a boy whom you believe is being bullied. Is that it?"

"Yes."

"So, briefly, what's going on, what do you see happening?"

"I see several things. They isolate him and ignore him if he tries to join any group. They talk about him behind his back and make fun of him. They even influence people like myself who are friends of his to ignore him too. Do you know what I mean?"

"Yes, I do. Very well. And what does he do or how does he react?"

"He's very quiet. At first, he wasn't aware of what they were doing and so he kept trying to join them in games and things. But now he knows he's not welcome so he just stays on his own. He tries to hold his own in class but, even there, they gang up against him and help each other to exclude him. I can see that this affects him and he has even missed a few days from school recently."

"Yes, I understand, that's awful. And tell me, how would you *like* things to be? What do you want from this chat? How should things be in your opinion?"

"I was hoping that you would be able to help me so I could do something positive to help him."

Real help!

"I understand, and I want to help, but for that I need to know how you believe things *should* be and how do you *want* them to be?"

"I would like this boy to be treated fairly and respectfully so that he is able to go to school every day and enjoy his study, without being abused or made to suffer. Doesn't that make sense?"

"Yes, it does, perfect sense. So, you would like him to be well treated, with respect and fairly, so that he is happy in school, able to do his study like everybody else?"

"Yes, I think that's fair and I think it's important."

"I agree, but why do you think it's so important?"

"Because somebody should not be treated like that, and he should be able to go to school every day without being afraid of being abused or bullied. I just think it's wrong and it's important that it changes. Even, quite apart from him, I don't think it's good for anybody that that kind of behaviour or environment exists."

"I agree completely. I think what you say is right and that it's important. So, what could you do to change that, then?"

"As I said, I don't want to go to the teacher, or the principal and I don't think he wants that either. I think he's probably not telling anybody at home about this too, because otherwise they would probably have done something about it."

"Yes, I think you're probably right. So, what do you think should be done or what could you do?"

"I'm not sure, Dad, that's why I wanted to ask you."

"Yes, I understand that so let's see what you could do. You seem very keen to tackle it because it's so important, so I wonder what you could do or try?"

"One thing I could do, which, to some extent, I am already doing, is to stay friends with him and support him and make it obvious to people that I am doing that. Yes, that's one thing I could do. What do you think?"

"I think that's great. That would give a very clear message and would help him in any case. What else could you do?"

"This might sound risky and I'm not sure I want to do it, but I thought of talking to and even challenging some of the people in the group who are being cruel to him. I don't know them all very well but I do know some of them. What do you think?"

"Very good, and what would you say to them or to one of them?"

"I think I would be quite forthright and strong and tell them that I don't like what I see happening and that I think it's wrong and unfair."

"Good, and how do you think they might react to that?"

"I think they would be annoyed and want to either justify it or deny it. But they know what they are doing so they would at least understand."

> "You can't be against bullying without actually doing something about it"
>
> **Randi Weingarten**

"And what do you think they might do after you've told them this?"

"I'm not sure at all, but at least I would call their attention to it and make them aware that I, at least, think it's wrong and would like it to stop. I think that would be a good first step. What do you think?"

"I agree. I think it would be very good first step. Well done. And what could go wrong with this? I'm only checking because I understand and like what you're thinking of doing."

"They might very well turn on me and try to take it out on me but, if they did, I would tell them that they are now doing it to me and that I think it's wrong and that I'll not stand for it. I would ask them again to stop and explain that what they're doing is not nice or right or good."

"And if that didn't work and they persisted – and I know I'm being very negative here – what would you do?"

"No, it's alright. This is helpful because this is exactly what may happen. I think I would keep asking them to stop and I might tell them that if they don't, then I'll take it further, but I hope that I don't have to. How does that sound?"

"I think it sounds great and, as I said, it's wonderful that you're doing this. If you're still happy to go this route, when do you think you might do what you plan?"

"I think, first of all, I'll begin by making it even more obvious that I support him and that I'm his friend. Who knows where this might lead or what might happen! Some other people might react or respond as well. But, if nothing happens, then by the end of next week I'll approach one or some of that group and do as I said and I'll do it in a respectful and honest but courageous way. Is that what you mean?"

"Yes, that's exactly it and do feel free to come and talk to me again about it if you wish."

"Thanks Dad, I certainly will and I found this chat with you very helpful. That was great advice."

> "Only those who will risk going too far can possibly find out how far one can go"
>
> **T. S. Eliot**

Mike smiled to himself knowing he had given *no* advice.

But Rose was not aware that all of the ideas were hers. Nor was she aware of the process Mike had been using, just "Coaching".

"Glad to hear that, honey, and are you now ready to go to bed? I know you'll want to read for a little while as usual."

Mike felt pleased about his chat with Rose and reflected again on what he did and how it went. Coaching was something he wanted to discuss in his own team.

Surprise visitor

He was about to read his book when Alex came into the sitting room having somehow escaped from his cot. He had no idea how he had achieved this. He picked him up and played with him for a while before returning him to his now very porous prison of the cot, still wondering how he had managed his escape.

He didn't return and so he got several things done, as well as some reading before Joan arrived in from her theatre meeting.

She looked excited but, before hearing from her, he told her briefly about his conversation with Rose and then about the Houdini act that Alex had performed.

"How could he have done that?" he asked.

"I don't know, but we can find out how he does it now because I decided to use the cameras your sister gave us months ago. I use them in case he wakes up and we don't hear him for some reason. So we can look at it to find out how he escaped."

"Yes, I'd love to do that but, first of all, tell me how your night was. It seems to have been very good."

"Yes, it was. It was great. Because it was our first meeting of the year when we planned what we'll do this year and it was truly outstanding. As you know, Maria is our director and she explained to us what she would like to achieve this year."

"What was so great about it?"

Joan told him all about the meeting. When she was finished, Mike remained enthralled.

"What are you thinking?" Joan asked.

"Oh, lots of things but let's leave them for now and get back to the mystery of our own escapee.

They connected the camera to the television and sat back to observe their very own Houdini.

In all, the escape process took less than five minutes and involved quite a few steps or stages. Sometimes it looked as if he were stuck. Other times he looked to have gone down the wrong track. But he kept trying until he found the right one and found escape and success.

Mike became intrigued and went in search of a pen and paper. He replayed the escape.

"You seem very interested, Mike," Joan asked. Are you impressed with him?"

"Yes, I am … but it's a bit more than that. We've just witnessed something extraordinary…right in front of our eyes."

"Hey. Easy on! What do you mean?"

"Well, it might not seem such a great thing to us, but look at it from Alex's viewpoint. What he achieved and why and how".

"Well, he can now get out of his cot on his own. That's what he achieved."

"Yes, and he did something he had never done before nor seen done. So now he can find freedom from the little prison that is his cot and which we use to control him. He can escape from his cot or prison and this would be a huge thing in real life if someone achieved that against all the odds. It's a big achievement, but it's *how* it happened that interests me even more. How did it happen or why did it happen? Remember it didn't *have to* happen. But in fact, from his viewpoint and his little world, he took on something that was impossible and solved it, made it possible.

"Imagine if we did that in our lives."

Joan knew Mike was probably thinking of his world of work as usual, and she wondered if she should go after the impossible in her own life – find a fulfilling way to live it, doing justice to it like Frankl and the others did, while being the kind of mother she wanted to be with her children. "Why not?" She asked herself.

> "Creativity is allowing yourself to make mistakes. Art is knowing which ones to keep"
>
> **Scott Adams**

Mike continued musing. "I suppose he decided that he wanted something different or better than what he had, even if what he had was alright in itself, comfortable and warm and where he had spent a lot of time already. For some reason he decided he wanted more than what he had."

When the status quo is no longer good enough
or acceptable

"Just like me!" she thought. "So, he decided that the status quo was no longer good enough, in a sense?" she said.

"Yes, exactly. That's the first thing I thought of too. He didn't *have* to do it. As you say, he has spent a lot of time there and become accustomed to it, but now he wants something better. Do you see where I'm going with this? I don't want to stretch it too much to make a point."

"I do and I promise I won't let you stretch anything beyond what it really means and is," Joan laughed. "So the first thing, you're saying is to not just settle for what he had or what we have but to want more and better?"

"Yes, exactly. And something more that seemed impossible to him, and, as I said, that he had never done before and that he had never seen happen before. Suppose I said that he mightn't have done that or gone after that, and that he hadn't done so on many other nights. If I asked what made the difference tonight or what made the difference between Alex and other children who remained tucked up in their cots tonight? What drove or enabled him to do it?" She was thinking of Alex but also of herself and her own life.

"I don't know. I suppose, for some reason, Alex believed he could get out. He believed it was possible because otherwise he wouldn't have tried. Am I right?"

"I think you are. But, again, think of how enormous this is too. He embarked on something, went after something that he had never seen done, had no evidence that it could be done and yet went after it. Do you follow?"

"You're right. It's huge. And before you say it, in the bigger scheme of things and in your world of work, this would be huge. Doing something that was never done before and still believing that it can be done, that it's possible. Now, even *I'm* getting interested!" And her thoughts reflected on her own life too.

Yes, and the interesting thing is where did this come from in him? He didn't learn it from us, did he?"

"No, he didn't" so it must be innate, mustn't it?"

"Exactly, and if it's innate in Alex, then, it must be in innate in everybody including, if you forgive me, everybody in my company. And what interests and intrigues me is, if this is so, then what's blocking it in them, in people at work?"

"I understand and that's very true and important. What next?" She laughed. "What other great learnings do we have from our little teacher?"

"Ha ha. Well, next came his analysis or assessment of the situation or problem, as we might call it, the bars! He saw this problem and shook them, tried to squeeze through them, went around all the sides and so on. His analysis was good, even if it might seem obvious to us."

"I can guess you're going to say that he identified the barriers of what was blocking him from getting what he wanted – the barriers to success – or whatever you would call them. Sounds jargonistic I know, but he really was taking stock and doing some learning and exploring."

"Well, yes, but don't dismiss it too easily. It may seem something small and obvious to us but he has focused on the main problem and saw it as a problem or challenge. In a sense, he was seeing his environment – his cot – in a new light. It has moved from seeing it as something inanimate and unchangeable to seeing it as a challenge to be overcome. He was no longer accepting reality as something separate and himself as a victim, but engaged with that reality in a meaningful way. Now I know all this was happening subconsciously in Alex but it was happening. Just like happens with the whole creative evolutionary process. How many of us are failing to do that today, right now? We're taking things as they are, accepting them as they are, maybe complaining about them like victims, but refusing to see beyond them to something more. I can see you're smiling, but what I'm saying is, I believe, hugely important."

Joan wondered if Mike could sense what she was thinking and going through, and if she too was behaving as a victim in a sense. But she kept with Mike and his world.

"No, I'm not dismissing what you're saying at all. I'm just smiling at how much you're getting out of it. Is there more?"

"Yes, lots of it!," Mike laughed. "As we said he explored different ways of dealing with the bars or the barrier until he found the one that he thought looked most promising."

"Yes, and the great thing is that he didn't give up. He persisted. I can't tell how many times he failed but he kept going."

> "I challenge you to make your life a masterpiece.
> I challenge you to join the ranks of those people who live what they teach, who walk their talk"
>
> **Tony Robbins**

The courage to risk and explore

"Yes, I really admired that too. It would have been so easy to have given up but he refused to let go of his goal. You might think I am labouring this again but so often I see people giving up because they want an immediate result. And, when it's not forthcoming, they give up. If nature and the universe had behaved like this we would not be here today. They encountered so many dead ends, so many failures, but the wonderful evolutionary process didn't give up, it persisted, just like our Alex did. I'm faced with this very same challenge right now. It would be so easy to just leave it and settle for what we have as normal. Heather often warns me about ending up disappointed and I can see that. And, of course, there's a real risk of that happening."

Joan knew exactly what he was saying, and the risk of disappointment which Heather spoke about. Was she not in the same boat?

"And, talking about risk, our little man is taking considerable risks. He keeps falling backwards each time but look at the enormous risk he takes once he gets on top of the bars. Now he has to fling himself into the unknown, something he has never done before. Of course, by hanging on, he has reduced the risk but it is still risky."

"Yes, you're so right. He is being very brave and is prepared to take a considerable risk in order to gain his freedom. It would be so much easier for him to stay with the known and comfortable. It's like that saying about ships remaining in the harbour being perfectly safe, but that's not what ships are for. Nor do I believe it's what human beings are for. We're not made for safety but for growth and development." She wondered who she was preaching to.

"I understand. That's very good."

"Yes, but there's one more. The lovely thing is that having got this breakthrough, he's now in a new place both physically and psychologically. He now knows that he can achieve other ones and go on learning, breaking rules, trying things and getting better and better. This is the final learning from our little video. Get to a new place and try new things"

"I can see where you're going with this, Mike. I can see how excited you are about it."

"You're right, Joan, but it's quite incredible and what is even more incredible is the fact that Alex discovered this whole process by himself. And it was a process. Just look at it.

1. He "decided" to do something about his reality and go after a new reality or better version of it or a transformation of the existing one.
2. He took stock of his reality or situation and identified the main barriers to getting what he wanted. All done very quickly and naturally of course.
3. He explored various ways of resolving his issue, tried a few of them and then settled on one.

4. He persisted and kept going even after many failures.
5. He took lots of risks along the way.
6. And he achieved his goal and got to a new place… and life will never be the same for him again … unless we create new and higher bars and barriers for him."

"So I take it you have learned a whole new methodology for your work situation?" Joan laughed.

"It's not so much a technique or methodology that I have discovered as much as a stronger resolve to keep going. I can see how we can, for very good reasons, fail on each of these six items. I can see how different members of my team might fail on each of these."

"Really?"

Life is constant change

"Of course. Most of them with, the exception of Teresa and Bernard, do not really want to go after or believe in a different reality for our company. Frank, wonderful as he is, can get blocked completely by problems or barriers, though I see how he's slowly getting a new understanding of what's possible from the work he's doing with his football team. Rarely do we explore different options and Tom will work himself to the bone but trying the same things over and over. We tried several things in the past but, unlike Alex, gave up far too quickly when it didn't seem to be working. Sally is wonderful at her job and looks after everything and us all, but usually she doesn't like taking risks, though there're some small signs of progress there too. But, what I find most heartening from what we have just observed happen, is the confirmation that what I'm after makes sense and is possible, but only if we follow what Alex did."

"And is what he did that important or significant? Really?"

"To me it is Joan. Several people in recent times have questioned the basis for going after a very different kind of company. They argue and bring up very convincing arguments and I can't give them any really clear and powerful examples to back up my belief. For some reason, I just believe it's so and that people want things to be different and better. This is not easy to achieve or realise and yet you and I have just witnessed how fundamental that drive and creativity and courage is and what's required to make it happen."

> "Nothing in life is to be feared, it is only to be understood. Now is the time to understand more, so that we may fear less"
>
> **Marie Curie**

"You're right. It's quite remarkable. But why are people so reluctant or afraid to go after a breakthrough, an improvement, like our little Alex achieved?"

"I think it's a few things and one of them is comfort or complacency. You know the theory that if you put a frog into a pot of boiling water

it'll jump back out again. But if you put it into a pot of cold water, and gently bring it to the boil, the frog, theoretically at least, will stay in the water and slowly boil to death. Why?"

"Because it doesn't realise what's happening. The water is only gradually getting hotter and one second is very similar to the previous one so it just doesn't notice what's going on," Joan answered.

"Yes, exactly. It gets comfortable and we all slip into that comfort. Just look at the mess the world is in environmentally! But no more than for the frog or for the alcoholic or for any addict, comfort is not a good criterion for what is best for us and therefore we have to shake ourselves and wake ourselves up."

Joan felt like the frog ... a bit.

"I see. And is it that important?"

"Yes, I think it is. Yesterday I took Teresa and Tom to Mark's restaurant and he told us that unless he keeps changing and improving, he won't survive. It's as basic as that, he said."

"That's very good. And what's the other thing you were thinking of?"

"Dishonesty and lack of courage to see and say things as they are and decide to go after something better. Don't forget what Alex did and the courage he had to do it. He set out to attempt something he had never done before and which was, to his mind, impossible. And he went against us in the process. Going against people and institutions is not easy. Easier to just fit in. He knew that what he was doing was going against our wishes. But that didn't stop him. This one is tied in to the previous one of comfort so we avoid risk, we avoid failure, we avoid stepping on people's toes and we avoid saying what we think. I'm facing this at work right now with this venture I'm embarking on and with going after something that my managers don't like. Tom, Natalie and others won't feel comfortable with it and I'll have to find the courage to confront them and their fears and believe that more is possible like Alex did, and believe in themselves like Alex did and take risks like Alex did and persist like Alex did ... and hopefully get to a whole new place and much greater freedom and life ... like Alex did. And maybe Alex, at some level wondered about how we'd react to his venture, as his superiors and parents. I have my own parents at work to worry about," he laughed.

"Yes, I know," Joan laughed, "but why do you think people like Tom or Natalie would do this?" Joan said with a yawn.

"I think it's about all of us. We fool ourselves about what's happening, we don't want to hear bad news and so we live life asleep, in a world of illusions. We prefer illusions to reality. We prefer to remain asleep. I mean look at our current world. Is this the best we can do? Is it good enough?"

> "He who is not courageous enough to take risks will accomplish nothing in life"
>
> **Muhammad Ali**

"Well, talking of sleep, isn't it time we got some? I think our young son has given you enough to think about for one night, and me, too." She thought.

"You're right about that. I'm more convinced than ever that I need to change lots of things. I think we can. But there's much I need to change in my own behaviour. If there's one thing Alex has taught me it's that creativity is a very deep and essential part of all of us and that we can make the seemingly impossible happen. Ok, let's call it a day … a good day in spite of some worrying developments. I learned a lot and I have to say that Alex has told me a great deal and been a great help."

He stood up and stretched. He felt he had taken a step forward. Still the challenge remained around how to change the minds of so many people on what was possible for them as an organisation, a company. And he first of all had to do some mind changing in his own team. Without them in agreement, nothing would happen. But it was not as easy as it sounded, and it was not something that could be commanded or forced. "But, for that to happen, I must persist with what might appear impossible. Like Alex did. And that's not easy, because there seems to be nobody who's really thinking like I am at present. It can be easy to give up and settle as we said earlier. Yes, that's the problem. And then there's the huge risk from Martha and Brad! Do I have the courage to throw myself into the unknown, like Alex did?" he asked himself as he slowly went upstairs.

Questions for reflection and action

1. What did you think of how Mike handled Rose's question and how he helped her? Do you recognise it?
2. Do you think she will actually *do* something about it? Why?
3. Do you recognise Alex's steps to creativity? Do you believe that is what he did, however unconsciously?
4. Why did this strike Mike so powerfully?
5. What do you think was most impressive in what he did? And most challenging? And how does this apply to you?

Chapter 12

Not just Transparent but Invisible Management

Learn what trust really involves and means for managing

The group were not too surprised when Mike told them at the previous meeting that their next one would be in The House of Harmony restaurant. Going off-site for meetings was not unusual for them.

Mike had reserved a table in the main restaurant but had booked a meeting room for after lunch. Before lunch he said he hoped they would all enjoy their meal but also asked them to make a note if they spotted anything special or different about the restaurant and they could talk about it afterwards.

When the meal was over, they adjourned to their meeting room and Mike asked them what they had each noticed. They all said they enjoyed their meal and that the service was also exceptionally good.

"But was there anything unusual that you noticed?" Mike asked.

They weren't sure. Some talked about the friendliness of the service and some talked about how efficient and yet how natural it all was.

"Very pleasant". "Friendly". "Attentive", "Efficient" were other comments from the team.

Mike persisted: "Yes, it's the service I'm talking about and the efficiency and performance of the waiters, but anything about that that struck you?"

"Well," Tony said, "there seemed to be nobody in charge, no head waiter or manager.

That surprised me a bit."

"Yes, I was going to say that too," Tom said, "I couldn't see anyone in charge but, despite that, they seemed to know what to do and to take responsibility for it without anybody telling them. And yet it seemed to work very well."

"Good," Mike said, "I wonder why? Why don't we ask the manager, Mark, to join us and you can ask him these questions. That might be the best way to find out what was happening or how it worked."

Why people need to be managed

It was clear that Mark had already been informed of this plan so he was ready and available.

Mark greeted everybody and, of course recognised Teresa and Tom, whom he had previously met.

"I was just saying," Mike said, "that maybe it would be better if people ask you questions, Mark, rather than you explaining how you manage or don't manage this restaurant. Alright?"

"Sure, I'm fine with that." Mark said.

"Okay, I'll jump in." Tom said, "Why don't you have a manager or head waiter, like most restaurants, to ensure everything goes well? Tony was remarking that you don't seem to have a manager in the restaurant. For me, management is everything and I place huge importance on good and strong management. The presence of a manager is critical, I would say, to ensure all goes well. No?"

"Please don't think me rude," Mark said, "but there *is* a restaurant manager. You just didn't see her. She just doesn't need to be around the restaurant always because the staff, both waiters and chefs, know what to do."

"But suppose there was a problem," Tony persisted, "what would happen?"

"They would solve it," Mark replied, "I should say they do solve problems. Believe me there's not a day without a problem. But there's nothing really that they can't handle or that would require the input or decision from a head waiter or manager. They are experienced people, at least many of them, and they've come across and dealt with most problems already. Some of that is due to how we deal with questions and problems when they arise. Instead of giving an answer or telling them what they should do, we ask them what they think, we coach them and, as a result, they come up with their own answers nearly always, and from repeatedly and consistently doing this, they're capable of dealing with any problem or emergency that might arise. This may sound strange but if there was a problem, their solution for it would very probably be better than the manager's. They have a better feel."

"I like that," Teresa said, "but how did you get there? I mean, you don't get that kind of culture or environment overnight. I'm having a struggle to change the culture in our own little house and I'm not finding it at all easy."

"No, you're right, Teresa, and we work hard at it. This restaurant and these people have a manager, as I have said, but it's not the manager's job to do things, or to get things done, or even to monitor and ensure that things get done.

But will you permit me to put all these questions back at you, Tom and Teresa, if I may. Can you tell me why not only restaurants, but all organisations need managers and managing? Why do people need to be managed?"

> "There is a new model of leadership in the world that rides on the premise that every single person in the organisation can be a leader. Titles are important for structure and order, but real power does not come from titles"
>
> **Robin S. Sharma**

Sally jumped in to help her colleagues. "Because people need to be told or directed on what they have to do. That's part of my job as the manager of Finance. This varies depending on the people, of course, or on the complexity of the issue. In the Financial area, we can't afford mistakes and it's a core part of every manager's job to ensure there aren't any and I'm sure it's the same for every manager.

"It's the same for us." Tom commented, "We have morning meetings with people to let them know what they have to do on the day and that's based on the weekly planning schedule and what has happened from day to day. There may be changes to schedules or orders or plans and they have to be informed of these and let know what they need to do as a result."

"But, Mark," Sally said, "even if the people know what to do, do you not think it would be good for the manager to be present, just in case, and to show support, and maybe even give a hand-out with things now and again?"

"I agree with Tom and Sally," Natalie added, "and quite frankly there are some people who have to be motivated or got to work. You'll always find some who just don't want to do what they should do or to do it as well as they should do it. I dislike having to challenge people when they're not motivated to do what they should but I need to do it.. Motivation is a key part of my job and of all my managers' jobs. Do you agree?"

"I promise I'll come back to you on that in a minute, Natalie," Mark said, "but for now I just want to hear all the reasons why you need managers and why I might need managers. And, believe me, we can't afford mistakes either! Poisoning someone is at least as serious as getting a wrong ledger Sally!"

What people need to work and perform well?

"Part of my remit as the manager of HR is training," Teresa said, "because you'll always have some people who are not able to do their job and so need help in the form of support and training or mentoring or coaching in some cases. I believe it's part of every manager's job to ensure that he or she has a group of people who are able to do what's required of them."

"I agree with all of you," Mark said, "I agree with you Sally and Tom that people need help to know what they have to do, both in general, and on a daily basis. I agree with you, Natalie that people need to be motivated, or be helped to *want* to do their job and to do it well. And I agree with you, Teresa, that we need to ensure that people have the capability and are able to do what's required of them. Where we might differ is that I believe that the things you have named as being part of the manager's job are, in essence, *all* that a manager should do; nothing more, this is everything ...virtually. Every one of my managers has the responsibility of making sure that everybody who works for them:

KNOWS what's required and what they have to do.

WANTS to do what they have to do and do it well.

Is **ABLE** to do a good job.

... just as you have all said.

As I and we see it, a manager's job is to work to ensure these three elements are in place, both for each individual and for the team. That's why your meal was, hopefully, so enjoyable and the service so good, because every one of those waiters, and the group as a whole, Know, Want, and are Able to provide really good service. Their manager would have spent her time working and taking advantage of every minute, every problem, every situation to have these three things in place."

And ...When things go wrong?

"I'm ok with that, Mark," Heather interrupted, "but that's not all a manager has to do. Things go wrong, problems occur – there are surprises. These all have to be dealt with too and this is part of the manager's job, surely?"

"I understand, Heather, and you're right. Things here go wrong every day... there are always surprises. Last week we had a person who was quite paranoid and was in dread of being poisoned. He made the most extreme demands and our waiters and our chef had to taste many of the dishes before he would eat. But they all handled it perfectly well and he and his group left very happy. Different from the kind of problems you and your managers meet, but still a very challenging one. The people in our case handled it all on their own because they knew and wanted and were able to handle it.

But the problem, as I see it, is that most times, managers do not fulfil these three roles or don't focus sufficiently and exclusively on them. And because they haven't done them well and put all their energies into these three, you're right, many problems can arise which they subsequently have to resolve and spend ongoing time doing so. So then they go around checking that things are being done properly and interfering and correcting where they see necessary. Do you know what I'm saying?"

Do they KNOW?

Do they WANT?

Are they ABLE?

"And this, then, gets in people's way?" Heather added.

"Exactly it has a counter effect; all of this supervising, monitoring, ensuring, interfering, correcting, which forms a large part of many managers' jobs, actually gets in the way of, hinders and slows down people Knowing, Wanting, and being Able to carry out their roles or functions on their own and do so really well. Do you know what I mean? It becomes a vicious circle that justifies or proves itself right."

"I understand what you're saying." Teresa said. "I've been making the same mistake with my own two children for a long time."

"Well, I think it's a bit simplistic, Mark" Tony said, "if you don't mind my saying so. In our area of Engineering there are issues that arise every day that people can't solve on their own. They need help, *my* help and the help of my other managers. That's what we're for."

"I understand, Tony, and, yes, there will be situations or issues that people can't solve on their own. But these are the exception, not the rule. And we use all of these 'problem' or new situations to educate and develop people. Nothing like it for learning. It is our greatest

"A hero is someone who understands the responsibility that comes with his freedom"

Bob Dylan

friend. And, with respect, Tony, some of our issues, while very different from your engineering ones, are no less challenging. Handling a very noisy table that is annoying people at another table is not easy to handle.

And, like you in Engineering, our staff will come across issues that they have never met before. Last week we had a very distinguished person who insisted he had ordered a special table for his group and the staff knew he hadn't. It wasn't easy to solve it in a way that he didn't lose face, but they did. And they did it without involving their manager or anyone else. They have the confidence, the skills and the common sense to handle things like this."

"I see," Tony said, "quite remarkable. Even if I'm not at all sure it would work for us."

Self-fulfilling prophecies

"I understand that. You see, I believe that seeing management as being about solving problems for people and being available to solve problems when they arise is a fundamental misunderstanding of the real role of the manager in my opinion. It generates an underlying loss of confidence, responsibility, ownership on the part of the people actually doing the job. That's why Clara, the restaurant manager, normally chooses *not* to be around. She thinks it might interfere with people and their sense of ownership and accountability. She believes they might defer to her. Then it becomes a kind of colluding game between managers and their people and does serious damage both to performance and to people. She believes that not being around most times gives a clear message to people that they're accountable and that she has full confidence in them. It might feel good and look good to be around and spot some small things that need attention, but it robs people of ownership and accountability. It's a bit like those football managers who jump up and down on the side-lines and shout instructions that the players won't hear, not to mention understand. Of course, jumping up and down and shouting or, as in our case, a manager hanging around and spotting things, makes managers feel very important and justified in their roles as managers.

But it also creates a negative and vicious circle or downward spiral. Because of this way of managing people, it turns out exactly like that, in line with the expectation that people need to be managed, and managers become confirmed in their suspicions and in their roles. They actually find lots of people who either do not KNOW what to do, do not WANT to do it or are not ABLE. And so, they feel justified in continuing to manage and monitor and correct and to feel that it's essential that they do so! And they're not aware that it is *they* who have actually and unwittingly created that very situation and problem. Is this making sense?"

"It certainly is to me," Frank came in, "and I think I could learn somethings from you about my own side-line behaviour with my football team. Do you know I manage a football team?"

"Yes, I do, and I would be delighted to talk to you about it. I work with some managers of football teams to help them give the kind of help that is really needed rather than satisfying their own anxieties and pressures. Yes, Frank, I'd be delighted to do that, and I've been hearing some interesting things that are happening. Seems things are beginning to turn around."

"I hope so. Still early days Mark, but I'd love to follow up with you on that offer"

Teresa spoke and probably spoke for everybody: "To answer your question, Mark, yes, it does all make sense. Too much sense, I'm sorry to say!"

"Good. So, that's why every manager's job here is to ensure that their people Know what

"You cannot hope to build a better world without improving the individuals. To that end, each of us must work for his own improvement and, at the same time, share a general responsibility for all humanity, our particular duty being to aid those to whom we think we can be most useful"

Marie Curie

they have to do, really Want to do it, and are Able to do it and do it well. A key part of this is about making sure that everybody truly understands what we want our restaurant to be and why that's good for them, for every part of their lives."

"Have you been talking to him, Mike?" Frank jibed.

"We come from the same school of philosophy," Mike answered "We were in kindergarden together."

So why have managers at all?

"If the waiters and the team are so autonomous and independent, why do they need a manager at all?" Sally asked.

"Well, maybe they don't!" Mark said, "And we're moving more and more towards using team leaders. By that I mean a person within every group whose function is, not to manage as somebody outside the group, but who has the responsibility for ensuring and promoting the overall health and environment and welfare of the group.

This is a responsibility they have to us as the overall managers of the restaurant but also a responsibility they have to their people and that the people give them and expect them to fulfil. But our managers, and the manager of the restaurant, have important roles without having to worry about things getting done, monitoring, interfering or controlling.

The obvious one is ensuring that every member of the restaurant staff, especially new people, **KNOW, WANT** and are **ABLE** or are equipped to do their jobs and fulfil their roles really well, and I know I'm going on about that bit and sorry for that.

They also have an important role in encouraging and helping staff to constantly look for, not only better ways of doing things, but find new things, new ideas and new services, so that the restaurant is unique and outstanding and is seen to be such.

> "The key to management is to get rid of the managers"
>
> **Ricardo Semler**

It's their role to make it easier to provide the service we provide and to find new and better services and new and better ways of delivering that service. This adds great value to their work and to them and makes their work exciting. They also act as the conduit between senior management and the staff so that senior management are aware of the situation and reality on the ground in the restaurant, and the staff are fully aware of what's happening and being considered at other levels or at the overall business level. But it's not about layers and levels but a more organic and dynamic kind of thing.

Of course, the manager gives time to each individual to help them review their performance, identify what they need to improve, and where they may need help, as well as hearing from them ideas on what could be better and what they want in terms of development and their career. This takes some time but, when done well, it's invaluable time. And there are other things too."

"These are very different things than I see managers in other restaurants or in other places do," Terry remarked.

"Yes, and I see that too, Terry. I feel very often that managers, at some level and in some strange way, don't really want things to go smoothly or faultlessly because they need problems and things to go wrong to justify their existence, even if they may not be even aware that this is what they're doing and would be horrified to be told that this is what they're actually doing."

They all laughed and Bernard said: "I think we all know some managers like that and maybe we are all a bit like that too if we're honest. But, I can see the benefits of this and how well it works, because things get done and with far less people and with far less pain and effort it seems."

"Yes," Mark said, "but there are lots of other benefits that may not be so obvious that we haven't touched on."

"What kinds of things? "Tom asked.

Before Mark could answer, a waitress knocked and asked would it be alright to bring in tea and coffee. Mark said it was and the waiter brought in a trolley with tea, coffee, biscuits, pastries and some fruit.

She put a cappuccino in front of Mike, a herbal tea in front of Teresa and a Machiato in front of Tom. Mark got an expresso, and the others were given cups so they could serve themselves.

"Hey, why are you the special ones?" Frank complained.

"It's ok," Mike explained. "It's just that we three were here a few weeks ago and she remembered what we like."

"Nice touch, Mark," Heather commented.

"I assure you I had nothing to do with that," Mark replied. "Absolutely nothing. They saw you are guests and they presumed you would welcome some refreshment at this stage.

The initiative was completely theirs. They do this all the time, for everybody.

"Freedom makes a huge requirement of every human being. With freedom comes responsibility. For the person who is unwilling to grow up, the person who does not want to carry his own weight, this is a frightening prospect"

Eleanor Roosevelt

No end to the benefits, no end to change

But back to your question, Tom, about other benefits. As you said, there are less people here than in other restaurants, but there are also less levels and ceilings between people. which is enormously beneficial in terms of relationships and communications and just keeping complexity out of things. Everyone is in touch with the overall goal and identifies with it. They know, they find out, what is needed or coming up on a day and what staff or other special things might be needed.

We don't need those morning meetings to do that. It happens seamlessly. Everyone sees themselves as being autonomous and free to take initiatives and do things and, as a result, everyone is in fact a leader, and will act as one whenever that's required. They see themselves as being responsible for the overall welfare of the whole restaurant."

"That's great," Tom said, "wonderful that people take such personal and individual responsibility."

"It is Tom but it's more than that too. You may think that our waiters are just six or seven individuals and the chefs three or four other individuals, but they're not. They're a team, an entity, a unity operating as a really intelligent "thing". That is enormously different and doesn't happen by accident either. It also means that we are a really *listening* organisation. Everyone is listening in all directions which is immensely powerful. And I can guarantee you, that if you come in here in a few weeks" time, you'll see changes, because we're forever changing as a result of listening to people and to problems that people identify, as well as to the many ideas that people contribute.

You may have noticed some things that are different from other restaurants. And some of these you may have seen in other countries where you were on holiday. This is because all of our staff are forever on the lookout for new ideas and when they find some, they bring them back and we look at them. It's a wonderful source of creativity, change and improvement."

"Why all this change?" Heather asked.

"Because we're very clear, Heather, that unless we are constantly changing adjusting to our ever-changing environment, we'll not survive. Flexibility, change and constant improvement are what differentiates us from other restaurants. Lose that and we die. Is it not the same for you ultimately?"

"Yes, you're right, Mark," Heather replied "it's essential for us too and it's something that we struggle with. We become comfortable with how we do things and get stuck in our ways."

"Good. I'm glad you see that. Another great thing is that people are always learning and trying to learn even more, and the manager really wants people to learn as quickly and as often as

> "Progress is impossible without change, and those who cannot change their minds cannot change anything"
>
> **George Bernard Shaw**

possible so that the group is as autonomous and independent as soon as possible. And people want to improve and get better and so look for feedback which may seem strange but it works really well.

Our Performance Reviews work really well as a result. I'm not saying that everything is perfect, but we're very happy with our way of handling things and I mean *all* of us, including those waiters who looked after you earlier."

"That wouldn't work in our place"

"One big difference between your restaurant and our company", Mike interrupted, "is that your staff have to be present, on the premises, every day. Ours don't. Or at least some can do their work from home and Heather here has probably worked more from home in the past few years than on the premises. But many others too can work from home."

"And we have that too, Mike. Even the waiters and others who have to be here enjoy great flexibility. If someone needs time off, they organise and agree it among themselves. We don't need to know. What makes this possible is that we all want the same thing. So things like lates and absenteeism are just not an issue here. People want to be here and do a good job. And that's why so few leave because they know they won't find the same flexibility and freedom anywhere else."

"I think that's great," Heather said, "I can really identify with that, and I know it works. And it's one of the really good things we do in our company and in this group. Or, at least, try to do … if we are let" she said laughing, after a glance at Mike.

Mike was pleased to hear this but he wondered how long he could maintain it so and how long, if at all, he could maintain Heather in her present position.

"Thank you very much for that Mark. Is that ok?" Mike asked? "I think there's a lot happening here that confirms what we're after, don't you agree?"

They all did and thanked Mark for the meal and for sharing his thinking and approach with them.

"I'm glad you liked how Mark operates and I'd like us to spend some time understanding what it means for us and for how *we* manage our people and situations. Would that be ok? I need your help with it."

Tom interrupted: "I understand that, Mike, but it's not as simple or as easy for us as it is for Mark? Do people agree with me on that?"

Several heads nodded and Tony's especially.

"Sorry to interrupt, and I don't want to interfere," Mark said, "but would you mind telling me, Tom, why you think you can't work in this way in your company and why your business is so different from ours?"

"Our people are different from yours," Tom answered. "They lack the drive and confidence your people have. I could never take the risks you take with your people, nor would people like me to, because they're afraid of making mistakes and I can understand why. It's very important for us to get things right."

"Yes, and the atmosphere is very different with us," Teresa added. "They rely on management a lot and blame us for things not being right and claim we're letting them down. They just don't have the same drive your people have. They are just not as interested and, unlike your staff, they don't find the work itself very interesting. They just want to do their job, get paid for it and go home. That's all they want, and they don't want hassle."

"Don't think I don't understand all that that you're saying." Mark answered. "It was the same in a restaurant where I worked once too. But it all comes down to the style of management or leadership. In fact,

> "Far and away the best prize that life offers is the chance to work hard at work worth doing"
>
> **Theodore Roosevelt**

I think it's probably easier for *you* to manage in this way and have this kind of environment than it is for us in a restaurant."

"How can you say that? "Tony asked, "ours is a very different environment from yours."

"Yes, it is," Mark replied, "but a much more difficult one.

It might look a nice job to be in a restaurant and serve guests, but that's only one bit of it. The preparation, laying tables and other duties are very tedious and onerous and have to be done well. Then the cleaning up afterwards is not very pleasurable either. Do any of you like doing that at home after a party? This is like a party every day and twice or three times a day. I imagine your people don't have to deal with unreasonable demands on a daily basis and unreasonable people. Nor, I imagine, are our people's schedules as consistent as yours. They have to be incredibly flexible. They often have to stay back or come in on days off because of some emergency or influx of guests. And, don't forget, waiters and restaurant staff are not the most highly regarded jobs nor the most highly paid ones in our economy. So, in all, I would swap with you any day," Mark finished, laughing.

All about belief in people and in the world

"So how is it possible then? What makes the big difference?" Tom asked.

"Well, I could say a lot about it and I already have, but basically to me it's about belief – belief in people and belief in possibilities. Most of managing is based on a lack of real belief in people, which means they have to be managed and controlled so they do what they are supposed to do. This is why people behave like both of you described earlier. And most managers don't believe in possibilities either and think that things are as good as they can be, with only little room for improvement. Leaders are different. They want things to be different and better and people understand and like this."

"Well, that's quite extraordinary," Teresa blurted out, "and both shocking and sad. But are you saying that really believing in people and trusting in them will be enough to get people to work well and be responsible?"

"Yes, I am, in essence. For example, the fact that everyone here wants to constantly improve things means that there are always challenges around and people love challenges. It's like an energy or fuel for them. Managers in other companies often manage challenges away, and in so doing rob people of the energy they need and want. Once people really buy into a goal, that supposes they don't need to be controlled at all. We have no controls on people's time because we know they *want* to do a good job, so we trust them. As a result, they feel completely free and love working here."

"But you can't just let people do what they want, surely?" Tom asked.

Let people do what they want; get people doing what they want

"Why not? That is *exactly* what I'm after in fact – to let people free to do what they want. I always want people to do what they want! What you have to do is to make sure that *they* want what *you* want and we do this by getting them convinced that what we want – a really top class company or restaurant – is really good for them.

You can do the very same, I believe. People who think that avoiding work or doing little is good for them are simply wrong and are being stupid. So our job is to help people to understand what they really want. Everyone here knows that the welfare of this restaurant is good for them, for every part of their lives and so they want to work and to contribute."

Many in the group smiled in recognition of this.

"And is that why they accept changes, as Mike said earlier?" Teresa asked.

"Yes, it is. There's such non-sense spoken about change and there are all kinds of manipulative change programmes, but change for us is synonymous with progress and improvement and everyone wants that.

> "Forget socialism, capitalism, just-in-time deliveries, salary surveys, and the rest ... concentrate on building organisations that accomplish that most difficult of all challenges: to make people look forward to coming to work in the morning"
>
> **Ricardo Semler**

We are forever beginning new curves as old ideas and initiatives die off and it's that that keeps us healthy and happy. And the time to begin a new curve is not just when there are problems with something, when a product or trend or menu or service is running out of steam because that can be too late. Here we are always changing – menus, layout, service, style. Believe me, no one here is ever bored or has time to be bored!"

"And is there never conflict, then, with staff?" Teresa asked.

"No, not really. We have lots of differences, but we work them out. As a matter of fact, we want differences and I worry if there aren't any. It's like the blind men around the elephant that Mike often talks about. Everyone's viewpoint and perspective is important and, if we listen to them all, we'll come up with really good ideas and decisions. It's nearly fool proof if you work in that way. But you have to park your ego and any idea of being a know-it-all superior management being," Mark said laughing.

> "The work environment can bring out the 'best' or the 'worst' in you"
>
> **Abhishek Ratna**

"But do you not honestly think that your people are not special people? You *know* you have very good people." Teresa persisted.

"Yes, I do, but it's not because they're blessed with a different set of genes from your or anyone else's people. It can't be that we were lucky and got all the good ones and you got a lot of the others! When you were talking about how different your people are from ours, I smiled because, not only are we taking our people from the same "pot", but some of our best people actually came from your company. And, some of them were let go by you, I believe. Sorry to say that. It's about how they are managed and led that makes the difference and that makes them or helps them to be "good" or "bad". All our managers see the great potential there is in people and they believe in that and find out how to release it. That's our job – to nurture people. I often think my job is like that of a gardener. I grow peas in my garden and my job is to release them from the packet and put them in the ground and look after them, nurture them. But that is all. *They* do the growing and the miracle working, and I only provide the rich environment. They have the innate intelligence around what to do to grow. It's the same here with our people. We provide a rich and challenging environment, and they do the rest. It is as simple as that."

"That all makes sense," Teresa said, "and thanks for the chat."

"Yes, thanks a lot, Mark," Tom added, "You have given me a lot to think about. In fact I feel a bit worried about myself and about how I have been managing so far, if truth be told."

"That may not be a bad thing or place to be, Tom," Mike interrupted, "it shows just how big and valuable the change we have to make needs to be."

But Mike knew they weren't fully convinced. He didn't mind. He wanted to just sow the seed – a different kind of seed – in everyone's head in the hope that it would survive and grow into something enormous and wonderfully beautiful. He wondered how he could turn Tom and the whole team around and get them believing that this new way of thinking and working was possible.

Possibility and pressure

"One last question, Mark, if I may," he asked, "if there was one thing you would say is key to all of this or one thing to get started, headed in this direction, what would you say it is?"

"I believe the most important key in bringing about this kind of organisation is to develop a mentality of possibility in people, that *they* believe that more is possible than they might currently think. It's much more than what people call a "can do" mentality. I think that's what enabled us to do it and that continues to enable us to work in this way."

Mike was happy with Mark's response, happy and intrigued. "I'd like to ask you another question, Mark", he said. "Back to what Tom and Teresa were asking earlier, about how your restaurant business is different from our company. I wonder if you appreciate the pressures we're under? We can't afford to take chances as we are faced with all kinds of challenges both from within our own corporation and from the competition. It's different and is something I worry a lot about, as do Teresa and Tom."

"Now Mike. I'm surprised at you," Mark laughed, "how many restaurants have you seen come and go even in our own small area in the past ten years? There's no riskier business to be in, believe me. There are predators, big and small, all over the place. And on top of all that, we know that one slip, one case of food poisoning or a serious burns accident, could put an end to everything. And, I know that even if your company did close, some of you and your people would get looked after.

Not so in my case or for my people and for that reason I have to always think of them. And, you know, that's exactly why I'm so strong and demanding, on everyone and on myself. I cannot

> "Leadership is not a popularity contest; it's about leaving your ego at the door. The name of the game is to lead without a title"
>
> **Robin S. Sharma**

afford to let them down but if I tolerate slippage then I'll be truly letting them down. But, don't hear this as a burden. We love it. It's exciting and we all share in that excitement. We love the challenge. And that's why, I believe our people stay with us. Our chefs are constantly being "head-hunted" and our other staff could find other jobs very easily. But they don't because I believe they like what we have created here."

"Yes thank you, Mark, and sorry if I was dismissive of your reality and challenge. I understand. Well done."

They all got up and thanked Mark again and his staff for the wonderful service and Mark in particular for sharing so much with them.

Tom was thoughtful and a little worried. "This is disturbing," he thought, "I've been very successful all my life because I always provided strong leadership. Yes, I've had a problem here and there, but, then, who hasn't? I'm not so sure I can change now. Or even that I should change."

Teresa was buoyant and full of energy. "I can see now how this could change my role dramatically. In a sense, this is what I always felt but couldn't really justify. Now I see a way. And as for my own children!"

Mike was in great form but still felt worried. "I can see that this is the way to go but does everybody else? And, if they don't, I could be left very alone. I can imagine that if something goes wrong everyone will jump ship and blame me. Still, this is the way I want to go and have to go. I will have to resolve that challenge of getting the others on board. He was particularly concerned about Tom. Not just because of things he had said at the meeting but in general about his style of management.

They happened to walk together to their cars and Mike took advantage to check in with Tom.

"Are you ok with all that, Tom? You look a bit puzzled."

"Well, I am in a way, Mike. I agree with all that Mark was saying but it seems such an enormous change for us … or at least for me."

"I understand, Tom. Maybe we might have a chat about it sometime if you think that would help?"

"Yes, I would welcome that, Mike. Let's do that when things settle down a bit and we return to normal. Thanks."

Questions for reflection and action

1. What did you most like about Mark's restaurant?
2. How was it possible to get away with not "managing"?
3. Do you know how you would get your people to want what you want, without manipulation?
4. What do you see as the biggest challenges to managing in this way?
5. How would you go about creating this kind of culture or way of working?

Chapter 13
The Golf Cart and the Tree

The enormous power of the organic and live organisation

The following Saturday, Tom, Tony, Bernard and Mike finally got to play their game of golf. It was Bernard who actually made it happen. He got permission from the group to nominate a date and take the decision and he did … and here they were. "Decision-making style number one" he told them.

All kinds of topics were discussed as they played their round of golf, but the conversation frequently returned to their meal and their experience in The House of Harmony restaurant. They were still talking about, marvelling at, and even struggling with the phenomenon of Mark's restaurant and how it all ran so smoothly.

"Not like that golf cart of yours Tom," Tony joked as they waited on the fifth tee box for a four-ball ahead of them to move on. "It seems to be always causing trouble and needing a lot of managing. Ever think of firing it?"

"Yes, firing it into a ditch or somewhere. It has my heart broken. I spend more time trying to get it going than I do playing golf. I think it's because it's so complex. Complex things seem to need a lot of attention, 'or managing' as you call it."

"Maybe it's the design that's at fault? Mike suggested.

"I'm not sure. This is my third one and I was assured it was the very best one, the best design," Tom grunted as he once more checked the leads.

"What you want, Tom," Mike said, is one that looks after itself – fuels itself, adjusts to hot and cold days, wet and dry ones and that repairs itself."

"Are you trying to annoy me more, Mike?" Tom asked. "Forget futuristic and pie in the sky ideas and be real."

"I am being real," Mike answered. "Right beside you, you have something that is designed exactly like that. It does all those things I mentioned – fuels itself, adjusts to hot and cold days, wet and dry ones, repairs itself and requires no looking after or managing."

"What do you mean?" Tom asked, as he finally stopped struggling with his caddy cart.

"The tree beside you, Tom. It's far more complex than your golf cart. What's going on in your caddy cart is of minor complexity to the managing of the carbon, hydrogen, oxygen, phosphorus, potassium, nitrogen, sulphur, calcium, iron, and magnesium in that tree beside you. And see that bark? Beneath that there's a band of what they call phloem, living tissue that transports material from the crown of the tree to the roots. Beneath that there's a different form of phloem that transports water to the crown of the tree. And then there is photosynthesis which plays the part your battery plays in your caddy cart and does so much more reliably, I would venture to say. I could go on but I won't. I like learning about these things as you know. But do you understand what I am saying?"

> "This most beautiful system of the sun, planets, and comets, could only proceed from the counsel and dominion of an intelligent and powerful Being"
>
> **Isaac Newton**

"I do," Tom answered, "but I'm not sure why you are saying it to me!"

"That's ok. So tell me, how does your troublesome caddy cart compare to our tree here? How do they differ?"

"What a crazy question!" Tom replied.

"Maybe it is, "Mike said, "but I'm not asking about how they differ, not in terms of what they do, but how they differ in themselves?"

"Ah ok," Tom replied, "well, it's still a crazy question but, leaving aside what the motor can do that the tree can't, let me see … you can take the motor apart and put it together again and if anything goes wrong, you can find out where the problem is, and what it is and fix it. So that's one big difference and advantage the caddy cart has."

"And the tree?" Mike asked, "doesn't it have parts, and don't things go wrong with it too?"

"Yes, the tree does have parts as you endlessly described, but you can't take it apart or put it together again and when something goes wrong, you can't do much. It more or less fixes itself, or doesn't."

"People are smarter than you might think"

John Astin

"So the tree is much more independent in that sense? What makes it so?"

"It has its own life or intelligence or internal dynamics and so it adjusts and responds to its environment. If the motor on my caddie cart runs out of power, unless I put some in, it will cease to function and die, whereas the tree won't, and it will go in search of water or one of those big words you used."

"So, it needs less watching and attention?"

"Yes. I need to look after the motor, whereas the tree looks after itself.

"Any other big differences?"

"Well, the motor will always remain a motor and as it is, but the tree is constantly growing and changing. Eventually, as I know well from previous ones, the motor will pack up and stop and become useless, the tree never will. Obsolescence is not built into trees, apparently," he laughed.

"But the tree will eventually die and disappear."

"Yes, but, even then, it continues because it sends out seeds to ensure that it or its species continues, albeit in a different form. How did I do? Impressed?"

"Ha ha yes …very impressed. Very good," Mike said, "and the greatest of differences and the one that I like best is that every tree has its own inner intelligence and just knows what to do to cope with whatever comes along, within reason, and this intelligence also means that every single tree is unique and different and special.

"Intelligence is the ability to adapt to change"

Stephen Hawking

So, Tom, which are organisations, like our own company, most like – trees or machines/motors?"

"Oh, machines or motors without doubt. They are complex and need constant looking after and problems dealt with when they arise. That's why I'm so important, essential in fact."

"Hey get ready," Tony interrupted them, "that's all very interesting but we'll be off soon."

"Sure Tony, but they still have not taken their shots. I agree with you Tom" Mike said, "but which would you prefer that our organisation was like – a tree or a machine?"

"Oh I see what you mean," Tom said, "well, it would be great if organisations were more like trees, required little or no attention, did their own thing, innovated and grew, but I don't see that as being very realistic, I mean I can't imagine it. Can you?"

"Well, yes I can," Mike said, "and I think you have actually seen one, an organisation that is close to being like a tree, certainly closer to a tree than being like a machine that needs constant looking after, fixing and correcting"

"You mean the restaurant?" Tom asked.

"Yes, exactly," Mike said.

"Well that would be great but I don't see how it would happen in our company, which is very different from Mark's restaurant. We have just been saying that earlier"

"I think it can happen and we can talk about this at our next meeting but now focus on your game, you're playing like an old broken-down machine. Obsolescence is creeping up on *you*. Ha ha. Ok, ok Tony, we're ready."

Making the complex simple at work

The senior management team met again the following Friday and Mike asked Tom to tell the rest about the conversation they had on the golf course about the tree and the machine. They all liked the story and had many questions about it, particularly about how one could move from being a machine organisation into being more like a tree or intelligent organisation, as Mike called it.

The intelligent organisation

"Am I being fair and accurate in claiming that The House of Harmony Restaurant is an example of an intelligent organisation, a bit like Tom's tree, doing its own thing, not needing attention, constantly changing, correcting its own problems, adjusting to whatever happens? Again, they all thought about it for a while. Some were going to disagree or query Mike, but then accepted that the two were in fact very similar.

"I sense some of you are not 100% sure. Why don't we have a go now at writing up a list of what an intelligent organisation would look like or how it would be? If we could get about ten of these. How Mark's restaurant is, or better still, how *we* would be if we were a truly intelligent organisation."

They did so and said that if their company were an intelligent organisation then:

1. It would be a *vibrant, live, dynamic company* run by the staff or workers who are passionately interested in doing a good job.
2. Everyone and everything would be *driven by a shared and meaningful goal* that all understand and have bought into.
3. It would be *a truly flexible entity* that adjusts and responds to circumstances and needs as required.
4. The staff would be *constantly trying to improve* and grow and be better.

5. They would be a *united entity* where each person supports and works for the other.
6. Staff would get their *information directly from the customers* and others and from what is happening.
7. The staff or workers would *need no direction* or to be told what to do.
8. It would be a *really exciting and fun place to work*.
9. The staff or workers would *control themselves* by their own desire to do a good job and *feel free to provide a quality* and efficient product or service.
10. Staff or workers would be *forever inventing and searching* for new services and new and better ways to do things.

"Ok?," Mike asked, "a pretty good description of the The House of Harmony I would say and I can see also a good description of how you would like our own organisation to be. Well done. And, if we can make this happen, Tom, you'll need to spend far less time fixing problems and messing like you do with your golf cart. Like the tree, people will look after themselves.

That's what I want. And I want it not just to make Tom's life easier or all of our lives easier, but to get that intelligence going in people and in the organisation. When you think of the wonders a tree can do, imagine what our people, rich human beings will do. I can't wait."

Mike thought back to that morning just some months ago when he drove into work and looked at the faces and demeanour of people arriving, realising that something was wrong and that something much better could be created. Was this it?

"I don't know about you," he said, "but I want an organisation that is and behaves like the tree ... only much better – is responsive to a situation, is intelligent with a clear goal and where everybody and every group has the ability to find and create its own way to making that goal a reality for themselves and for all of us. All those things that you all identified. I believe that's possible. I believe it's terribly important to go after making it a reality for the benefit of all our people, and for our business, for society and for ourselves. Please tell me if I'm wrong in this. Please tell me if it's a dream or that it's not worth going after, or that pure business success is enough for us?"

He looked around the table, at each member of his team and knew by the looks on their faces that he didn't have to ask them for a verbal answer.

It was Teresa who spoke for the rest. "Let's go. But where do we start?

"We start right here," Mike answered, "in this room, with ourselves, and I know each of you well enough to know that you can do it and that we can do it together. As Teresa said, "let's go". And by that I mean that we – each one of us in this room – has to give leadership and be real leaders in bringing this about by how we manage and lead our people. But leadership is a much overused and misused word and can mean anything from Gandhi to Hitler. What I would like each of you to do, before our next meeting, is to think about what it means to be a leader, but in particular what I'm calling a "Facilitating Leader".

> "In the long history of human kind (and animal kind too) those who learned to collaborate and improvise most effectively have survived"
>
> **Charles Darwin**

But we have to live it and put it into practice every day and in the problems and challenges we face. Don't look so downcast, Tom, it's easy and you'll love it."

The Tree	The Golf Cart
1. The tree moves on its own, develops on its own.	The golf cart only moves when moved or started, and has no inner development.
2. Grows continuously.	No growth apart from what gets added on from the outside.
3. Changes and has an inner knowledge or wisdom to change and adjust to light, water, wind.	Is changed. No internal knowledge or wisdom to adjust. Handles elements poorly.
4. Trusts in itself and has confidence that it will cope with most things. A broken branch will either be repaired or replaced.	No trust itself, passive and a victim. If broken will remain broken, unless fixed by someone from the outside.
5. Relaxed and quietly relentless in its growth and renewal.	Listless and waiting, and slowly decaying.
6. Appears dead but a life is there that never dies.	Slowly dissipating and disappearing.
7. Innovative – grows in different ways and gets around problems of obstacles to the light etc.	No innovation. Will always remain the same.

The Tree	The Golf Cart
8. In touch and in harmony with its environment, shares, adjusts and cooperates with birds, soil, air.	A foreigner or stranger to environment with no interaction or relationship.
9. Complex in how it works, operates and lives.	Simple and inoperative and inactive.
10. Unique – all different. Has freedom to be as it chooses and can adjust.	Standard and can be replicated over and over.
11. Thinks of the future and of continuing life.	No future, only this and when this is over, that is it!
12. Part of something greater, a whole, a greater purpose.	Isolated … cut off, on its own, for itself.

Questions for reflection and action

1. How relevant do you see Mike's connecting the machine with the tree or the organic?
2. Can you think of examples – close to home – where only the organic and the organism work and resolve issues?
3. What are the major challenges to managing in an organic way, through organisms, rather than through control? And are your particular challenges?
4. What experiences have you had where you have seen this way of working and relating to work? Or in life or society?
5. How big do you see the shift to managing in a more organic and live way? Do you know how you would do it?

Chapter 14
Getting on Top of ...
Or to the Bottom of Things

What managing in a new way means and why it works so well

Tom was far from happy. He wasn't feeling good about himself at all. Part of his difficulty was because he felt that Mike wasn't feeling good about *him*. Despite his best efforts, Mike had been unable to arrange a meeting to follow up on their promised discussion on how to put into practice some of the lessons they had learned from their visit to Mark's restaurant. And then there was the whole issue of the golf cart and the organic tree – esoteric, troubling but true.

And Tom knew some of the blame for not meeting with Mike on all this fell on him. It was the same old story. Yes, some meetings were scheduled but eventually were cancelled because of one crisis or another. There always seemed to be some crisis. And very often Tom was at the heart of the crisis. It came with the territory, and it came with Tom. He was at a loss as to what to do. He was giving the company and this issue his very best shot.

The Operations Department was a large and extended one where most activities began and ended. And there was never a shortage of problems, setbacks and upsets on the way from one to the other. Tom knew this and he also believed he was the right person for the job. He thrived on problems and on eventually overcoming them. He drove himself and others to go after and take on problems and eventually break through all barriers that they came across. This present problem was big and one that was going on for some time. For that reason, he was not surprised when Mike pulled him aside after a morning meeting.

"How are you doing, Tom? It seems we're finding it difficult to make time for that meeting we discussed. I know you said that we would wait till things became more normal, but will things ever be normal?

"I understand your frustration, Mike, and I was thinking the same thing myself. It seems to be one thing after another now. As you know, the Quantum Logistics System is taking all our time and atten-

> "Time is the coin of your life. It is the only coin you have, and only you can determine how it will be spent. Be careful lest you let other people spend it for you"
>
> **Carl Sandburg**

tion and I know you understand how important this is. We still haven't solved it and it's imperative that we do so, as you know."

"I understand that, but I wonder why it's taking so much time. Will this be the case with every problem that arises? On that basis, we'll never find time for our meeting which I think is also very important."

"Yes, I know what you mean, but it's hard to know what else I can do. I just seem to have so many meetings. I spend all my time at them. But I feel I have to because I want to get to the bottom of it. That's my job. And that's why I'm giving it so much attention and ensuring that others do too. None of us is ever out of here now before 7 o'clock in the evening … at the earliest. The problem is slowing down everything else and costing us a lot of money. Sally has had to deal with no end of questions about what's happening, and I have dealt with no end of suggestions. So that's what's taking up so much time."

Getting to the bottom of things – root and branch work

"What takes so much time, Tom? I know we give it priority at our weekly meeting when you report to the group, and we thresh it around among ourselves and that in itself annoys some people like Bernard as you have noticed. "

"Yes, there's that, and it takes time to prepare reports for that meeting, because I know I'll be asked questions and I need to have my answers ready. I have to explain why some of the suggestions didn't work or wouldn't work. You can't take every view on board, but I hate to appear defensive. Most of the time is spent on a meeting I hold every Thursday with everybody involved, where we try to get to the bottom of things. I did this because there were more and more meetings of small groups happening and I wanted to pull it all together. Much gets discussed at that meeting and there's a lot of preparation involved.

Then we have all the follow-up. There are five separate groups working on specific lines of investigation and exploration at present and this all takes time. But we'll get there, I know we will. I also have a special daily meeting of my own Operations team to see how we can make the most of what we have and minimise disruption and cost. Then we agree plans for the day and people take responsibility for following them and report back on them the next day. Additionally there are my normal team meetings devoted to other issues. I know I promised to reduce my meetings and I did for a while but they keep creeping back in.

So, you see there's a lot going on, but I believe we'll will get to the bottom of it eventually, providing we get the support of all of the other functions. Everyone has a part to play and getting the cooperation of the other functions is essential and not always easy. There were times when I thought of asking you to attend our Thursday meeting to mediate or arbitrate on things, so that everybody is pulling together and resolving them. What do you think?"

"No, Tom, I don't think I'll do that, although I'd like to help."

"We're getting some help as it is, and Teresa has been great. She has arranged great training in problem-solving, communications, negotiations and conflict management which has made a big difference to our meetings. Quite a few people have gone on those courses and found them very useful. She has dedicated one person full-time to provide this training. On that front, there's one area where I think you might be able to help, Mike, around resources. We could really do with the help of one or two more people."

"What kind of people?"

"One obvious area is administration. If we had one or two people who could handle that work it would free up some Operations and Engineering people for other tasks. And if we got some suitable contract people, that would relieve other staff. Do you think that would be possible?"

> "How did it get so late so soon? It's night before it's afternoon. December is here before it's June. My goodness how the time has flown. How did it get so late so soon?"
>
> **Dr Seuss**

What Mark would do!

"Maybe it would, but as you were talking, my mind went on a different route. How do you think this would be handled in Mark's restaurant or by Mark?"

"I've no idea. I don't think it's the same thing at all," Tom laughed.

"I know that, but just for the fun of it, between *us*, what do you think *he* would do if a problem or emergency like this arose in the restaurant?"

"I really don't know. It's just so very different from our situation."

"I understand, Tom, but what do you imagine he might do if he had a similar situation in the restaurant or something truly important wasn't happening or wasn't working well and was going to damage performance, service, and results – just like ours?"

"Well, as he said, I think he'd probably get the restaurant staff together – waiters, chefs, other support people – and ask them to come up with some solution. Something like that. And leave it with them. But we can't do that."

"But why could you not do something like that? Something along those lines, even?"

"I don't think so. I just don't see it working. Our situation is much more complex and requires more expertise and a lot of coordinating."

"But could we not give it a chance? Suppose you, and maybe I, met with the Operations people, professionals, technicians and some of the operating staff – the frontline people directly working on this?"

"And what would we ask or get them to do?"

"Just ask them to work out a solution for this and leave it with them. But let them know that we're available to help, *only* if they want it."

"I'm prepared to give it a try but I don't think they have the expertise or resources to solve it, because it needs managing and coordinating, and we're doing most of that already."

"Maybe you're right, but this is a bit different. We would be leaving it to them to resolve. Why don't we give it a try and see what they come up with?"

"As I said, I don't see it as very different from what we are currently doing. It would be the same thing, but without me and some others present. But I suppose it wouldn't do any harm. Are you saying that we stop everything else to solve it?"

"I'm sure you've done a lot of good work and there are lots of initiatives that have been taken that the group could avail of as they see fit. So why not pause all of that now, and see what happens?"

The handover of responsibility

And that is what they did. Mike and Tom met with a group of Operations people and those from other functional areas – all those involved in the problem.

"I know you've all been working very hard on this system issue as have many other people and thanks for all your good efforts" said Tom. "Much good work has been done and I'm sure we will solve the problem eventually. But Mike and I have had a chat about it and what we would like to do is tvo ask you as a group to meet and take responsibility for trying to resolve this. I know some of you have already been involved. and so too have a lot of other people and we'd like to simplify it for now and leave it with you all, just for now, and see what you come up with. We won't interfere and you'll get all the help that you ask for, but only what you ask for. Is that understood?"

> "In a very real way, ownership is the essence of leadership. When you are 'ridiculously in charge,' then you own whatever happens in a company, school, etcetera"
>
> **Henry Cloud**

At first the group were a bit mystified. Nobody said anything. People looked at each other. Eventually some asked questions like who would lead or manage the group, what reports or information they would be required to provide, what parameters there were etcetera. Tom and Mike answered these, basically along the lines that they were free to do whatever they required and needed only to report as they saw fit.

There was a mood of disbelief in the group but also one of excitement, and some looked eager to get going. Albert, the recent recruit was one of them. He looked enthusiastic and actually stood up, showing he was ready to start working on the issue immediately.

And get going they did. They followed some of the lines that had been worked on previously, but also looked elsewhere. Initially there were some small but immediate improvements, as well as an overall air of excitement and confidence. But then, towards the end of the week, a fine thread that one of the group had been suggesting from the start looked promising. Everyone focused on it and were delighted when they saw it led to a complete solution.

It was a combination of several things rather than one single thing, but it was a complete solution. Lots of little threads came together into a strong rope solution. Parts of it had been mooted over the previous weeks in some of the meetings but never really gained support or momentum and got swamped with so many other ideas and suggestions and initiatives, or over-ruled by some more senior manager.

Now the whole group went after it and worked to make it happen. And it did. Actions that had previously required approvals from senior levels happened immediately. Trials were carried out quickly and adjustments and improvements made. The group asked for a meeting with Tom and Mike to share the good news and to make sure it really was good news. Quite apart from solving the problem, something else occurred. They had developed and were following a very different way of working. Gone were the demarcations and divisions between functions and gone were the different reports, presentations and justifications. Whole new lines of thinking came from this and several breakthroughs or "aha" moments happened.

A leader had emerged and was given authority to make decisions, but she did so most of the time based on ideas and suggestions from the group. They were operating to new standards and were taking on and doing things that they would previously have regarded as impossible or not practical. There was also a great sense of freedom in the group and allowances were made for particular situations where people needed time off and other people covered easily and naturally. Technicians were doing things that previously only engineers did, and operators were doing things that technicians normally handled.

Trust grew and all kinds of checks came to an end. More problems were resolved easily and there seemed to be fewer of them. Everyone on the team seemed to be enjoying themselves and to be full of energy. Other groups were curious and interested in what was going on.

But not everyone was happy. Some managers who were not directly involved, especially at middle level, had misgivings and seemed loathe to agree with some of the new ways of doing things. There was no shortage of potential risks that they identified on a daily basis. Tom and Mike heard these but paid little attention to them and hoped they would go away.

What happens when people are treated and behave like real human beings?

Two weeks later, Tom arrived in Mike's office with a big folder under his arm and a smile on his face.

"May I use your bin for this folder, Mike," he asked, "it's the notes from the 150 meetings held over the past month. And maybe I should throw my golf cart in as well. I feel so stupid."

"No need to be, Tom, I'm surprised too – agreeably so – by all that has happened. Why don't we go for a coffee and chat about it and see what sense we can make of it and what we have learned from it?"

"Sure, I would love that but please not in Mark's restaurant! I don't think I could face him right now. My ego would not allow it nor survive it." Tom laughed.

"So, Mike, I think you understand what happened and why it happened a bit more than you're saying," Tom commented after they had got their coffees.

"Well, in a way I do, but there's never a guarantee that it will always work and every time you do something like this, you still wonder if it will work *this* time. Deep down I knew it would work, but because I'm living in an environment, which operates in a completely different way I fret and doubt … a little. And I did this time as well. Especially after a few days when nothing seemed to be happening and more and more managers were coming with complaints about their lack of control and influence."

"I understand that, and I know I'm part of that same environment! Sorry about that. Maybe I'll begin to change after this experience. So, what did happen or why did it happen so unbelievably well?"

"This is going to sound very simplistic and trite, but we got that behaviour and breakthrough because people, human beings, were given the opportunity to behave as full and rich human beings and do so as a team. Something that we don't do very often."

"What do you mean?"

"I mean that we use a particular approach to managing which prevents people from behaving in this way, in this wonderfully human and creative way. It's a long story but it goes back a few centuries to when people like Galileo and Newton and Bacon and others achieved wonderful breakthroughs in understanding how things worked in our universe. From previously thinking that things happened by chance, or at the whim of the gods, or by some form of mysterious magic, they discovered some very fundamental laws about how things worked.

"I believe to be a leader is to enable others to embrace a vision, initiative or assignment in a way that they feel a sense of purpose, ownership, personal engagement, and common cause. I was very affected as a child by my father's positive example as a civic leader who inspired others to share his commitment to improving our community"

Melanne Verveer

These were based on very clear connections between cause and effect. Things happened because something caused and determined them to happen. This was great because we were no longer left with the vagaries of a haphazard world, but now we had control over it. If we knew the cause, we could control the effect. If we came across a negative effect, we could find out the cause and put it right. Isn't that what we do when we have a problem – use analytical problem-solving as we call it. Analyse it, find the cause – the root cause we often arrogantly call it – and we're done."

"So, what's so wrong with that?"

"First of all, there's a lot that's right with it. Newton and others discovered some laws about how the physical world really works that are still valid and very valuable. We now know that the sun doesn't rise, that some things in motion need something to put them into motion and without that understanding we would have no aeroplanes and we would certainly never have sent anybody to the moon as it belonged to another and very mysterious world. We would have been lost without those scientific breakthroughs and even this little problem might not have been solved without those insights and breakthroughs. But the problem was that they were given universal application. Everything fell under these laws including the human, and the whole domain linked to the human, including society. This is where our management thinking has come from. Managers are given responsibility for making things happen in a real cause-and-effect way and people become an essential part in this. It all becomes fixable and we, managers, can fix it,"

> "The world is so unpredictable. Things happen suddenly, unexpectedly. We want to feel we are in control of our own existence. In some ways we are, in some ways we're not. We are ruled by the forces of chance and coincidence"
>
> **Paul Auster**

"I understand that and what's wrong with that?"

"Only that it's not true and it doesn't work. It's untrue at the physical level as we learned from quantum and chaos theory and it's certainly not true at the social or human level. Things are far less predictable, controllable and manageable than we thought, but we continued to operate as if they were completely predictable and controllable.

Most of our social sciences fall under this category and we even use the word "science" to give them an air and aura of certainty that they don't have. Real science doesn't claim to have absolute certainty either. It's a constant pursuit of what really works and always on the principle that there is more to be discovered, that we never have the full truth."

"And you're saying that applies to management also?"

Why managing doesn't work

"Yes I am. Management is another social science and it was founded during the industrial revolution which saw human beings as equally controllable, predictable and manageable as parts of a machine. Laws and principles of management were developed on how to predict and control everything, including people, and we're still in the grip of that same way of thinking. Just like you were doing in your efforts to solve this problem. Forgive me for raising it again, but it's like your famous golf cart versus the tree. We're treating people as if they were parts of a machine instead of as inherently intelligent beings. This worked so well because you switched intelligences! From the intelligence of the cart to the intelligence of the tree. All along you were working with the group as if they were the golf cart, needing constant analysis and intervening and fixing. Then you left it up to them and they found their own innate intelligence just like the tree and magic happened. They became a completely different entity, Tom."

"I see. Incredible difference and result!"

"Yes it is. And that's why workers the world over complain about how they're managed, how little they are involved and respected and taken into account. And this in all kinds of different cultures, but the one common denominator is the philosophy of management. Of course, this is not only confined to business and management. It affects all of the ways we handle people and society, but here we're talking about our own world."

"And you're saying that that is what we do here, as well as and why the environment you referred to earlier is prohibitive of people doing quality thinking."

"Yes I am. It's very simple. You're responsible for your area in operations."

"Yes."

"And you're responsible, for what happens, for making things happen and for the results in your area?"

"Yes."

"But, you can't do all the things that are necessary and need to be done to achieve those results. You have to achieve them through others. Isn't that so?"

"Yes, that's my job as manager".

"Of course, and that job means getting people to do what is needed to deliver the result, or ensuring that they're doing what is required and doing it in the right way to achieve the results that you want and are needed. Isn't that it?"

"Yes, exactly, that's my job and that's how I spend my time – ensuring that things get done and get done properly so that we're successful. Is there anything wrong with that?"

"No, it's just that that little word "ensuring" covers a multitude and could mean very many different things. Can you tell me, briefly, what are some of the things that you do to ensure that people do what they should do and do it properly and well?"

"Well, first of all I make sure that they know what is to be done, both as groups and as individuals. And then I get them to understand and accept their roles and responsibilities, agree their key performance indicators (KPIs) etcetera. And then I regularly check in with them to make sure that they're carrying them out properly and well."

"And I take it that this means that you have to be happy with what they're doing, or they need to satisfy you that they're doing what they should do and that they are doing it well?"

"But, of course, that's my job."

"What else?"

"Well, I was talking about individuals there, but the same holds true for the various functions and areas that I manage. So, it's here where I spend most of my time, planning, checking, reviewing, dealing with problems and improving things, of course. It's my job to keep on top of things and to answer to you for them. So I must be sure that things are happening and getting dealt with and that's where most of my time goes. As I said, I answer to you because you want and need to be happy so that you are able to

> "As long as habit and routine dictate the pattern of living, new dimensions of the soul will not emerge"
>
> **Henry Van Dyke**

"ensure" – to use your words – others and everyone that things are getting done well and will happen properly. Isn't that how it is?"

"Yes, that's definitely how things are. It's a bit different from how Mark and his restaurant manager and waiters work and how trees work. I take it that the team that you put in place to address that issue has been disbanded and no longer operates as such, is that right?"

"Well, yes, once we got the problem resolved we went back to normal, the normal way we work. Why?"

"I was curious. And how is it working? Are things going well?"

"Yes, we're back to normal and I think everything is going fine. I have heard no complaints. We're very busy as you know."

"Yes, I can see that. It seems you're now as busy again as you were during that whole problematic time?"

"Yes, you're probably right. I like to be busy as you well know," he laughed.

"Yes, I know. A few things interest me. Remember when that group we set up were working on the Quantum Logistics System problem during those few weeks? Why was it that you had so much time then and were not so busy?"

"Well, it was a temporary situation, of course, but in that time the group were doing the work and we weren't involved. It wasn't that we were idle, but we had lots of time for other things. Is that what you mean?"

"Yes, that's exactly it. And in that time, they got everything done, and done very well as we know, without all those things you mentioned earlier, around the planning, checking, problem-solving, reviewing etc.?"

"Yes, I suppose so!"

"And can you tell me how the group now compares to how they were then? How are they performing or thinking or how are they feeling, do you know?"

"I think they're fine. They're getting on with things. Maybe the same buzz that they had then is no longer there, and they are not nearly as busy, but I think they are okay."

"Would you mind finding out how they are and ask them what made that period of work so different for them? I'd love to know."

"Sure, I can do that. I'll get a group together and ask them that very question."

"Great. Perhaps you might have them for our meeting on Monday. I would like to share them with the rest of the team along with some other things I'd like to discuss."

"That's perfect Mike. I'll get that done and have something for you on Monday."

Questions for reflection and action

1. Do you know why Tom's enormous efforts failed? Ever had similar experiences? Despite your best efforts?
2. What was different with the group working on the problem compared to the previous approach?
3. Why did it work? Do you believe it will work? Why?
4. Do you understand Mike's explanation of where "management" came from?
5. Why did Tom revert to his normal way of managing? Why is it easy to do so? What would be so good if he hadn't … if he had continued with how the group had been working?

Chapter 15
All You Need is COACH

The five differences that make the difference

As agreed, Tom met a group of those who were involved in solving the Quantum Logistics System problem. First of all, he asked them how things were going and how they were working and feeling since the issue was resolved. He again thanked them for this, but the group didn't seem all that pleased. The meeting didn't look like being it was going to be an easy one. They seemed at a loss and to have little to say. They all seemed unclear as to what Tom was looking for.

"Things are fine and we're working away as usual", was the general response he got.

"What things are going well? Are you satisfied enough, then, with how things are going overall?" Tom asked them. He was relieved that he would be able to bring back a good report on how things were to Mike.

Again, responses were few and slow, and given with some reluctance.

"Ah, yes, things are going fine, and we're getting things done as usual and in the usual way. Nothing has changed."

"Good, but you don't all seem too happy," Tom joked, provoking them a little.

"Well, you know how things are," John spoke up.

Mike was not surprised it was John who spoke. John was always critical of things.

"You've heard it all before, Tom, we do more or less what we're told. We get the job done, as you well know, and we

"A sure sign of a soul-based workplace is excitement, enthusiasm, real passion; not manufactured passion, but real involvement. And there's very little fear"

David Whyte

give our opinions when we're asked for them. That's what we're doing. What more do you expect?"

"Not that you feel much confidence that your views will be listened to." Harry, a sidekick of John's, joked

The mood was sombre, the tone dull and the energy poor.

Tom persisted. "But, now I *am* asking for your opinions. So are there things that you would like to be different or better? Other things that you're unhappy with? I get the impression that you're *not* very happy with things."

Eventually, Ellen, normally a quiet person, seemed to lose her patience.

"I don't know what you're getting at, Tom. You know how things are. Have you got some problem with what we're doing? Because if not, I, for one, would like to get back to doing it. I'm not sure how the rest of you feel."

It was clear how they felt. They felt cross, frustrated and agreed completely with what Ellen had said.

"Yes, I'm not sure what this is about either. What are you getting at?" Caroline asked. "Is this some exercise you've been asked to do?"

"What do you expect us to say? We come in, get our instructions for the day and get on with our work. What else do you think? Or what do you want us to say, Tom?" John repeated.

"Okay, What I'm getting at, or trying to get at, is if you all feel strongly about your work now is different from how you were working for those weeks on the quantum logistics system issue? Or if how you are working now is better or worse than the way you were working then and which approach do you prefer? That kind of thing. Do you understand?"

A very different world

Suddenly the mood changed, and a torrent was released.

"But, you know that it is completely different." Harry said, "Normally we are *told* what needs to be done, whereas during that time we decided ourselves. So, when we saw something that might affect the process or something that needed attention, we used our own initiative and dealt with it, so that a constant flow was kept going."

"Yes," Veronica said, "and people took their own initiative and jumped in, rather than being told to. Being told can cause conflict."

"The big difference for me," Ellen came in, "is that we were able to see things for ourselves and because we could see for ourselves what was needed, we responded immediately, rather than being told, as if we are incapable of seeing it for ourselves."

And so on.

"Why is that so different? Or is it that different?" Tom asked

"Yes, very different." Stephen, an experienced engineer said, "It was just there was better overall awareness and consciousness of what was going on and involving the project, so we were constantly interacting with people and knowing where work was required and not. You didn't have to ask or be told.

You just did it. We just did it."

"Yes," said Gerry, a very experienced operator, "and then we were able to decide if people needed to spend time on other activities and we could decide for ourselves and we didn't have to wait for managers to decide."

> "Find joy in everything you choose to do. Every job, relationship, home ... it's your responsibility to love it, or change it"
>
> **Chuck Palanuik**

"In fact, *we* would tell managers what we were doing, rather than the other way around," Veronica added.

"Okay and I understand that you felt much better about that way of working? Why?" Tom asked.

The answers came from everywhere

"It was because we were all much more engaged and there was more job satisfaction".

Yes, and it was more exciting. We were continuously working for ways to improve things. Spotting things that needed attention and giving them attention. We were forever changing and improving things."

"Yes, and spotting things in other areas too that we were not doing, and we would then raise it among ourselves and decide if they would work for us".

"And we were left alone to get on with things. We were trusted. We did what we thought was right and not what someone else thought and decided".

"And we all got on much better. There was better communication with everyone … we talked more about what was happening, even during breaks. We spent most of our breaks talking about some work aspect, rather than something we saw on television. Maybe not during a complete break, but We were just so caught up with things."

"That's great. I hear all that and I believe you could go on and on listing things. But could I ask you to work in small groups for a few minutes and see if you can zone in on what the most important, the most basic, the most fundamental things about how you were working during that time were. Is that clear?"

In a while Tom heard back from each of the groups.

Ownership and relationships of trust

"We felt that ownership was what most mattered," said Carmel speaking for her group. "We were given and we took ownership for the whole project and we wanted to get it done and we did what we had to do rather than waiting for the supervisor to come along and tell us. We were in control … previously we had to explain and convince others and layers of management if we wanted something done... Isn't that what we said?"

The group agreed.

It was Albert who spoke next. Mike had been wondering what he had been thinking earlier in the meeting as he had said nothing.

"We would agree with what Carmel and her group say about owner-ship, but for that to happen, you have to have trust. For us it was about trust and being more trusted. And to be fair, you did trust us Tom – you and Mike. We heard and felt it. As a result, we had the confidence to go after things, to take decisions ourselves and to implement them. Confidence and trust ran right through the way we were working. But that lasted only for a while and then things returned to the old way of doing things."

"The one *we* came up with is a little bit strange and it's something that we mentioned earlier," John came in. "The big difference for us was that we were really aware of and in touch with what was happening and what was needed ourselves. We were able to see things for ourselves and because we could see them ourselves we responded immediately, rather than appearing as if we were incapable of seeing it for ourselves. We knew what had happened on the previous shift and we were aware of what we had to do.

Do you all know what I mean?"

They all visibly did.

Albert spoke again: "What we most liked about the way we were working was the actual challenge itself. The fact that we were working on something important and meaningful was very exciting and changed everything. While it wasn't nice that things were not going well and we couldn't find an answer, it was great to have something to think and worry about. You never stopped thinking about it actually. People at home even noticed that I seemed distracted. But, we actually looked forward to coming to work, because there was something really worthwhile to go after. We had a goal, and it was ours and made sense to us."

"Trust is the glue of life. It's the most essential ingredient in effective communication. It's the foundational principle that holds all relationships"

Stephen Covey

"And what about you, have you anything new to add from your group?" Tom asked the final group.

"Well, the others have covered everything, but because of all those things, every one of them, we had great relationships both among ourselves and with everybody else. We all got on much better. This was because we were a team with a clear goal, which gave us a great sense of power. There was better communication with everyone, and with other functions and areas as well, and with other managers too, because there was much more trust in us. We felt more self-worth ... because we felt we were being listened to and because we were more involved, it gave us more drive to do what was wanted. Isn't that so?"

"Even the other functions changed, didn't they, didn't you?" Ellen asked looking at some of the engineers and technicians."

"Yes, we did, because we did what we thought was right and felt free to do, rather than being pulled all over the place. But I got all my other projects done too," Alan said. "I think we all did, even if not everyone was always happy. I think some managers felt they had lost power or something."

"There's something else I'd like to mention if I may that I think is important," Albert said. "This may not sound all that important and certainly not to you or management, Tom, but we had a very different sense of freedom while on that project. We paid no heed to time and worked all kinds of hours. And some couldn't do that and that didn't matter and some needed time at home and that didn't matter. The way of working changed and even being at work felt different. We weren't tied to hours or structures and yet we probably worked more and harder than we normally do. But it felt different. We felt free. We did what we wanted, and it was great. Isn't that so?" They all heartily agreed.

"I find that very interesting and intriguing," Tom replied. Thank you all very much for that. It was very revealing and interesting, and I can clearly see how different it was from how you normally work and, indeed, how we are currently working. It gives my colleagues and myself something to think about. Based on what you've been saying, I think there has to be a better way of working than the normal one we use. Yes, much to think about. Many thanks to you all.

How we should always work

"Tom and I have had some discussions about what was going on in the recent saga around the Quantum Logistics System issue," Mike said, opening their next team meeting. "We were talking about how differently people were working during that period when we gave them control and responsibility, compared to how they had previously been working, or compared to how they are currently working. We were trying to find out what made the difference that time, and I think we all saw the big change that occurred. Would you all agree?"

They all agreed wholeheartedly.

"Where Tom and I didn't agree was whether that was just a once-off or whether it might, in fact, be a better way of working all the time. Tom told me that things are back to normal and I asked him if he would find out how people were feeling about that and how it compared to how they were working when they resolved that big issue. Tom?"

> "Don't lower your expectations to meet your performance. Raise your level of performance to meet your expectations. Expect the best of yourself, and then do what is necessary to make it a reality"
>
> **Ralph Marston**

"I did what you asked, Mike, but it wasn't really very easy. What I mean is that when I asked everybody about how things were now, they hadn't much to say. Okay, there were a few suggestions and one or two complaints about not being listened to and not being involved. The kind of thing you always hear. But that was it."

"I see," Mike said, "so you really found out very little or nothing?"

"No, not exactly. I found out a lot, but it was more around how they felt they were working *during* the time of the problem. That was interesting. So, I gave up asking them about how things are currently, and focused on hearing from them their description of how they felt and how things were when we left them on their own."

"That sounds good. Let's hear it."

"It's quite a list, so I'll just show you all or most of what they said. It's more a description of how they worked in general at that time rather than just trying to fix the problem.

Tom gave them feedback on what had been said at the meeting and described how the people involved would like things to be.

"I love all this", Bernard said, "and I agree with them and with Mike that it would be great if we were able to work like this all the time. One thing I noticed during that time when we let the group deal with the issue was that we didn't have so many meetings. It was great."

"I agree," Teresa said, "but I wonder what would be necessary to make that way of working possible all the time, Tom, or even if it's possible?"

"Well, I remembered my discussion with Mike so I asked them a few questions about what they thought might be required to make this work. See how open-minded I am, Mike?" Tom said.

"I'm impressed," Mike commented, "and I'm curious."

"Well I have some things in my head and some things written down but maybe in the spirit in which they were talking, it would be better to hear from everybody what you all think we need to do to work in a different way. Would that be okay, Mike?"

"Absolutely. I'm all for it. What do you all think?"

Teresa was first up, "I think we have to have more respect for people, trust them more and show more confidence in them."

"I agree," Tony added. "Trust and confidence can make a huge difference. I think that's what happened when they were working on the other issue. I can't say I found it easy. It doesn't come easy to me."

"But, for that we have to have the courage to give them real ownership and be able to stand back." Heather said. "This to me is the most challenging thing, to hand it over to them. Isn't that what Mark does in his restaurant?"

Mike caught Tom's eye and both smiled but said nothing.

"I agree with Heather and with Tony, especially about how difficult it is," Sally said. "It's very difficult to do that when you're a manager.

It's very hard to let go and to hand over responsibility. It's risky too. Especially in the Finance area. Do you know what I mean?"

"I think I do," Bernard answered, "but maybe it's about the kind of managing that's required. I'm not clear about this but I can see that there's something fundamentally wrong about how we currently manage. People need managers or leaders, but it's what *kind* of managing or leading that will make all the difference. I'm not sure. But we have often spoken about this … and with Mark too."

"Apologies for dragging this in again. It seems I'm always going on about this damn football team", Frank said. "But I have to shout my agreement with what Bernard has said. This is the big change that I'm making with my team, or trying to make. It's a completely different way of managing.

Now they have much more ownership and responsibility and they're handling that very well. I'm still the manager but I'm managing it very differently now.

> "There is nothing more difficult to take in hand, more perilous to conduct, or more uncertain in its success, than to take the lead in the introduction of a new order of things"
>
> **Niccolo Machiavelli**

"I think I understand what you're saying," Terry added. "I'm not clear enough about this, but I think we have to come up with a different and better way of relating to people if we want them to enjoy that confidence and ownership that Teresa and Bernard were talking about, and what Frank is finding and creating with his team. I feel that at present we make people feel inferior to us. We're even called 'superiors', which is bound to make people feel "inferior".

"One of the things that struck me as you were talking, Tom," Natalie said, "was that they got all the information themselves and not through us. I think they said that they saw it for themselves and that this made a great difference. We were out of the picture. They were able to respond themselves based on what they were seeing. It was first-hand. In my own area, very often, people are doing things because of information that I give them.

I coordinate all the information on what is happening and what is needed and then share it with them. Morning meetings are all or mostly about that. They were saying that it made a great difference when they were seeing it for themselves. Do you know what I mean?"

"Yes, I think I do, Natalie," Frank said, "but what struck me also was their drive and resolve. I believe they worked well together because they had a goal that they all subscribed to and one that made great sense to them. Maybe it was because of this that all other efforts have failed but whatever the reason, they certainly focused in on the challenge and this, as they said, helped them to work well together."

"Yes," Teresa added, "they were very clear about how well they worked together. I mean, don't forget, these just weren't Tom's Operations people. It was a group made up of different functions and expertise and very different personalities."

"What I've just now realised," Frank came in, "is the similarity to what happens with footballers and sports people in general. As managers of teams we want things to go well and we train and plan and develop strategies to try to ensure that. But, no matter how well you prepare for a game, no matter how much you try to configure what kind of game it might be, the reality is always different … always. This can be hard to handle when you want, and when it's your job to get a result – a good result. It can seem an impossible ask! But, what you have to do is trust the lads, the players, and rely on their intelligence to do the right thing in the moment, in the situation. So, developing that intelligence in them as individuals but, more importantly, as a group or team … team intelligence, is what's most important, just like the intelligence of any organism. It's so powerful and a bit humbling too!" he laughed.

They were all struck by this and continued to ask Frank more questions about what he meant and to discuss what each of them had noticed from Tom's report on the meeting.

Eventually, Mike brought the discussion to a close.

"How are we all doing, Tom? Are we covering many of the comments that your meeting came up with?"

"Everybody here is doing brilliantly. This is exactly the kind of things the group were saying to me."

The five essentials of good performance and the good life

"I thought so too," Mike commented, and I've been listening to you for the last while and I really like and admire what you've been saying. I say that, not just because it concurs with some ideas and models of my own, but because it just seems to make sense. But let me check if my model does concur with what you have been saying. Am I right in saying that the following elements work or are what made the difference to their performance to their success.

And, I would very much like to hear your comments on this also Tom. First of all, as you have just said Natalie, they had a very clear and challenging goal that they saw as important and meaningful, and they really wanted to achieve it. I mean this was a problem that was critical and one that we had been trying to solve for some time. So, it was a real and exciting challenge. We can't forget that. Very different from the normal day-to-day work that people do. Okay?"

> "Everyone you work with, in order to achieve a goal, must have something to lose if it is not realised and something to gain if it is realised. These are the people that are going to stick around you through thick and thin until the job is done."
>
> **Saidi Mdala**

They all nodded.

"Secondly, what you said Heather about ownership seemed to come up over and over. They really felt they had ownership and we gave them ownership. I think that made a big difference and always does. Would you agree?"

Again they all agreed.

"Then, Natalie, there was that whole question about how aware they were themselves of what was happening – fully and directly aware. And because they were aware themselves, they could respond immediately and, I would add, intelligently to what they saw and perceived was happening. This might seem nothing but it's very different from how we normally filter information to them. Things come to them through us rather than directly. Real awareness, direct awareness of what is happening is very different."

"Teresa and you Tony, spoke about confidence and how important they said that was. Uniquely, maybe for the first time, they felt that by giving them ownership for the problem and trusting them to resolve it, we were also giving them the confidence to resolve it. It seemed, from what they were saying, that they grew in confidence as individuals and as a group or team. I think that too was very important from what they were saying and very different from how things normally are. Do you agree?"

Once again they all agreed.

"Finally, they talked about relationships. Relationships among themselves and how well they got on with each other, but also relationships with other people and with us and with other managers, as you were saying Terry. By giving them ownership and showing confidence in them we stopped seeing and treating them as inferior to us. As they said, they were telling us things and letting us know what was happening, but doing so knowing that we were not going to interfere, unless, that is, we saw something very amiss. Is that what you are saying Terry?"

"Yes, that's exactly it, Mike, very different from the normal relationships we have with them where we are above or superior to them."

"Everyone happy with that, I take it. Now, these are your words or Tom's words, the words of the group. They're not mine. But they make sense to me, and they fit neatly and perfectly with a model that I believe in and that I try to follow. Here's how it goes in terms of what is always present when people perform well and is, in fact, necessary for people to not only perform well, but to enjoy what they're doing. For that to happen the following elements are needed and present. Have a look at them." And he wrote them up on a flipchart.

Clear, Challenging, attractive and meaningful goals.
Ownership of the task or project or area and accountability for it.
Awareness of what is required and of what is happening, real and direct awareness.
Confidence and trust, in oneself, in others and from others.
Healthy relationships with respect, equality, team working and adult to adult.

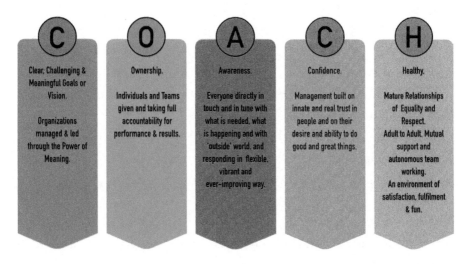

"What you think of them? Do they cover everything you've been saying?"

They all murmured their agreement. It all made sense. They looked at and went through them a few times and chatted about them,

"Is there anything you notice about them and about how they are written?" Mike asked

Commitment to COACH

It was Teresa who spoke first. "Yes, it is a mnemonic. They spell **COACH**. Is that it? I've come across this before." Mike could guess where she had come across it!

"Yes, it is." Mike answered.

They all smiled.

"Just in case you might think that these concepts only apply to that particular group or to some people, would you take a little test for me? Think of some situations or jobs or projects or assignments about which you felt really good, whether that's because they went really well and were very successful or simply because they were very enjoyable and satisfying. Can you all take a minute to do that? You won't find it difficult! You have lots of them."

They all took two or three minutes to write down some examples of what Mike was talking about.

"Now, can you tell me whether these five COACH elements or qualities were present or not? Or which of them played the greatest part?"

They all gave different examples, and they were all very convinced that all five were present.

"Good, so I take it then that we all agree that we have five very clear keys or principles around what leads to not only good performance, but to satisfying and enjoyable work. Is that understood?"

They all agreed.

Then Teresa spoke. "I mentioned earlier that I had come across this already and, in fact, not only have I come across it, but I've been applying it over the past while, with my own two children. Many of you are aware of the frustrations I've felt with them for some time now, but I believe I now understand what has been happening. It's just this. I've been blaming them for how they were behaving when, in fact, they've been simply reacting or responding to the reality that they have come across. In short, they have not come across one organisation that comes near to working in this **COACH** way.

Now they understand, and I understand, what has been going on and what they need. I'm not saying they will find a perfect organisation but at least they now know what they are looking for and that they are justified in wanting and insisting on that.

Mike and I had this same conversation way back when we were considering hiring Albert and I can see clearly now what Albert, and Mike, were saying. So, I'm fully behind this model because it has fundamentally changed my relationship with my own children."

"I'm delighted to hear all that, Teresa," Mike said. "Well done. Now, can I ask you all if you believe that, while all of these are important and maybe in different ways are there some in there that are not so necessary, that we could do without?"

They all looked at them again and went through them one by one. But they were silent.

Eventually Frank spoke:

"Personally, I think they're all necessary, there's none that could be left out."

"I agree," Heather added.

And, in fact they all agreed.

"So, this is how it is, then and wouldn't you all agree that if this is so, then we have to do everything we do in such a way that it respects, honours and observes these five principles. Do we all agree? How about it, Tom?"

Mike was referring to the conversation he had had with Tom around the existing and normal way of working. They had discussed how, after the problem was resolved, things returned to normal and Mike had queried Tom about how satisfied he was with this, with the normal way of working and ensuring things got done.

"I think I know what you're getting at," Tom laughed. "I suppose you're asking me if I'm happy that the way we're doing things fits with and delivers on these five elements?"

"Yes, that's exactly what I'm asking."

"I can see clearly that they don't, but I'm still at a loss on what to do or how to handle things in a different way, in line with these five COACH principles. But I think we have to find a way."

The key to real freedom

"One of the things that wasn't mentioned was something that came up at the end of the meeting which sounded a little strange to me, was freedom. It appears they just came and went as needed and worked all kinds of hours. I was struck by how an operational group like this was able to work in such a flexible way. But it did work. They got so much done and they loved the freedom and flexibility that went with it and was part of it. Now they are, for the most part, back working as usual but I was intrigued by what they said and how well it went."

"This topic keeps coming up and I think we need to spend some time on it sometime soon. What I would like us to agree for now is that, based on what we have just said, our current way of working is not good enough, and is not working. Can we all agree on that, even if we're not sure at the moment exactly what to do, including this business of flexible working and working from home?"

"Move out of your comfort zone. You can only grow if you are willing to feel awkward and uncomfortable when you try something new"

Brian Tracy

There was unanimous and genuine agreement.

"In fact, I think we've already taken some big steps to understand and put in place what we need to do and how we need to manage and lead. Does anybody have any idea what I might be referring to? Work we have already done?"

There was a long silence, but eventually Bernard ventured:

"Are you referring to the work that we did trying to identify what kind of company you want us to be? A bit like what that man in Joan's theatre did that you were telling me about?

"Well done Bernard. That's exactly what I was referring to. It all comes down to power. The kind of power that's most effective and that's in actual fact empowering. But let's leave that for today. We'll revisit that and work on it another time. For now, let's all commit to the search for a better way to work, out of an agreed conviction that the way we're currently doing things is not good enough.

They all agreed but Sally had a question:

"This may sound all wrong after talking about these five elements and I want to say that I agree with them all. But … what about the question of money and rewards? Surely it's critical to reward people well. I don't think you would get many who would vote for the five elements of COACH if there was no mention of money or rewards. Do people understand what I'm saying?"

They all did.

Yes, you're right, Sally. Money and financial rewards are very important. And, it's because it's so important that we need to handle that issue with great care."

"What do you mean?" Sally asked.

"What I mean is that because it's so important in our lives and in our world, that it can take over and end up being the only thing that matters. Consequently, these critical areas become swamped or eclipsed by the money topic and we lose sight of them and pay an enormous price for doing so. I'm saying that these five elements are of even greater importance than financial rewards in terms of people's overall welfare and that of the organisation. I'm not explaining this adequately but do you understand what I mean?"

They all seemed to agree, Sally included.

"That's good. I promise we'll come back to this and I'd like to leave things for now. Is that agreed? I think we did a good day's work today. Thank you all very much.

They all were in full agreement and happy.

Mike was pleased about the meeting and felt they had taken some big steps forward to finding a better way of working. He was particularly heartened that Tom seemed to believe that a different way of working and managing was possible, even if he was not entirely clear yet what to do in practice. He knew that more work was required on this matter and in particular to find out how the way of working the group had experienced could become the norm.

After the meeting, he remarked to Teresa: "I like the way you're thinking. I wonder where all those ideas are coming from?"

Teresa blushed and laughed saying: "You know I love to learn, Mike."

Mike was still thinking of this when his phone rang. It was his boss, Martha, asking if he would be free for a call later on. He wondered what it was now! Teresa had mentioned to him that Martha had asked her about the so-called staff committee she had learned about through a colleague who had been talking to someone in his company. Teresa had passed it off and made little of it, even though it had worried her.

"Yes, I can hold on here for an hour or two, Martha. I'll let Joan know. Is there anything in particular you want to cover or want me to prepare for, Martha?"

"No, Mike, nothing major. I'm just following up on our last call. I wanted us to have a chat to see if we can move on the whole topic of our communicating prior to our visit."

"Sure, Martha. Anything that helps improve things is good for me."

Questions for reflection and action

1. Can you identify with the group and with their confusion? Why did they find it difficult to explain it to Tom?
2. Which of the things they said were most significant in your opinion? And which most challenging or difficult to implement?

3. Do you think this is real and will work in your organisation?
4. What risks would changing to this way of working involve? Why might it be very enjoyable?
5. Are you happy with their sense of freedom and how this worked for them? Do you think you could operate in that way?

Chapter 16
It's All About Power – Good Power

The key to passionate, excellent and sustainable performance

"I can tell from looking at you that you won again," Tom said to Frank as they arrived for their team meeting.

"Yes, we did have another good win and, against all the odds." Frank replied

"What happened this time?" Heather asked. "There always seems to be some miraculous story of late!"

"Yes, you're right. I really can't explain how it happened. They looked down-and-out and

> "The kind of people that all teams need are people who are humble, hungry, and smart:humble being little ego, focusing more on their teammates than on themselves. Hungry, meaning they have a strong work ethic, are determined to get things done, and contribute any way they can. Smart, meaning not intellectually smart but inner personally smart"
>
> **Patrick Lencioni**

it looked all over and then they found a new lease of life and – cliché as it is – pulled the game out of the fire."

"So what's happening?" Tom asked. "It's the same team as last year more or less, and you had a poor start to the year and yet you seem to have reached a new level. What magic have you brought since you took over?"

"I'm not sure. I think we have a new resolve. We had a very honest meeting at the beginning of the year and asked ourselves realistically what we wanted to achieve. We, as a management group, set very high goals for ourselves and for the team and I have to say that everybody bought into them. We continue to return to them and to review all our games in the light of them, even when we play badly and lose. We keep returning to what we had agreed and to the goals we set ourselves.

I keep telling our players that we're working in a very different way. After all, they're the ones who have to do the business – a bit like our own people. We trust the lads and they respond to that trust. That's the only explanation I can give."

"But there would seem to be nothing new in this, Frank. Didn't you always do some of that?"

"Yes, I suppose we did, but it was very different this time. We were kind of going through the motions before … saying all the right things, but the real, genuine meaning wasn't there. Now it is and it's very different. I can honestly say that any other team will need to be a lot better than we are to beat us. And I must admit that I got some help from Mark on all this. It's really following the same principles he practises."

"I didn't know Mark played or knew much about football!"

"He knows a bit, but it was not around football that he helped us. You may not remember that he spoke about sports managers that day after our lunch and how they behave at games. How they are forever shouting instructions on the side-lines at games and trying to get their team and players to do what *they* want."

"Ah yes, I remember that," Tom said, "and how you were interested in all that. So, what did you do after that?"

"I met Mark and we talked about control and the lack of real control that managers have. What I learned from Mark was all about power. What I mean is that, effectively, we were taking the power away from the players and holding onto it ourselves.

We changed all that completely and found ways to give *them* the power. It's not that we handed over everything to them, but we brought them to a point of great clarity about where they were at, and what they wanted to achieve and why that was important to them. We also helped them to come up with ways to achieve success, the kind of style of play to use, the principles to follow, clear commitments from everybody – that sort of stuff. As I said, this didn't mean we had no control or power, but that it was a way of really empowering them, so, they agreed and knew what they wanted to achieve and then we worked with them to help them to do that.

I know I'm not making great sense of this, and it's an ongoing struggle not to intervene and trust the lads, just like Mark trusts his staff, but it's a struggle well worth engaging in, because the good results keep coming in. Long may it continue," he laughed.

The secret core of real power

"Well, whatever it was, it seems to have made a great difference," Mike observed "and, you know, it may have some connection to ourselves here and what we're trying to do. Remember when you all said how well we worked on that issue with our customer and how we have plans to deal with every eventuality? Why do you think we worked so well that day and please don't give me all the credit!" Mike laughed.

"I think we identified several things," Teresa said, "but what struck me as being of real significance was that it was something very important to us all. Therefore, it got rid of some of the differences of opinion and personality that normally dominate. And your handling of the decision-making was very good Mike."

Others nodded in agreement with that.

"And how do you think we could make that the norm for how we always work?" Mike asked.

"I'm not sure, Tony answered, "it would mean that we would have to make sure that we're always working on something that's important. I don't think that kind of performance is sustainable or can necessarily be the norm."

"Yes," Sally said, "but could we not always bring everything back to what is of most importance?"

"I like that," Mike said, "and I would like us to do some work on that issue to see if we can always work in this really focused way. I think if we can identify and agree on what it is that is most important, that we all believe in, then it'll help us to make sense to each other and work well together. I think, that if you can do the same with your own people and teams, the same thing will happen there."

> "Great theatre is about challenging how we think and encouraging us to fantasize about a world we aspire to"
>
> **William Defoe**

"And how do you think we could do that?" Teresa asked.

"This may seem irrelevant, but I was telling Bernard recently how just two nights ago my wife, Joan, came back from her theatre meeting. It was the first one of the year and I can't explain how happy and excited she was."

He tried to explain what happened. He recounted and described the conversation with Joan that night.

"The theatre can be a bit of a drag at times for Joan, and she has often felt like getting out of it. It's not easy to come home from a day's work and head back out again, especially when you have to work hard at learning lines, practising different parts and being constantly corrected. But, on Tuesday Joan came home very changed and very fired up.

"What's got into you, I asked. You seem to be on a high."

"I am, "she said, "all of us were, and it was a really great night."

"Why?" I asked, "what made it so special?"

"It was Henry," she replied, "Henry made it special. Henry is the director, of course".

"Why, what did he do?" I asked.

"He simply told us about what his plans and hopes for the year were and they were so exciting and interesting that we all became very enthused."

"And why was what he said so exciting? What was so new in it?"

"He described what he wanted us to do and achieve in this year. For example, he wants us to put on three plays, which is a big step up for us, but a challenging and exciting one. And, on top of that he wants us to get into some genres that we haven't done before. Everyone was very excited by the challenge", she said.

"I told her I understood that, but asked her what else made it so special apart from those fresh challenges. She said that Henry spoke of full houses every night and full houses of genuinely enthused people, where those attending could feel the buzz at the interval and hear the applause at the end. He said he wanted people going away excited and talking about their performance.

He also said that he wanted them to go after some awards this year which they have never done before. She said it was a great and stimulating night. I told her it certainly sounded like that and I asked her why she thought it worked so well".

Meaningful and integrated work and life

"She told me that Henry appealed to something in every one of them. He seemed to talk to each one of them and was inviting them to go after something really worthwhile. And they all saw it as something worthwhile. Joan told me that if it went half as well as expected, it would enable them to spend some money on areas that need attention and, who knows, they might do something very special by way of celebration at the end of the year.

I became nearly as excited as Joan was after listening to her. She told me that they then spent nearly an hour when Henry got them all to think about and propose ways in which they could make all his vision materialise. He listened to it all, took notes, and of course added in some of his own ideas. Joan told me they didn't close on those comments, but Henry said he would come back to them with a summary of what they had said and his own conclusions about what they needed to do."

"That sounds great, Mike," Teresa said, "and I think we can see where you're going with this." she laughed.

"Believe me," Mike answered, "I didn't make this up or arrange for it to happen. I just found it very interesting and, you're right, it's exactly what I would like us to do and what I would like each of you to engage with in your own teams.

Think how wonderful it would be if you were able to get your people as clear and committed and excited as Joan and her fellow theatre group were about their year ahead. Or as excited as Tom's group was. And why not? Why do I think that our doing this will be much more important than what Henry did, and in a sense much easier?"

"I actually think it will be both of those," Bernard answered. "Like, important as Joan's theatre group is, it is not nearly as important as what *we* are about. People's lives depend on us and on this company and so it is of enormous importance that we do something like Henry did. I also think it will be easier because it will be easier to make sense to people. If we can do something like Henry did, then people will see that what we're about is important for them and important for every aspect of their lives."

> "I would rather die a meaningful death than to live a meaningless life"
>
> **Corazon Aquino**

"That's great, Bernard," Mike said, "But is what Bernard said true? Is it a fact that this company is important for every aspect of people's lives? How can that be so? Is this not a job and one that people simply do to earn money to be able to live their lives outside of here and work as Sally referred to recently?"

"I agree with you, Mike," Natalie said, "and, yes, this company does provide people with the finance or money that they need for their lives but it also provides much more like, for example, their careers, what they want to do with their skills and gifts. We, or this company, can play a huge part in helping people to fulfil their ambitions and to achieve what they want in life."

"Yes," Frank came in, "I think Natalie is right and, when you think of it, people's families too depend on and are affected by who and how we are as a company. I'm not just talking about money but having a job is important for people's dignity and even identity. That's how they're perceived and appreciated and valued at home with family and relatives."

"And not just for their families," Heather added, "but also for their friends and for their place in society. Belonging to a company is important, and you only have to see what happens to people when they lose a job to realise that."

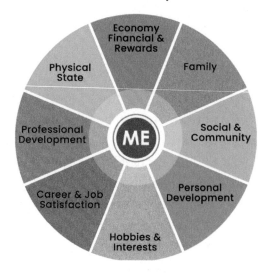

"And even for their hobbies," Tom said, "I can see people in the golf club who want the game of golf to last as long as possible because it's all they have. A hobby is great once it's a hobby and a diversion from other things you do in your life. Take work away and it ceases to be just a hobby."

"It may be strange to say this, but, even at the personal or spiritual development level," Tony commented, "belonging to a company and rubbing shoulders with other people and being challenged to relate and communicate and change are, in my opinion, hugely important for personal development. I know that getting on with you inferior lot certainly challenges me and brings out the best in me ... and at times, to be honest, the worst," he laughed.

"That's great," Mike concluded, "and we could add a few more like professional development, one's contribution to society, job satisfaction and other considerations and it's easy to see why Bernard is right that being clear about what we want for our company and areas within the company is more important, much more important than what Joan and her theatre friends are after. So, are you all convinced about this and are you all up for doing it with your own people?"

There was a unanimous positive response.

The magic of the vision and the 'X' meeting

"That's great, and, if you're going to do it with your people then we have to do it here first of all, and that's what I would like to do now. Teresa is right, I have given this some thought and, just as Henry did, I would like to share with you what I would like us to achieve this year and in the future."

Mike did that, and like Henry, he spoke of really satisfied customers, not just satisfied but extremely happy and frequently surprised at the level of service they were receiving. He spoke of the relationship he wanted with their suppliers, much to Natalie and Frank's delight, and how he wanted them to feel real partners with them in achieving their goals, loyal and benefiting from that loyalty. He spoke of the importance of delivering on their goals for the corporation and ultimately for their owners.

> "Setting goals is the first step in turning the invisible into the visible"
>
> **Tony Robbins**

"We have a responsibility to those who have invested in us and taken a risk with us, and we want them to feel pleased about that decision and happy to continue investing and supporting the enterprise."

He spoke of their place in the local community and how they wanted to feel part of the community, contributing and feeling welcome, and doing this also in the wider society. This sounded strange to some people and Mike was not surprised, as he knew it sounded strange to Martha and Brad and others too.

There were some knowing looks exchanged around the table, but nobody said anything. Finally, he spoke at some length about what he wanted for all of the people who worked in the company, that they would feel truly engaged and involved in bringing about the success of the company, proud of what they achieved and recognised and rewarded for doing so. He spoke of his dream of changing how people viewed their work so that it became something they enjoyed doing and wanted to do, rather than seeing it as a chore and a means to the end of just making money. Again, he could sense that some were a little surprised at some of those points.

"How did I do?" he asked. "Was I as good as Henry and do you all feel as excited, enthused, and committed as Joan and her colleagues did?"

They laughed but they all agreed.

"What did you like about it?" Mike asked them.

"It really has everything in it," Terry replied. "I think it ticks all the boxes and is really comprehensive."

"Strangely, Mike," Sally commented, "I liked that you mentioned the corporation or our owners or investors. We can often, not so much forget about these, but resent their interference and fail to understand how important they are. It would be fine if we were working for ourselves but that's not how it is right now, and we have to make the most of this particular situation. "See it as if you were working for and supported by a rich uncle," a manager of mine once said to me when I was complaining about the corporation and having to work for them. That doesn't mean that we should not challenge them in an adult way to do what's right. As Mike knows I am having to face that just now. But, as I said, I'm happy that you included them in your vision and not just because they will like to see that when they visit," she laughed.

"And I of course I liked the inclusion of our suppliers." Natalie commented. "These people very often are forgotten but they're critical to us. And it's easy to just treat them as suppliers and do battle and negotiate with them on prices and drop them in favour of others when it suits us. We have a lot of power we can use. But I think it is better for all of us if we have trusted suppliers, just like we like to be trusted, as Terry and the rest of us all know and as Sharon in KEY Services now sees us. I just hope we can do that. It'll be a change for us."

"Nobody will argue about the importance of including either customers or employees in our vision or goal," Heather said, "so I imagine that Teresa and all of us agree with that. But I think including our community and society in general is very good. We can give lip service to this very often, but we're part of this community and we're part of and dependent on society, so we should ensure we always keep them in mind in how they see us and in how we see our company, our mission and vision. I think we need to be more aware of this. Do you all agree? I know *you* do, Bernard and I can see that wise look on your face, Bernard, as if this is just normal and common sense."

Bernard laughed and they all said they agreed. Mike smiled to himself in some relief, knowing that he was not alone and that a serious issue was at least mentioned.

"You're right, Mike, I'm happy with this and especially about our role in the community," Bernard came in. "I know this does not always make sense to people who can see our obligations being to customers, and our people and, of course, the corporation itself. But I don't think that is good enough any longer. Companies and businesses will have to see themselves as part of everything and contributing to everything.

It's the only way they'll be sustainable in the long term and the only way the two-way relationship thing will be sustainable. In fact, I think companies can or could serve as models for how all organisations could be and so should play a major and positive part in our world, compared to the normal one they are so often accused of playing. I know not everyone sees eye to eye with me on this, but I appreciate how well you have cooperated with our efforts to be a real and vibrant part of our community."

"And of our *society*," Sally added. "As Mike knows, this is something I've been working on with government departments and it's in line with what Bernard is saying, but at an overall country or society level. I will talk more about this when it's appropriate. So, I too am happy with this aspect, Mike."

"One thing that I see," Teresa added, "is that more and more people will be working from home and, already, many of our colleagues are doing that. I see this as being absolutely essential to making relationships work well. It means, as we have been saying, that people do things because they make sense, because they believe in them and in the overall goal and not because they are supervised and obliged to do so. They will do things because they *want* to. I'm not saying that this is enough in terms of the change to working from home but it's a completely essential part of it. As you know, we're working on other things to make this change and make it work well, but this has to be at the heart of it all."

Which gets priority – the company or the individual?

"There's one thing I want to ask you," Mike said, "do you all really believe in this and want what I just described? Often these things can look like an exercise and that's the reason why they rarely work. Just like with Frank's football team in the past. Maybe I should ask you a different question! Do you all believe that you really want this and that it's what really matters to you, not only in terms of work, but in terms of your whole life. Do you all believe that?"

> "When I tell the truth, it is not for the sake of convincing those who do not know it, but for the sake of defending those that do"
> **William Blake**

They all said they did and with great seriousness.

"Because if this is what really matters to all of us, then it means that *everything* we do has to be done to achieve this. This has to be like our compass that we use in every situation to decide what direction we take. Does that make sense?"

Again, they all fully agreed.

"If what we're saying is true and valid and is of real importance, what do you think I might expect you all to do with that?"

"We'll, do as you said, Mike," Tom answered, "and make sure that everything we do is done in line with this and in bringing it about."

"I think that what this does, Mike," Bernard with great enthusiasm said, "is ensure that we are all focused on the overall goal, the bigger picture and not our own individual or functional or vested interests. I see this all the time, people focusing on a party or faction or movement and going after that in everything. This is something that I see with the Chinese system that we don't understand. I spoke to a lot of people there about what we call "human rights". What they mean are individual rights while the Chinese focus on the overall rights of everyone and that's what ultimately decides."

"So, are you, or they, saying then," Tony asked, "that the overall or the group is more important than the individual? That the welfare of the individual is sacrificed for the larger welfare?"

"Yes, this is how it's often seen, as if it's my good over the good of the whole or the overall. But they don't see it like that and it's not like that. What they believe, and I do too, is that the individual good depends on the overall or greater good. Like any of Frank's team will be happy – relatively so, of course – not to be selected or get taken off for the welfare of the team and so that the team wins. It's a different mindset and we in the Western World with our individual focus, don't understand it. Trees and nature get it all the time and so there is huge cooperation going on all the time in nature. No tree would survive for any length of time without the heat of the sun, the nutrients from the soil, the oxygen from the air."

"I agree Bernard," Natalie said, "and when you think of it this is exactly how we and our bodies work. A lung or pancreas or kidney is useless without the overall goal or purpose of the body. So, what we are doing or saying is simply reminding people that their individual welfare and rights depend on the overall welfare of the body or organisation of which they are a part. I see it as of huge importance and probably our most important role as managers."

"I think that's great," Mike said. "I believe we all have to think in that way for us to survive and thrive both as a company and as a society."

Everyone nodded and were intrigued with the input from Bernard and Natalie.

"Good. That's great. And what else do you think I might expect you to do? Teresa?"

"Do the very same with our own people," Teresa answered, "in other words share what we want for *our* areas in exactly the same way. We must make sense of it in the context of our own areas. That would mean that I would meet with my team in HR and let them know what I want and believe is important and get their agreement about what we want to achieve and do it in a way that is really convincing and makes sense to them."

"Yes, that's exactly what I meant." Mike said. "And what, do you think, will make this different this time because, as you said, people have been through this many times already, just as Frank was with his team?"

"I think we'll have to do it in a way that they really believe and understand what we're saying and know that we truly see it as important." Bernard said. "They won't be fooled, and they'll only be convinced if *we're* convincing. And we'll only be convincing if we ourselves are convinced. We have to ask ourselves that same question you asked us, Mike, if we genuinely come across and are convincing in what we say."

Handling different personalities and needs

"Well said," Mike commented. "I think that's exactly it. I believe that if we truly believe in this and go after it to make it a reality, then, we'll be adding great value to every aspect of people's lives. And if we're able to get everybody really convinced, believing and committed to being this kind of company then something quite wonderful will happen to the people in our teams. What do you think that might be that happens? What are you smiling at Frank?"

"I think it could unite them," Frank said. "This is quite like what happened with my own team as we talked about earlier. What we did was quite similar to this at the beginning of the year and it had an extraordinary effect on people. It's not that they became different people. They all remained who they were, but they became imbued, inspired with something that united them and made them one. If I could draw this for you, Mike, on the flipchart it's like this.

Let's imagine that all of them are like some geometric shape, with different personalities, experiences, hang-ups, needs and backgrounds to everybody else.

Now, when we shared our goal for the season with them, they didn't become different people, they still remained essentially the same people or shapes they were previously, but they became coloured, imbued with something great in common that united them

and made them strong. Not just strong as individuals but strong as a team, as a unit. But also better as individuals as a result. Does that make sense?"

"It certainly does for me," Terry commented.

"What strikes me about it," Heather came in, "is that it could deal with or explain that thing that Tom talked about around flexibility of working. I can imagine that if this really worked, we could disband or get rid of some of the controls and rules we've set.

You might not like me saying this, Teresa, but once you have something to work for and it makes such sense in every way, you don't need controls, or, at least, not externally-imposed ones.

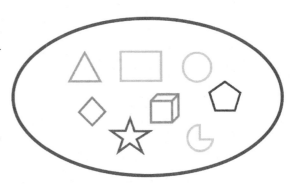

I think Tom's group understood this and worked in this way. And two things happened at the same time: they felt free to work as they wished and were flexible around how much individuals worked, and they worked a lot more than they normally did. Now I know this works.

I've been here. As you know I was entitled to so much maternity leave and I took what I was obliged to take. But that didn't mean I stopped working. I kept at it and not only for the welfare of the company but also for my own welfare. I'm not very happy if I'm sitting down all day doing nothing. I found it enormously helpful to have such interesting and important things to keep my mind active. Nor did it affect my children's welfare. Someone said to me once that a mother's greatest responsibility to her children is to be the best she can be as a person. Being involved in work helped me do that and I'm so grateful to Mike and to everyone's understanding. And, I'm not trying to win you over to my side in this tug-o-war over my appointment."

Everyone was impressed by what Heather said. They knew the pressure she was under from the uncertainty around it all. And some knew of the resentment towards her from her own family who had never been too happy with what they regarded as her overly ambitious drive. And in her wider family there was resentment from a few sisters-in-law who had opted for a different and more exclusively home oriented lifestyle. Her colleagues knew there were many who would be very happy to see her

eat some professional humble pie. Of course, she could opt for the security of her previous position. That would deal with the pressure from all sides, family and corporation. But it was not what she wanted.

"And why do you mention that in this context, Heather?" Teresa asked.

"Because I believe that if we can get everyone bought into our goal and what we're about, then we'll be able to allow people much greater freedom that will add to their lives and equally add to the betterment of the company, as we saw with Tom's group. Does that make sense, Teresa?"

It did make sense to Teresa and to everyone.

"And tell me, coming back to you, Frank," Mike asked, "what did you do with your team after you agreed all that with them? I'm interested."

"Very simply, as I said, we worked out together everything we needed to do to ensure we achieved our goal. In fact, I led that session, a bit like you do, Mike, and it was very good. We constantly go back to it and check what's working and not working and upgrade and improve it as we see fit or as needed."

"Great Frank," Mike said, "and that's exactly what I would like us to do now. So can I ask you all to take just about five minutes to think of what we'll need to do in order to make our vision a reality and to be as successful as Frank's team?

When they had done that, Mike led or facilitated the meeting and got over thirty ideas about what they should do. Some of them agreed with his own but they came from everybody on the team. And they covered all kinds of areas like products and

"Only mothers can think of the future – because they give birth to it in their children"

Maxim Gorky

services, marketing, sales, relationships with the corporation, a whole lot of people-management ones, competition and handling change, cost management and performance improvement.

"Is everybody happy that we have touched on everything that we need to in order for us to realise our goal or vision?"

Everyone seemed content.

"Good," Mike said, "I'll tidy them up into a greatly reduced number of areas to focus on and we'll come back in a week or so and close on them. Is that acceptable? And then we'll do, as Frank did, continue to revisit our strategy or plan and see how we're doing against it and if there are things that we need to change or improve. Once we have the compass of our goal or vision, we will know where to go and what to do. I think that if we do that really well, we won't fail and we can't fail. Is that okay?"

Everyone agreed and everyone seemed clear and enthusiastic.

"I bet we'll do better than Henry and Joan's theatre project," Terry said.

"Or maybe as well as Frank's team." Natalie added. "Though I'm not convinced we can be *that* good."

"One last thing," Mike said, "I would like each of you to begin to think about what you individually can do and need to do in your area of responsibility to make this a reality. What do you need to do in your function and with your team to contribute to realising our goals by following this strategy? Do you know what I mean? It's like asking you what your unique contribution is to making this a success. You could ask yourself, putting it a bit negatively, "how could you fail to play your special part", and then turn that into something positive that you will do to make sure you *don't* fail. Part of your special contribution will involve the part you play in this team for the overall management and leadership of the company. So, there are two parts to your role – your head of functional role and your role as a member of this senior team. Is that okay and clear?

Everyone seemed to understand and agreed.

"I'll meet each of you in a few weeks on this initiative to hear from you what you're thinking and help you to make sure that you're happy that what you're doing will make the difference you want it to make. And in those conversations, I'll be covering both your role within your function, like yours Tom or yours Heather, and your role as members of this team which has a broader role to fulfil. Okay?"

Everyone was fine with that proposition.

"That's great and thanks everybody for your part in this and I hope that it is, in a sense, the beginning of a new phase in our existence as a company and that it adds greater satisfaction to you all both in your work and in your life in general. That's what we want for everybody, isn't it? Why or how can I say that?"

"Because," Teresa answered, "as we said earlier if we manage and lead the company well, it will affect every aspect of everyone's life. I'm all for that, Mike."

They all agreed wholeheartedly.

Questions for reflection and action

1. Do you believe that Frank's approach could make such a difference with his team?
2. Can you believe and identify with Joan's excitement? What created it?
3. Why do you think Mike's goal or vision might work where many others don't?
4. Do you think you could be as convincing? What would make you so? What would you do?
5. Do you agree that doing this, holding this kind of meeting is the most fundamental and most important thing you can do as a leader? Why? If you have not done it, when will you?

Chapter 17
You are Far More Powerful than You Think!

Taking ourselves seriously and changing the world

At the end of the meeting, Mike asked Natalie, the Purchasing Manager, if he could have a word with her. Natalie who was 41 just a few weeks earlier, had a lot of experience both in the company and in other companies. She was very reliable, very efficient, and very hard-working. She was not opposed to any of the changes that Mike wanted to bring about. But then, Natalie was rarely opposed to anything. She went along with most things. She was easy to get on with and everyone liked her. But, while not opposed to any of the changes, she was not a strong driver of those changes. Mike had the impression that not too much was happening or changing in the Purchasing Department in terms of bringing about a different and more vibrant and involving culture.

Natalie was a little surprised that Mike wanted to talk to her. It sounded different and a bit ominous. But she showed none of this. As always, she was happy to go along with whatever was required and not to cause any problem or anxiety.

"Let's go back to my office," Mike suggested, "and we can talk better there. I could do with a coffee anyway."

Armed with their capuccinos and black coffees, Mike explained what was on his mind. "I just wanted to hear from you, Natalie, where you're at on this whole transformation we're working on. You seem to be fine with it and never oppose anything I suggest or put forward, but I wanted to hear how you really think about it."

"I've no problem with it at all Mike. I think it's a good plan and it will make a difference. But if I don't seem all excited it's only because we have a lot on at the moment, and just keeping things going well is quite enough to have on my plate! I'm probably not a great person around change anyway, and once things are going along satisfactorily. I like to keep them that way. So, I don't find it easy when I hear you asking us to change everything, "change the world". I probably struggle a bit with how we

> **"If you change the way you look at things, the things you look at change"**
> **Wayne Dyer**

can do that on top of everything else that we have on. I want to support you on this, Mike, and I will. I'm not at all sure that this is the right time for all this But then, with me, is there ever a right time?"

"I understand that", Mike replied, "and, you're right, I am expecting and asking us to "change the world". I appreciate how you feel about change. It can be easier to handle change when one is making the change, rather than when one is on the receiving end. But, let's take a look at changing things. If I asked you to change the world, how risky and difficult would that be on a scale of 0 to 10?"

"Well, a silly question, maybe, but I would give it a 10 on both fronts!"

"Okay, fair enough, and if I asked you the same question about changing the company, how high would your scores be?"

"I would put them also pretty high – maybe eight or nine! That's what I'm saying. Doing what we have to do to keep things going and going well is hard enough, without having to change things at the same time."

"Okay, I hear that, Natalie. Now if I asked you the same question about changing your own area within purchasing, how would you score it under my two headings of how risky it would be and how difficult in terms of effort?"

"Ah that would be lower, probably around five or six."

"Fine. And if I asked you to score how risky and how difficult it would be to change yourself Natalie, and how you're doing things, how would you score it?"

"Well, in that case it would only be between three and four, even though changing oneself is never easy either, especially for me. You have tried hard enough to change some things I do, Mike, and on some you have failed", she said, laughing.

"Good, so how about if we went after changing the world but we started with you, and with each person in your area? Then, if we work in this way, going from you to your area of responsibility, to the company itself, we may finally get to actually "changing the world", but we will be doing so intelligently and practically. Does that make sense?"

I'm only me ... just one person

"Yes it does," Natalie responded, "but I can't see how changing just one person, like changing me, is going to have such a major effect. I am only one person, after all. And, I have a lot on as it is, and I don't want to slip up on anything. It's too important and too risky."

Then Mike explained to her that it was not really true to say that she was only one person because, in actual fact, she was a Centre of Relationships and he drew the model for her.

"You see, none of us is really an isolated individual but is part of a Circle of Relationships. We're human not because we have a head, eyes, mouth, arms and legs etc., but because we have been humanised, socialised by our parents and by many other people in society. People who were born and reared without human contact never became people, human, subsequently.

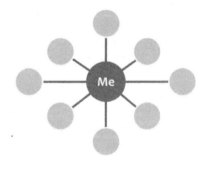

And we continue to exert this influence on people and to be in turn, influenced by people. Now you, Natalie, are at the centre of a very important and powerful set of relationships, both in Purchasing, in the company and beyond it, and how you are and how you relate to people in your circle of relationships, in Purchasing, with your peers on the senior team and in general, has enormous effects on how *they* are and how they in turn relate to and affect people in their corresponding circles of relationships. Do you see that?"

"Yes, I understand, but I'm not sure I see how it helps me."

"Do you not see, Natalie, that you are enormously powerful and you can have very powerful and impactful effects on everybody who's in your Circle of Relationships here in the company? So by changing or transforming yourself, there's no telling where the effects of that change and transformation will end. Now you might think I'm preaching or talking at a high and intellectual level but it's not like that. On my way into work, I come on to a busy road and sometimes there's an unending stream of traffic. I remember one morning feeling that the line of traffic was so endless that I would never get in. Then I saw a person slowing down, flashing their lights and letting me into the traffic. I waved and used my hazard warning lights to thank them. But then a strange thing happened. I found myself, quite unconsciously, doing the very same later, on my way into work. Several times.! That person, by that simple action, affected me. I learned a long time ago that my mood at work has an effect on how other people feel and behave. And that's happening all the time unknown to anyone."

"Yes, I see that," Natalie replied, "so are you saying to me that I have been underestimating the extent of the influence I can have and that I am far more influential than I had thought?"

> "A teacher affects eternity; he can never tell where his influence stops"
>
> **Henry Adams**

"Yes, that's exactly what I'm saying, and you're not alone in this because most people take themselves for granted and are unaware of how they can impact on other people in their lives. So, you have to take yourself very seriously and take your power and influence with people also very seriously. Now, let me ask you a question. How will doing this help you with what you first asked me at the beginning of this chat? How will it help to get all the good, normal things done as well as all these changes that I want as well? What difference will this make to that?

"A big one, I imagine. If I can get all these people really fired up and working and really aware of how powerful they are, how much more powerful they are than they think, then I'll have enormous resources available to me. No end to them."

"Yes, that's exactly it. And to achieve that and get all those resources awake and moving, you have to look at Natalie, at yourself first of all."

"And what does that mean or what will that involve? I try very hard and work very hard, as you know."

Who are you?

"Well, it means asking yourself the question who you are and what do you represent? If you are the centre of a set of relationships, then you need to be clear about who you are, what you stand for, what you want etc. as the centre of things, in order to positively influence those around you in your circle."

"But, I think I know who I am and what I stand for and what I want. I'm a manager in this company, a wife and mother of a large family. I stand for what's good for this company and I'm loyal to the company and to you. And I want the company to do well, both for all of us who work here as well as for my family … and for our customers, too, of course."

"Good and these are good answers to very important questions to ask yourself. But, good as they are – and there is nothing wrong with them – I wonder if there's more, Natalie, more that's in you and more that you can do and contribute? I mean within your present role, so that you get in touch with your real meaning as a person, get in touch with your real vocation, decide on what your role in life is, and the part you want to play in the world. Once you do that there's no telling what you can change and transform, not only in purchasing, not only in the company, but also in life."

"Well, it would seem that I have some work to do here! I'm not sure how to go about it but I need to do it."

"Yes, you do. If we look at the Circle of Relationships again, what really matters is *you* and who you are and what you stand for. People see this and notice it. They will respond to you or react to how you are and so it's important to be clear about who you are and what you stand for and what's important to you and why."

> "The key to successful leadership today is influence, not authority"
>
> **Ken Blanchard**

"What do you mean, "*who* I am and what I stand for?""

"Well, for example, to put it bluntly, you, Natalie, can be a nice friendly person that people like and get on well with. Or you can be a very ambitious person who wants to get on irrespective of what anyone else wants and so you ruthlessly go after that. Or, you could stand for something that's really good for everyone, including you, like having a wonderful Purchasing Division that is making a big contribution to creating a wonderful company for people to work in, contribute to and belong to. So you have choices and, of course, I'm in no way trying to shape your choices, Natalie!"

"Ha ha ... I can see that. So I need to think about that and about standing for and representing something that makes sense and is good for everyone and that has real value? And, you are saying, that if I do that, I will have a big influence on my people and on my world, are you? This reminds me of what we were talking about around the X meeting, no?"

"Yes, that's exactly what I'm saying. Who does Natalie want to be and how need and how does she need to be? But not just so that you influence your people or others, but because it really matters to you and is really important for *you*. There are lots of questions and aids to getting clear about all this and I can go through these some other time with you. They involve getting in touch with what's really important both to you and in itself. What I'm trying to bring about here is also very important for this part of you, Natalie. I could continue on and let you feel that you're doing a good job, earning a good salary and so looking after your home and family. But I believe there's more. I want to do great things and make great things happen and I want you to be part of that, of doing something very different and special."

"I think I understand and I can see that people, my own people, need to see more possibilities and to see more in me and in Purchasing. I can't let them down or let down their own aspirations either."

"Well said. I think you have a responsibility to them, to their deep needs and to their dreams however unclear these may be. And this will involve spending a lot of time thinking of the people in your "Circle of Influence".

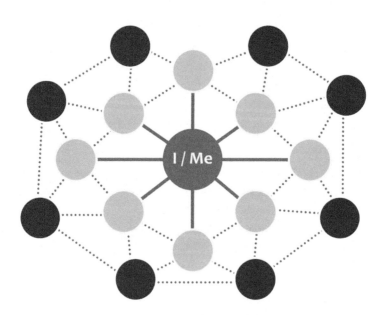

It's easy to forget your people because of being so focused on getting things in Purchasing done, but they need attention ... every one of them. And individually they can also make a great difference in their own Circles of Influence."

"Yes, I can see that and I'll do it, knowing it won't be easy. I will probably have to take some risks and, as you know, I'm quite risk averse"

"Yes, I know, Natalie. This will stretch you and you will have to wrestle with things in yourself and taking risks is one of them. Remember that risk and reward ride side by side. Avoid one and the other passes you by."

"I know, I know!"

And don't forget the words of Marianne Williamson, which have often been attributed to Nelson Mandela:

"It's our light, not our darkness that most frightens us.

We ask ourselves: Who am I to be brilliant, gorgeous, talented and fabulous?"

Actually, who are you not to be – you are a child of God.

Your playing small doesn't serve the world.

There's nothing enlightening about shrinking, so that other people won't feel insecure around you."

All in our heads?

You've been doing a great job, Natalie, and I really appreciate all you do. However, I believe you've been selling yourself well short of your potential. When you do this, you'll arouse and inspire others to also go after much greater things."

"I hope you're right."

"I think I am. But it's only you who can ultimately decide if I'm right or not. It's up to you and how you handle things. When I say that, do you know what I'm referring to?"

"Ah I think so. Is it about your image of the "Person and their Situation"?"

"It's exactly that, and what do I mean by that in this context, do you think?"

"I think you're saying that how I see and handle my situation will to a great extent determine what and how my situation is. That's what you mean by saying it's up to me."

"Very good, so do you think, then, that I'm saying that everything is subjective, that it's all down to how we see things, and we can make things good or bad, depending on our perspective?"

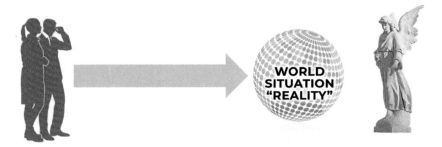

"No, I don't think that's what we said. It's like what we said around Michelangelo, that the angel was already present in the stone or marble and he simply found and released it. But that was up to him and, without him, it wouldn't have happened. And the angel in the marble doesn't exist apart from Michelangelo.

They're both part of one and same thing. It's a play, a relationship between the two. So I think you're saying the same to me, that those great things you talked about are to be found. But I have to see them, believe them, and release or make them real. Is that what you mean?"

"That's exactly it. And the main reason is that it's there to be done – it makes sense in itself. In a sense, it's not a tactic or means to an end but an end in itself. And I'm not being manipulative of you in all this, Natalie. Because this will be great in itself it will be great for you too." So are you happy with all that, then?"

"Yes I am, though I think I need to work on it and may need some more help."

More management "help" in creating a plan

"Okay, Natalie, let's try this. Without telling me, can you just make a little note about how you're feeling about all this now. You needn't show it to me, but just take a minute to get in touch with how you're feeling about this right now. Alright?"

Natalie thought and scribbled for a few minutes and after a while told Mike that she had finished.

"Good, Natalie, so I hear you saying to me that you would like more help on how to think and work and be like this, so that you achieve those great things? Is that it?"

"Yes, that's exactly it, I'd welcome more help from you on that, on how to practically do it and to bring it about."

"Alright, to start can you tell me where you are at present, or what currently is happening, what is the current situation around this?"

"Well, it's like I said, I'm very busy, I have a lot on, I want things to go well, I'm nervous about taking on more things and, to be honest, I often doubt myself and whether I'm able or good enough to make this happen. Because of that, very often I hold back, avoiding taking risks, and I don't aim too high. This way I can't fail. If one doesn't expect too much, one won't fail and can't be disappointed! That's about it, not that I'm too happy with the task ahead."

"That's fine. And can you tell me how you would *like* things to be? How you would love things to be if they were very different and much better?"

"I'm not sure. I think things are pretty okay as they are and I'd just like things to continue to improve a little."

"I understand. But if, as we've been saying, you were to go after making some great things happen, what might they be? What might your angels or David's be? Don't worry for now if they are realistic or how to make them real, just try to tell me what you would really love to happen be it realistic or not."

"Okay, it's not easy, but it's like we said earlier and like we have been talking about, that work would become something very different for people, something that they really enjoy, love doing and love doing better and better. A bit like Frank's football team or Joan's theatre group."

> "Where there is no vision, there is no hope"
>
> **George Washington**

"Great. And why is that so important or valuable, or is it?"

"I think it is. It would make a great difference, not only to the people doing it but to all of us, how we work, what we achieve, and how we are as a company, as a group of people. And, I think it would inevitably lead to much better performance and results, which would please you too, Mike. And everything would be that much easier and more enjoyable, including both my work and my life. Definitely, there's no doubt that it's important."

"That's great. And can you tell me or describe to me what might be happening if that were so? How would you know that you had achieved your goal?"

"Things would be very, very different. You would see it in how people work, in their enthusiasm, in their interest levels, in their contributions. There would be a whole new sense of freedom, with people taking initiatives and surprising us. And, like we said some time ago, people would be feeling trusted to do things and would be doing them in ever better ways. And they would feel real responsibility, that it was down to *them*."

"Yes, that sounds great. So, what might you do to bring that about and make it a reality?"

"I don't know. That's why I said I needed help."

"Yes, I understand that, but what are some things that you might try that might at least begin to make that kind of difference?"

"I'm not sure. I'd have to think about it."

"Yes, I understand, but how might you get things going, at least?"

"I don't know. One thing that I might do, even though it feels risky, is to actually lay my cards on the table and tell people what I would like and why – like we spoke about before. I feel nervous about this but maybe I have to be courageous and honest with people in sharing with them how I would like things to be and why. That kind of thing. What do you think?"

Being realistic

"That's a good start, and what do you think might happen if you did that?"

"I don't know. There might be people who could be cynical but there could also be people who would love this approach and who have been longing to hear it for a long time."

"Great, and especially if there are some people whom you know will welcome this new approach. But what about those who are cynical and who don't believe it, or have heard it all before and think it will be a one-month wonder?"

"Yes, there might be some of those and I think it would simply mean that I have to be courageous and honest, and by that I mean acknowledge and recognise why they might be cynical and ask them to give it a go. But I would need to do that in a convinced way, not as if I were asking for permission. What do you think?"

"That sounds promising. So, what I hear you saying is that this is something that is of real importance to you and to many other people and that you are going to go after it. And, to do that you're going to be explicit and honest with people about what you want and why, and invite and request them to come on board. Is that it, more or less?"

"Yes, that's what I said and I still go along with it."

"That's wonderful. So, are you confident? Or are there some other concerns you have or things you need to think about, or things that might go wrong?"

"Yes, there's one thing, and it's a mistake that has been made in the past where we go with something like this but try to do it our way without really involving or listening to people. I think that's a big mistake I could make."

"And what would you do to avoid that happening?"

"Radically change how I go about it and, while sticking to what I want very closely and without deviating from it, getting people's views on what we need to do differently and to be very open about that. This might mean going against how things have been done for a long time. But I think that would make a big difference."

> "If you set goals and go after them with all the determination you can muster, your gifts will take you places that will amaze you"
>
> **Les Brown**

"Great, Natalie. So, when do you think you'll begin all this?"

"I want to begin it soon, and I will. I would like to think it over for a few days just to make sure that I get it right. I want to handle it really well. Do you agree?"

"Yes, that makes lots of sense. I think that's very important. So when do you think you'll meet your people to break the news?"

"I'm due to have a meeting with them during the week after next and I'll make sure I'm ready to begin the process with them at that meeting. That feels right and I think it will work."

"One last thing, Natalie, and this might sound a bit strange. I can hear from you that this makes sense and that you believe it's the right thing to do, but can you tell me how you feel about the whole thing? I don't mean worries or anxieties or positive emotions but how you feel in your body."

"I'm not sure I understand what you mean, Mike."

"That's quite alright. I know it can sound a bit strange. What I would like you to do is when you think of the changes you're planning, ask how it feels in your body. What sensations do you experience? Take a few seconds to find them, if you can."

"I feel a bit nervous. It's hard to describe. It's like uncertainty, not being sure of myself, like skating or walking on ice."

"Great, that's exactly what I meant. So, what would you do if you were skating or walking on ice?"

Natalie went quiet for a minute or two. Then she said, "Normally I feel nervous and I become very cautious and do very wrong things."

"So, what will you do this time that will be different?"

"I will walk confidently on the ice without being afraid of falling. I will trust myself that I will not fall and that if I do, I will know I will be alright."

"That's the spirit Natalie, so you are all set now?"

Real and empowering help – coaching

"Yes, I am. I found it very helpful and really appreciate your help."

"Do you know how I helped you?"

"Of course, you gave me great ideas and I have a really good plan that I think will change how I work and bring big improvements to everything and to all of us. You were very helpful, Mike."

"But you're not sure how I was helpful, are you? Because, in actual fact, I didn't give you any ideas at all. They were all yours. So what did I do, then?"

"I don't know. You asked me questions, and you listened and you challenged me and you seemed to agree with what I was saying. And I felt you trusted me, that you believed I could do it and do it well. Those kinds of things."

"That's not a bad description of what I was doing. While it may have looked or felt like an ordinary conversation, I was following a very specific process and six very clear steps. Any idea of what they were?"

"Well, you asked me what I wanted, I remember. And you kept asking me what I would do. It was all up to me really. Now that I think of it, I did all the work," she said laughing.

"Yes, Natalie, you did all the work. In fact, I asked you six questions or took you through six steps.

1. What would you like to talk about or work on?
2. What is happening at present, what is the current situation?
3. What would you like to have happen or want to happen? Why is this important? How would you know you've achieved it?
4. What can or might you do to achieve this?
5. What I hear you saying is: "Is this right? Is it enough? Am I happy with it?"
6. When would you like to begin?

Remember those steps we took?"

"Yes, I do, or some of them, even if at the time, I wasn't aware of what was going on."

"That's alright, Natalie, but I'd like us to talk to the rest of the team about this meeting and about the process and explain how it worked and how well it worked. Would you be happy with that?"

"Absolutely, no problem at all."

"And would you be able to explain how each step is important even if it might appear simple and straightforward?"

"I could try! The first one, when you asked me what I wanted to talk about or work on. I'm not sure. I think what it does, or did in my case anyway, was to invite or encourage me to look at something that I wasn't giving enough attention to, for whatever reason. Yes, it was a kind of challenge but an inviting one to get me to look at or do something different. Yes, that's it."

"Good. And the second one where I asked you what was happening or what the actual situation was? Is this not asking you to say what you already know?"

"No. It was very different. What it did was it helped me to actually see and accept what is happening and allowed and made it alright for me to do so. That was hugely helpful. It's so freeing to be able to acknowledge and admit something to someone. And you didn't comment or make any judgement on anything I said, so I felt really encouraged to be honest and open.

Yes, it seems innocuous but in practice it was really important and freeing as I said."

"That's good to hear, and the next step, Step 3, asking you about what you want etc.?"

"This was great too. It can be easy to settle for the existing state of affairs and to remain comfortable, especially for me. Wishing or dreaming can seem futile sometimes and also risky, so this is one step a person definitely needs to be pushed a bit on, especially someone like me… but in a good way. And then when you asked me why it was important for me, that was good too, because I realised that it was important and so something I needed to go after. Oh, and yes, asking me how I would know when I had achieved it, made me imagine or visualise what would be happening and I found this very powerful. I could see it and, then, didn't want to let go of it!"

"Well done. You're doing great. Then to the next step. A challenging one!"

"Yes, it was! I was kind of waiting for you to advise or tell me what to do. I found that a bit tough, but you wouldn't let go! You refused to take it back from me and eventually, to my surprise, I came up with a really good plan, I thought. And it was *my* plan."

"Yes, I understood how you felt and that's what nearly always happens. Do you know why I did that and why your plan might have been better than anything I might have suggested, brilliant as I am?"

"Yes, because it's mine, then I will probably achieve it rather than something you would advise or tell me. So I have full ownership for it. Is that what you mean?"

"Yes, it is, exactly. And why else might your plan be better than one I might come up with?"

"I'm not sure. I think your ideas would have been very good too and maybe even better. You have a lot of experience and skill."

"That may be true but there's a great risk here too. What we're looking for is what is right and best for you, and experienced and skilled as I may be, I still don't know what is best for *you*. We very often think we do but we're wrong. You know yourself and your reality or version of reality far more closely and better than I do and so you have much more wisdom around you and your situation than I have. What I have to do, then, and what I did in fact, was to help you get in touch with that great wisdom. Does that make sense?"

"It does, even if it feels a bit strange. We're so accustomed to being told and given advice, from early days in our life, that we don't trust ourselves to use the wisdom that you talk about. Then it becomes a kind of downward spiral where you don't make the effort to even think about what to do and, instead, take on board and go with what someone like me tells you."

"Exactly and so you end up with no real ownership, that ownership that Bernard spoke to us about a while back, and I'm justified in doing the thinking for you... because you aren't doing much. Do you follow?"

"Indeed I do. It's exactly as you describe. Boy oh boy, it's so common and we all think it's ok. How terrible."

There are three questions that every manager – and indeed every person in any kind of authority need to ask themselves before they give anyone advice or direction:

"Am I really sure I'm **RIGHT** in what I'm saying... meaning right for the other person and right in general. Will the other person **UNDERSTAND** what I'm saying or suggesting or advising? Will the other person be **ABLE** to do what I'm advising or saying?

The answer to these three questions should not and cannot be presumed. I believe that they can only be answered positively in very few cases."

"Now I understand. It's frightening when you think that it's what we do all the time in management!"

"Yes, it is frightening. And the awful thing about it is that working in this normal or usual way ends up with us both feeling happy. I feel great because I feel proud of how wise and powerful I am and you feel comfortable because the risk has been removed for you."

"I understand. That would be so comfortable for me."

"And now to step 5. What value does this one bring, where I played back to you what you were going to do or thinking you will do?"

"While it's only playing back my own thoughts, I found it very reassuring and encouraging to hear them understood and articulated by another person. It was not that I felt you were approving of my plan, but more that it made sense … in general, to the universe. It felt great to hear it described by another person. I felt, well I'm not off the wall with this."

"I'm really glad to hear that's how you received it. You have done great. And my final question, Step 6, where I asked you when you were going to move on your plan. Was that not about going back into my doubting or controlling you? Typical manager stuff?"

"Well, you're right. I could have heard it like that, but because of how you handled all the rest of the conversation, I didn't. I felt challenged again but I liked the challenge. It can be so easy, at least for me, to believe that because I *think* something, that it is enough. I can feel good about myself and leave it there. For that reason, being asked concretely when I was going to begin to act was very helpful. Of course, the earlier questions, especially around Step 3 about what I want and why it is so important, made this final step possible."

"And what about me and how I did Natalie? I am your manager but it seems I didn't do much managing! Just asking questions, listening and repeating things and checking in now and then! Not great management performance, would you say?"

"Yes, I know what you mean but it was enormously helpful and far more than normal managing usually is. I'm not sure why or how to explain it. As we said, you helped me to become clearer about everything but it was a lot more than that. You made me or helped me to be more confident about everything. As a result, I ended up being more powerful, better equipped and better able to act and handle things well.

You could say you transformed me from feeling small and unsure to feeling strong and confident. You see, if the aim of our session was to help me to be more effective and more influential and overall stronger and better, then *this* is what you achieved. And, whatever it was you did, be it listening or questioning, you achieved all of that. And that would seem very good managing to me, even if it's not what managers normally do."

"I'm pleased, and relieved, to hear that Natalie. A key part of my job as a manager —and that of any manager – is to *help* people to perform and be better. We can often forget that. What I did and the coaching approach I used is a truly and really powerful way to help. It makes you more powerful in practice, and so helps you to do what you need and want. One last thing, how do you feel now about this whole topic or area? Take a second to check how you're now feeling."

After a while Natalie said, "I feel very good, actually – very clear, confident, full of energy, quite excited about it all and looking forward to doing it. Is that what you mean?"

"Yes it is, and would you take a look at how that compares to what you wrote down earlier about how you were feeling."

"My goodness, it's hard to believe. Before this I wrote that I felt nervous, confused, uncertain, worried and very unsure. I'm a changed person, a new woman! It's a miracle," she laughed.

Mike laughed too. "Yes, Natalie, that's the power of coaching and we can talk some more about it in the full team."

"I think we should. It's enormously powerful.

"And, don't forget you're the centre of a set of relationships and so you can help make all these people feel and be so much more powerful too."

"Yes, I see that, Mike. But, I was wondering as we were talking if you would come along to one of our community spiritual meetings and share some of your thinking?

"Oh Natalie, you know I'm not religious or knowledgeable about spiritual matters. "

"Yes, I do and that's why I say it because what you say makes so much sense but it has none of the syrupy religious language or thinking. It's how things are and you show that so clearly. It's what we talk about in our sessions, as you do here. We use words like the "Kingdom" and a whole new world, and yet that's exactly what you're doing here. I think you believe much more than many of the people in our group do," she laughed.

"Well, Natalie, you know me and the way I talk about things, so I would be happy to join your group some evening or day if you wish, but I won't lead on the prayers or hymns if that's alright."

"You won't have to Mike. Just tell us what you're trying to achieve, why you see it as so important and what you believe is required to make it happen. That's easy for you."

"Ok … I'm prepared to talk and answer questions on those things of course and if that helps people bring in a new world or the Kingdom as you and they call it, why not? It would be a privilege."

"Ah great, Mike. Thanks. There's more world changing to be done."

Questions for reflection and action

1. Do you know what *your* "circle of influence" is and what it looks like?
2. How clear are you about "who" you are in your circle? Do you know what you stand for? Is it truly worthwhile and worth following? What do you stand for? What do you want? Do you know what your unique contribution to life and the world is?
3. What would you need to do to be a powerful centre in your circle of relationships that would inspire everyone you relate to and manage?
4. Why is this so important and why would doing it make you so "powerful"? From today, begin to make a big difference – even bigger than you have made to date.
5. Are you clear and happy with the process and power of coaching?

Chapter 18
Getting to OUR Promised Land

Bringing about transformational change in performance and culture

Mike was still a bit worried about what he perceived as a lack of real conviction on the part of some members, at least, of his team. Sally, Tony, and Bernard, at times, among others, were in full agreement with what he was saying but he was not sure the whole team appreciated the enormity of the change that was required, even though real progress was being made. These changes did not look easy and the benefits from making them would need to be clear and seen as valuable by everybody. He felt much better about Natalie after his conversation with her.

Notwithstanding this, he was happy with many things and matters had definitely improved on many fronts, such as managing meetings. There were now fewer meetings than before, and their own meetings were much better. Despite all that, he knew he had not got even close to what he was looking for. So he decided to go after it again. At the next meeting, after they had spent some time dealing with some more immediate and practical topics, he brought up the topic again.

"I hope you don't mind but I want to return to the topic of what we mean by a very different and better way of working – the topic we talked about some weeks back. Remember?"

They did.

"After our conversation about the X meeting, I had a strange feeling that there were still some misgivings felt by some people in this group around the real value of what we and I want to achieve. What do you remember that was about or involved?"

"Wasn't it about finding a way of working in line with those five COACH principles we talked about." Terry ventured.

"The ones that we saw working for the group on the Quantum Logistics System and the ones that we subsequently agreed were essential for high-performance as well as for satisfying and fulfilling work. Wasn't that it?"

> "It's only after you've stepped outside your comfort zone that you begin to change, grow, and transform."
>
> **Roy T. Bennett**

"Yes, Terry, that's exactly what I meant. And why do we want that? *Do* we want it? Why is it important, Tom?", he asked laughing.

"Okay, okay, I understand and I agree. How we're working is fine and it delivers what we want. But it works at a great price. Because, as Terry just said, people are not working in line with those five principles and so are not performing nearly as well as they could. We do have to find a better way for that and for other reasons."

"What are the reasons?" Mike asked.

"I think Tom is right around the kind or level of performance we are currently achieving," Teresa said, "but it's not only about performance. It's about people's well-being, their satisfaction at work and their enjoyment of what they're doing. In fact, that goes for all of us. The people in that group you met with, Tom, said it all. They don't see it happening yet."

"I agree completely," Tom came in, "and, as well as that, everything is just so much more difficult. You and I talked about this, Mike, and about how there's never time for anything else. Remember we were unable to meet and to find time because so much effort was spent on other meetings? Yes, there are some improvements, but there's more to be done.

That is just one example of how we can get stuck in our ways and find it so hard to get out of them. And our people can be in the exact same position. We are changing and improving. Don't get me wrong.

But I still think we have a way to go. A bigger shift to make. I wonder if others feel like I do?"

Heads nodded around the table.

Our promised land

"Well said, Tom, I think that realising and accepting that something isn't working is always a critical and vital first step. I know it's a bit far-fetched but I think the Moses story explains the kind of change and the kind of thing I'm after. I'm no biblical scholar but my simplistic version is that Moses took advantage of an incident in Egypt where some of his people, who were slaves, were killed by the Pharaoh. Using that incident, he convinced them to leave and go in search of a better place, his promised land. Like us, he wasn't quite sure what that meant but he was very sure that it would be a very different kind of place and was what they wanted and needed. And, very much like us, he had no idea how to get there," he laughed.

> "When you lower the definition of success to such a level that any person can reach it, you don't teach people to have big dreams; instead you inspirit mediocrity and nurture people's inadequacies"
>
> **Shannon L. Alder**

"Well, we trust you," Heather said, "we know you'll lead us there." She laughed.

"I can do my part, but we all need to want to get there. As I remember from the story, some of them wanted to go back to Egypt when things got tough in the desert. I bet that will happen with us too. I hope I'm wrong but it's easy to give up and settle for the tried and trusted even if, as Tom says, it's not really working."

"I don't know the story very well either," Sally said, "but didn't all kinds of miracles happen in the desert? Food falling from the sky, water pouring from the rock, seas parting and other wonders? Maybe we will get some miracles or lucky breaks along the way too!"

"I agree with you, Sally," Bernard added, "I think we'll get miracles or lucky breaks if we really are united in going after what Mike is suggesting or inviting us to. I mean getting that breakthrough with Sharon in KEY Services or on the Quantum Logistics System, were kinds of miracles. They came from nowhere."

"I'm delighted to hear you say that, Bernard, and I believe we'll need them. There are some things that I'm struggling with and I could certainly do with some miracles," Mike laughed.

"But, in terms of our promised land, I think it will be fundamentally, radically different from what we have now. So … what would you think of this kind of organisation?" said Mike before showing them a slide which described a special kind of organisation:

1. People have to perform to a very high standard.
2. Very clear and very challenging goals are set.
3. There are lots of rules to be complied with and people understand this and follow them.
4. Good performance is always highlighted and recognised and poor or unsatisfactory performance is never let go unchallenged.
5. People have to perform well to belong and, if they don't, they leave or are let go.
6. There are strict disciplines that are applied and that people adhere to. Sloppiness is not tolerated.
7. People's personals likes or dislikes or preferences or wishes are not always met and often take second place.
8. Everyone is held accountable for their performance and for the fulfilment of their role.
9. People cooperate and work together but, when the need arises, one person calls the shots.
10. People are expected to make extraordinary efforts to be successful and for this are expected to endlessly practise and improve their skills in their roles.

There was silence. It was plain that people were taken aback.

"Well, what do you all think of that kind of organisation, and would you like to belong to a company like that?"

"There are some things about it that I like," Tom came in, "I like the accountability and the very high standards. But it seems a bit strong, even for me," he laughed.

"I think corporate management would like it, Mike," Sally came in laughing, "they will be delighted with this change of mindset on your part. Sorry Mike!"

Mike laughed, but he understood what Sally was saying and he thought of his next conversation with Martha.

"I have to agree with Tom and Sally, Mike," Heather added, "it looks very strong and very strict."

"Yes," Bernard said, "it looks very like old management style, autocratic management to me."

Others commented in a similar fashion.

"So I take it that not many of you would like to work for this kind of organisation?" Mike asked.

They all remained silent but their silence seemed to suggest that he was right.

"Suppose I told you that there are thousands of people, hundreds of thousands of people, who want to work for or belong to organisations or entities like this and actually love doing so, what would you think?"

"I can't imagine that," Terry said, "unless it's in some very different culture or environment. I can't imagine people in our world wanting to work for or belong to that kind of organisation."

Everyone agreed.

"I'm telling you that people *do* want to belong to and be part of this kind of entity or organisation, – thousands and thousands of them. What kind of organisation or entity do you think I might be talking about? Any ideas Frank?" Mike laughed.

"Oh, do you mean football teams?" Frank answered smiling.

"Yes, Frank, well done. That's exactly what I mean. Or any sports team, or any group that are genuinely interested in and passionate about what they do. Talk to my wife, Joan, about her

> "Believe in your heart that you're meant to live a life full of passion, purpose, magic and miracles"
>
> **Roy T. Bennett,**
> **The Light in the Heart**

theatre group if you don't believe me. Think of some orchestra or musical group, or mountain climbing group, or exploratory scientific group. Have a look through them, all ten of them and see how they apply and are true for those kinds of entities or organisations."

They all did and nobody doubted or challenged any one of the ten points.

High performance and high standards

"So, if that's true of not only high performing groups, but also of groups of people who are passionate about, really love and enjoy what they're doing, why would *we* not want to be like that?"

"I agree with you, Mike," Teresa answered. "I can't argue with you about that, but it still seems a long way off from where we are."

"I understand, Teresa, but which or how many of these do you think we could do without or live with them not being present?"

They went silent for a while. Finally Sally spoke.

"You might be surprised to hear me say this but what about number three, that one about lots of rules. Is that not one that we could do without?"

"What do you all think?" Mike asked, "Do you think we could do without that one, or with less of those rules?"

"It's an interesting question," Tom answered, "it depends on what we mean by rules or what part they play. For example, in sport, like golf, rules are just part of the whole thing. They're what make the sport meaningful, how it works. In golf we have books and books of rules.

You could say the same about rules in work situations, like there are rules around what you get paid, what you pay, costings, so these are just part of life and can't be done without."

"Yes, I agree," Bernard said "but there are other kinds of rules too that people agree to and respect. I'm sure Frank has lots of these in terms of his football team but the same would be true of mountain climbing, all the rules that would apply in your wife Joan's theatre, that everybody agrees to and see as being critical for their success. So, in this way, I think rules are essential and not something that can be done without, Sally."

"I agree with you, Bernard," Tony said, "but I understand what Sally was saying too. I think it's about how rules are viewed and approached. They can be seen negatively if they are not properly understood and their importance is not appreciated. I often wonder if we should spend time educating people around the rules so that they understand the rationale for them and so respect them. Just like you people do so honourably, I understand, with your very strict golf rules. Then, people will want the rules. But I agree that, if this is done, then they're also essential."

"What about number five?" Heather asked, "is it not a bit strong to say that, to say that if people don't perform, they will be let go?"

"This is something that we will come back to some other time when we talk about handling some people whose performance is unsatisfactory," Mike answered. "But, for now, let me ask you a question, and I will take Frank's football team as an example, even though I could equally take the theatre group, music group etcetera. So, here's my question: if somebody is not performing well on Frank's team, should Frank not do the nice and kind thing and keep selecting that person rather than dropping them as number five is saying?"

"Definitely not," Frank answered, "I couldn't do that. It would be wrong and unfair to the others and to the whole team. I mean, it could probably lead to our failure to be what we want to be – a good and successful team. I have no problem with any one of these."

"But to speak for Heather for the moment, is that not being too hard on the individual?" Mike asked.

"No, not at all," Frank answered, "if the team fails, that individual fails too, so it would not be doing him any service to keep him on the team out of kindness or something. Everyone agreed and subscribed to the overall goal and the welfare of the team and to do whatever it takes to promote that welfare. They know how it works and agree with it and

> "Better to get hurt by the truth than comforted with a lie."
>
> **Khaled Hosseini,**
> **The Kite Runner**

know that if they're not performing well, they should not be on the team. Of course it has to be handled fairly and well, but the principle in number five stands – you are part of a team because you can make a contribution through your performance and that remains the condition for being part of the team. That seems very clear to me."

"When you put it like that, it makes sense to me as well," Heather laughed.

"Any more that are problematic? Mike asked

"What about number seven," Natalie asked, "the one about personal likes and dislikes taking second place?"

"I think that's similar to what we've already said," Tom answered, "it's like Frank said, it's the welfare of the team that most matters and, by being a team, people understand that their welfare depends on the overall welfare. Remember the "Balanced and Integrated Life" that we spoke about? It's not that there's a conflict between two sets of interests but simply that one interest, the overall welfare, comprises or contains a subordinate one – the individual one."

All on the side of the company or organisation

"Very well put, Tom," Mike said, "and we'll come back and talk about this another time. A question for you all. I take it you would be very happy if we had an organisation thinking and working like that? Think of the difference it would make to our performance and results. But, do any of you think or feel that this is a bit one-sided. That we, the *company*, would benefit enormously from this and that, therefore, it could be a bit unfair, or lopsided as I said?"

"Absolutely," Heather said, "of course I see it as a dream in terms of managing and getting things done. It would make things so easy and, as you said, we would achieve great things. But, to answer your question, yes, I see that it is one-sided, very much in the company's or management's favour. And I'm sure the people would see it like that too."

"I agree," Natalie said, "to me it would be like a return to the old days where workers had no rights and management could do what they liked."

Everyone seemed to be in agreement that, good as it would be, it was hugely beneficial for the company or management at the expense of the people.

"Okay," Mike said, "tell me, Frank, if these ten elements are not only what you want, but what actually gives or operates in your football team, do the lads feel, as everyone here seems to feel, that they are making huge sacrifices for the benefit of the club? Is that how they see it?"

"Ha-ha, not at all," Frank answered, "in fact it's what they *want*. They love it and they see it's for their benefit, for their success. They're very happy to go along with all ten of these elements, because they see them as being vital for their success and, you could say, happiness or well-being."

There was silence for a few moments. Then Bernard spoke. "It's because they identify with the success of the team and the club and see it as theirs. They see that the better off the team or the club does, the better it will be for them. It's very different for how our people see things, or, indeed, how we see things. They see that they're working for the company or for us, and that sacrifices they make are for the benefit of the company or for our benefit."

"Yes it's completely different," Tom added, "they see working for the company as a job they do and are obliged and requested to do things and for that they get paid. They don't really identify with the success of the company and, for that matter, why would they?"

"I think this is enormous," Teresa said, "maybe they see things that way because it's how *we* see them and structure them, and it's

> "When 'I' is replaced by 'we' even 'illness' becomes 'wellness'"
>
> **Scharf**

how we manage and relate to them. But remember some weeks ago we all agreed that people's welfare is absolutely linked to the welfare of this company, so why should that be any different from Frank's football team?"

"I agree," Sally said, "and, if you think about it, our people can achieve far more, be much better rewarded and benefit every way, including personally and professionally, far more than Frank's footballers can. Their very lives and welfare depend on it, much more than Frank's lads do, but they don't see it like that and it's not how they think and it's not how we think or operate or manage either for that matter."

"I agree," Bernard came in, "and it's even much more important that we and they think and operate and relate in this way because, while Frank's players spend time training and practising, it's minimal compared to the amount of time that people spend working with us. For that reason, it's even more important that we get across that they are part of the company, that they *are* the company to a great extent."

Mike spoke up and very seriously stated, "I take it that most of you around this table would agree that I've been trying to bring about those very same ten attitudes for more years than I care to remember. Do you agree?

Everyone nodded.

Enjoyable and Fun Leadership

"But, I hope you can see the difference in this whole approach compared to what I was doing." Tom came in. "I was trying to get people to think and behave in this way by pushing them, controlling them and driving them. What I now see is that these very same attitudes and behaviours can be achieved, not by my pressurising people but by getting them bought into the overall goal or vision, wanting what *we* want, because it makes sense. For me this is truly enormous. As you said, Teresa, it changes everything for me. I now see that I can achieve what I always wanted but do so in a very different way. I can't believe how I didn't see it before and yet I can understand why not, because it is subtle and very new. I think you all understand what I'm saying."

"This is great," Mike came in, "and how would we go about bringing about what Tom is so excited about? Let me leave Tom out of it for now.? "

"I think we've already spoken about this," Teresa said, "and agreed how we would show and convince people that their welfare and they, are intimately linked to the welfare of the company. Remember our famous X meeting?"

"So is that what we have to do and is that all we have to do?" Mike asked. "Will simply doing that be enough?"

"Not at all," Terry said, "we would have to work with them in a very different way, and probably not too dissimilar from the way that Frank works with his team. Frank is forced to rely on his players because they're the ones who are playing the game. All he can do is help them do that better and better.

"Exactly," Heather said, "remember what Mark and the restaurant told us that the job of his managers was to make sure that people, the staff, had three things:

• That they knew what was required and why.
• That they wanted to deliver it.

- That they were able to deliver it. I think that Frank's role is a bit like that and it's what ours should be too."

Tom came in to say, "I'm a little shocked and, to be honest, a little embarrassed. All that managing I've been doing! I can now see for the first time that much of it was doing more harm than good. We've been taking all the fun out of it for people. At least I have."

"It's funny you should say that and use that word "fun", Frank said, "I was on a coaching course some years ago and, strange as it was, the person running the course ran most of it through tennis and we actually spent time on the tennis court. Learning about how people learn and perform. At one point he took two of us and put us on either end of the net with our tennis racquets and proceeded to give us instructions. So he told one of us to run to the baseline and swing their racquet and the other person to stand in the middle of their court and swing theirs and then the first person to run to the left and swing their racket backhand and the other person to come to the net and swing their forehand etc. After a few minutes he called us together and told us he wasn't happy with what we were doing, that we weren't working hard enough, weren't running fast enough, not showing enough enthusiasm and interest etcetera.

Then he told us to try harder and we went back on court for a few more minutes doing what he told us. Then he stopped and threw in a tennis ball and told us to play if we wanted. We did, of course, and we ended up doing *all* the things that he had been telling us to do but doing them willingly, happily, with enthusiasm and, doing them very well. He then explained how this was a good example of what managing

> "Most people do not really want freedom, because freedom involves responsibility, and most people are frightened of responsibility"
>
> **Sigmund Freud**

does. Exactly as Tom said, we take the tennis ball away from them and they do as we tell them. We take the challenge, excitement, fun out of it. In fact, we take all five **COACH** elements out of the whole thing. Mad!"

"That's great, Frank," Mike said, "does that make sense to everybody?"

It obviously did, judging by the nods of approval.

Management and people want different things?

"Let me ask you then, if we forgot all about us and about the company, and suppose we only thought of the welfare of our people, our staff, what you think we would do? What I mean is, what do they *really* want, and, by that, I want to exclude the rewards or money piece, for now. What do you think they would really like and want in terms of their work, how it is organised, how they do it etcetera? Do you know what I mean?"

"I think so, Bernard said, "I think they would like work that they would see as challenging, as valuable, as worthwhile."

Yes, some few might want the "easy" life of minimum effort but these would be the exception and we should not base how we handle things by the few exceptional people. Which is exactly what we do. Someone abuses something and we introduce a new rule or law and these build up and affect and change the whole culture."

"I agree," Teresa spoke, "and I think the vast majority of people would like to feel in charge, that it was theirs, that it belonged to them and was up to them."

"Yes," Tom came in, "I agree completely with you, Teresa, and I think if they felt that it was up to them, and they were accountable, they'd feel free. I don't mean free to do any old thing, but free to do things *their* way. And I do actually believe that they would love really high goals and big challenges. That is what the group told me in no uncertain terms when I met with them."

"That makes sense to me too," Sally said, "and I can see them wanting to be left alone and let get on with things."

"I agree," Tony said, "and for that they would like to feel trusted, treated like responsible adults and, bit like Tom said, feel free in the sense that they have things in their own hands."

And so on and so on they continued describing what they believed would make people happy at work and happy with what they were doing."

"Isn't this very interesting, then," Mike commented, "that if we were to think of what *they*, the people want, and only what *they* want, it would coincide exactly with what *we* want – namely the ten points we talked about. It's a perfect match. We get what we want by giving them what they really want – all those things you mentioned. Isn't that wonderful?

They all laughed and agreed.

"And what's also wonderful," Mike added, "is that we know how to go about this, don't we?"

"Yes," Frank said, "it's about getting them to Know, Want, be Able by holding that famous X meeting and getting everybody clear and in full agreement about what we want for everybody's benefit. And then we help and support them to make that happen."

"That's the tricky bit," Tom said, "finding out and practising what really good support and help would mean, as distinct from the kind of help I've been giving for all those years."

"I think you're right, Tom," Teresa said, "if we're going to allow or enable them to work as we have just said, we'll have to find a different way of relating to them, of managing them, of getting things done. And, it will come as no surprise to any of you to hear that, for me, this comes down to two critical areas or approaches or skills – facilitating and coaching."

> "The interesting thing about coaching is that you have to trouble the comfortable, and comfort the troubled"
>
> **Ric Charlesworth, Hockey**

"You're right, Teresa," Heather said. "We know well how strongly you feel about facilitation and coaching, but I've always felt that the problem is that we don't really see how facilitating and coaching fit with managing and leadership. They can give the impression that we simply hand things over to them and have no other real part to play. Do you know what I mean?"

"I think I do," Mike said, "and I think what you're saying is very important. And I believe you're right that they can fear they will come across and be heard as weak, "whatever you like" kind of interactions. But that's looking at them, as it were, in a vacuum, outside the whole context in which they're done.

On their own, they could appear weak and lacking in real power – leadership power. It all comes down to power and the kind of power that we want and that's most effective. If we take Frank and his football team, or the manager of Joan's theatre group, or the leader of some band or music group, where is their power and where does it come from?"

"It comes from the goal," Terry answered, "from what they want, from what they all agreed is most important. I imagine that Frank, and the others you mentioned, are very intolerant of anything that's getting in the way of the achievement of that goal – just as the ten points that you showed us are demonstrating. So I imagine that it's this power that underpins the facilitating and coaching that Teresa talks about."

"I think you're right, Terry," Mike said, "this power, of what is meaningful, of what everybody wants, underpins everything, enriches everything and what Teresa is saying is that we would relate to people in a facilitating and coaching way to support and help them in achieving the overall goal. And part of that would involve dealing with situations or people where the goal is not being achieved or is in danger.

As I said before, we'll come back and look at this too. Now I can't spell out in detail exactly what any of you should do about this in practice, but I hope that we're all clear that we have to fundamentally change how we have been managing people, as Tom is very clearly recognising. Is that okay for now?"

They all agreed.

"But isn't this hard to believe?" Bernard asked, "it's like the piña colada song where they both wanted the same thing but didn't know they did!

1. We want our people to be really committed to the company and our goals ... and that's exactly what *they* want, something to really commit to.
2. We want people to do a good job and be responsible and accountable for what they do, ...and *they* are pleading to be left accountable.
3. We want people that we can trust, in whom we have confidence... and *people* want to be trusted and to feel that we have confidence in them.
4. We would love and want people to get on with things and react and respond well to whatever happens.... and *they* want to be in touch with whatever is happening so that they are able to respond to it properly.
5. We want people to behave responsibly, like adults... and *they* want to be treated as adults and with respect.

Can you believe it? What fools we've been... And I mean us, managers, not them."

Everyone laughed embarrassingly.

Then Frank spoke, "I have been relatively quiet here but there is something that I want to say now. I know many of you have been asking what brought about the change in our results as a football team.

We've won nothing yet but we're in the final and if we keep playing as we have been doing,

> "All coaching is, is taking a player where he can't take himself"
>
> **Bill McCartney, American Football**

I feel very sure we'll win. I can honestly say that the reason for this turn-around is that we have been operating in line with those principles that Mike named. They may not be the exact words that we use but they're the values that we all share and the commitments we all accept and live up to. This has meant a very big change for us all and it did take some time to get people to buy into it. But it's true to say that there's not one of those ten principles that we don't live, and Mike and I haven't even spoken about this until now. The coincidence is quite amazing."

"Amazing indeed", Mike said, "that is most extraordinary Frank, but I have to say I'm not surprised. I was quietly wondering what was going on in recent weeks and months that brought about such a remarkable change in your team's results. And I'm not overly surprised about what has happened, as you'll easily understand."

Everyone was equally surprised to hear Frank's explanation of what had made the difference and everyone commented on what Frank had said, each one asking a different question and querying alternative examples of what had gone on.

"And I can vouch for how well this works," Natalie said. "I had a session with Mike a few days ago where I was really stuck on something and quite unable to move on it. Mike and I spoke and I ended up not only being clear about what I was going to do but confident in doing it and committed to doing it. The transformation I experienced was quite extraordinary. And, you might all be thinking that that happened because Mike gave me some good ideas and support. He didn't. Not one! He coached me through the whole way forward and it really was quite transformational."

And Natalie explained what Mike did and the steps he followed.

"These steps look very easy," Teresa came in, "but there's a wealth of skills working behind and through every one of them. I think it would be good for us all to learn and practise these skills so that we can get the kind of transformation Natalie is talking about, and that Frank has experienced and enjoyed with his lads on the football team. Ok?"

They all agreed. There was little more to be said. They all were fine and seemed excited to explore how they might manage in line with the **COACH** principles and bring about an equally remarkable transformation in how their teams performed.

"You mentioned rewards earlier, Mike," Sally said. "Are they not pivotal to all this? After all, at present they're the main reason why people work, aren't they?"

Everyone seemed to agree.

"Yes, you're right, Sally, said Mike. That's how it is and I said we needed to talk about them. And we will, I promise.

Questions for reflection and action

1. How big is the jump you believe you need to make to be the kind of organisation you really want to be?
2. Do you see how you can be faithful to all ten points but in a good way, by being your true self?
3. Are there any of the ten you think you could do without? Which do you most need to work on?
4. Where does facilitating and coaching leadership fit in with bringing about this transformation?
5. Why can "comfort" be the greatest challenge to be overcome? Where does it fit or not with management … and with leadership?

Chapter 19
Money Makes Us Poorer

How money robs us of life

In recent meetings when working on the new kind of company, Mike's "Promised Land", the question of rewards and money kept coming up and he and Teresa had assured

> "One can't have power without committing oneself"
>
> **Aldous Huxley**

everybody they would deal with it. He knew how powerful money and rewards were, but also knew the limitations of the power of money to motivate and get the best from people. Some saw it as all powerful. But was it? And was it the best kind of power to use to get the best from people? So what *was in fact* the best kind of power? As he continued to search, news came on the radio and the first item was how the military in Egypt violently quashed a protest by the Muslim Brotherhood supporters of the ousted President Morsi.

"Well that's one kind of power," he said to himself, "the power of physical force and violence, and that's one we certainly won't use, common as it may be."

The second news item concerned a UN debate on Syria where, it seemed to him, wider world political issues were being played out, namely the overthrow of a leader.

"No," he thought, "that kind of power, political power, will not really work, if it ever does." He knew many people in the company at different levels who believed in and used political power, but he also saw the downsides of it.

Thinking of politics and statesmen, Nelson Mandela jumped to his mind, and he thought about the enviable power the man had – charismatic power – but this seemed to him something one had or hadn't and not something that Tom, or Sally, or Fred or Natalie would learn easily or that he was sure he had himself either. He couldn't base everything on something so elusive.

> "Mastering others is strength. Mastering yourself is true power"
>
> **Lao Tzu**

He continued thinking of this and, as he neared home, his mind turned to his family and to some things he had to do. He had become very aware of his conversation with Joan around home and spending more time there. And she was right, there were things to do, lots of things that had been neglected. And she was right that the garage was a good place to start.

It wasn't only because of Joan. He had been planning for a long time to do a really big and badly needed tidy up of his garage which, as he had told Tom, had become a mess. In actual fact he liked this task, including the physical and earthy nature of work, a different kind of work. He didn't see the job as a kind of distraction. In fact, he felt it was more a kind of meditation or spiritual experience. The work had its own reward. How could he achieve that for his own people? he mused.

Getting a helping hand

The garage tidy-up was a big job and he reckoned he could do with some help, not that Tom ever intended providing it. He wondered if Harry, his son, would assist him. But would Harry want or be willing to help him? Harry wasn't lazy, but he had his own things to do with his friends. Mike knew that his son had other things to occupy him that he would have to forfeit if he was going to help him out. He believed it was good for Harry to do physical work like that, and he also felt it was good for his son to do things with his dad. But would he want to? And how could Mike get him to want to do such work? That brought him back to what he had been thinking about earlier – power. Suppose he wanted to get his son to help him, how could he go about it and what kind of power could he use to influence and persuade him?

The first one that sprang to his mind was not one that he liked or would use, but it was his power as father and a head of the house. So, as Harry's father, he could use his position as one of the heads of the house, and simply *tell* him to dedicate some hours on Saturday to cleaning the garage.

And, while he was clear that he would not use that power, he realised that it was this kind of power, hierarchical power, that was used most often at work in the company. In Harry's case it would not really work and he knew that, apart from damaging the relationship, Harry probably would not do a very good job.

But thinking of the work situation brought to mind the other power that is very frequently there – money, the power of reward. So, he could offer to pay Harry something for helping him on Saturday and Harry would certainly welcome that. That would definitely work. Yet, for many reasons, he had serious misgivings about it. He did not want to encourage that attitude towards work and life in Harry and so he resisted following that course of action.

He got on well with Harry, so he could also take advantage of that goodwill and use his personal relationship to request Harry, as a favour, to help him out, knowing that Harry would cooperate, giving him another option. But still he was not happy and continued to search for a solution.

The strange and underlying power of meaning

He was going to pick Harry up from football at his school on the way home and he looked forward to hearing his excited story of what had happened,

"You can have everything in life you want, if you will just help other people get what they want"

Zig Zigler

providing they had won of course. Otherwise, it would be a quiet fifteen minutes' drive home. He knew Joan would have a nice warm fire going and he had left it all ready for lighting before leaving that morning.

Dinner would be ready, as Joan had an early finish and he had bought a nice roast beef the day before. He reconsidered this question of power again and he reflected that all these things were done by Joan and himself, without any power being visible at all.

What was all this about? How could that be? "Why do I undertake those things and much more, like looking after repairs in the house, cutting the grass, looking after the garden, paying for many things? And I never have to ask Joan to have hot towels in the hot press, or to iron my shirts or a hundred other things she does? Then he realised that they both did those things simply because they made sense.

They were important and worked in terms of the whole project of running or keeping a house or home. "What's the power at work then in such cases?" he asked himself. "The power of meaning, of what makes sense! Of course!"

As he got near Harry's school, he decided he would try something. It felt a little manipulative, but he vowed to be open with Harry afterwards. After he had listened to Harry's account of the match – they had won easily in a bit of a non-event – he took advantage of a lull in the conversation to raise the topic of cleaning the garage.

"I was looking for a cylinder of gas in the garage last week Harry, and I couldn't find it. The place is in such a mess. Have you been in there recently?"

"I have. I was looking for an old pair of boots for training last week because my good ones were wet, but there was no sign of them. I asked you about them some time back, remember?"

"Yes, I do. Could we have a look at it when we get home, as I was hoping to tackle it next Saturday and wondering if you could give me a hand? Unless you have something else on, that is."

"Sure Dad." Harry replied, "No, I have nothing on next weekend."

After dinner he asked Harry if they could take a look at the garage and out they went.

"Well, what do you think Harry? A mess?"

"Yeah, it sure is."

"I was thinking of dragging out all the rubbish first of all, and then putting the rest away in some order, what do you think?"

"Yeah, I agree, and maybe we should get as much up on shelves as possible."

"Good idea Harry. We could do a nice job on it, what do you think?"

"Yeah, it would look good, and you might find that cylinder in there somewhere, maybe with my boots on them!"

He slapped his son on the back and they headed back into the house.

A Good and Enjoyable Day's work but why?

Saturday came and all went very well. Joan had a day's rehearsing, so she was gone most of the day and planned to eat with the theatre group. He knew how important this was for Joan, so he got breakfast for her before she left. He loved to see her so exhilarated. The theatre really brought out the best in her. Rose was spending the day with her best friend Mary and was having dinner in Mary's house, so Mike was in charge of everything. He got Alex settled and he and Harry then set about the work on the garage. Mike let Harry choose what he wanted to do, and he got really stuck in and within a few hours the place looked ordered. There were a lot of things to be thrown out and a gas cylinder and a pair of boots had appeared in the process.

When they had finished and cleaned up, Mike told Joan – who had arrived home in the meantime – that he and Harry were going for a snack and he took a delighted Harry to his favourite chicken and chips restaurant.

When their meal arrived, Mike squared with Harry about his hidden agenda and told him that he had promised to pay a fine of €10 for being devious, slipping a note across the table and he genuinely said he was sorry and that he wanted Harry to know he would never do that again.

"But why Dad," Harry asked.

"Well in getting you involved in helping me with the garage, I decided to use a particular approach. I wanted to see how that approach would work compared to other approaches I might have used. There were two in particular I could have used and I would love you to tell me honestly what would have happened if I had used either of them."

"Sure, Dad," Harry said, "and this chicken is delicious so thanks for bringing me here."

"Well, as your father, I could have, at least kind of, just *told* you what I wanted and that you had to pull your weight and play your part in looking after the house. How would that have worked do you think?"

"Well, it would have worked and I would have done the work with you, but I think I would have done it but very reluctantly and probably not very well. I would probably have complained about how tired I was and maybe found an excuse to get out of it early... training or something! You know how I can be sometimes. I can be awkward when asked to do things. I like to keep my football gear tidy but when Mum gets on to me about it, it takes all the good out of it. Today, I actually wanted to do that work and that made all the difference. And you let me decide lots of things too so I felt it was *my* job."

Mike was surprised by the mature answer Harry gave but, then, he was getting lots of pleasant surprises about how people behave when handled well.

"Good man. Now the other way is a really dodgy one, so I want you to be really honest. Ok? Suppose I had offered to pay you something for helping me? Given you €10 or €20 for pocket money as reward?"

"Oh I would have loved that Dad! Of course! That would have been great.

"Yes, I know that, Harry, but please try to imagine what might have happened and how it might have differed from what you did today. Be honest as your lying father has not been with *you*."

"No, I understand Dad. Well, I think a few things would have happened. I would have only done what we had agreed both in terms of time and the amount of the work. My friend, Andrew, has that kind of a deal with his dad and I hear him talking about jobs that he could do when he needs money for anything. It seems now that he won't do anything around the house unless he gets paid for it.

The same might have happened here and I would want the same deal for everything else you might ask me to do. And, nice as the money would be, that would change the kind of relationship we have which I like Dad. And it wouldn't be fair to you or to Mum who do so much for us anyway. We're in this together to some extent. Is that what you mean?"

Mike was again surprised at the wisdom and fairness in his son and delighted with the response which matched his own thinking on money and rewards.

The real reward!

"Yes, it is. You're great Harry. I agree. And the money will come to you anyway some other way. And Harry, here's a difficult question. You know how you felt after we finished today. How do you think that might have been different if I handed you over your money?"

> "This joy of discovery is real, and it is one of our rewards. So too is the approval of our work by our peers"
>
> **Henry Taube**

"I know exactly what you mean, Dad. I loved the satisfaction of seeing that place so neat and tidy and I felt proud of my part in it, as well as being happy to have found my old boots. I felt proud when mum complimented us both on how it looked. But I think that all that would have been lost if the money was the reason for doing it. I would be just thinking of the money and not of all that tidying and brushing we did.

And I wouldn't enjoy the feeling of having helped you either. I would have done my part and you your part and we would "owe" each other nothing. No, you're right Dad, that would have changed everything.

I am kind of proud of the garage now and of the part I played in tidying it. It's mine, in a sense."

Mike was again surprised but very happy with his son's response.

So Mike then explained the power of meaning to him and told him all the things his mother and he did just because they made sense.

"That's what I want to try to achieve in the company too Harry. Just as you *wanted* to tidy that garage and had a clear idea of how good that would be, I want all our workers to think and work in the same way, because it makes sense, because it's meaningful and so do it all because they *want* to. Thanks for all you did today"

"Do I now get paid for the experiment too?" Harry joked.

The following week, Mike told his team that he wanted them – at last – to work on the key issue of money and rewards and began by telling them what he and Harry had done the previous Saturday. When Mike had finished telling the group the story of Harry helping him with the garage, he asked Sally:

"So, what you think Sally? What do you make of all that?"

"I like it and I understand it, Mike, but I think it's a big jump from where we are to that kind of thinking. Our people may not be as fair or mature as your son is! It would be a big change for us, but imagine the change it would mean for others and for corporate management? You know the struggles I have on other topics. But, I agree that it would be great if people see and do their work because it's rewarding in itself and if they enjoyed the sheer achievement of it, like Harry did. However, I do think we're a long way from there."

"I know what you mean," Bernard said, "but I'm not sure that I agree that we're that far away from it as you suggest. I think it depends on the people and the job and how they perceive it. I'm not saying that any of us will do our jobs for nothing, but I think that many or some of us, at least, really enjoy our jobs for the same reason that Harry enjoyed his. And, don't forget Tom's group working on the Quantum Logistics System and how that was for them and why they both enjoyed it and did it so well!"

"Yes, and let's not forget," Heather said, "that Harry did get financially rewarded as well for what he did. And it was important, but it was not the main reason for doing it or the greatest reward that he got. As you say, Bernard, we're like that too in that we might not do what we do for nothing, and couldn't afford to, but it isn't what drives us."

"I agree with that, Heather," Teresa said, "it's not that the money or reward doesn't matter but whether it is the only or main driver for people doing what they do. When it does become the main driver, you lose, and everybody loses."

"I agree, Teresa," Terry came in, but in my world, the world of Sales, targets and getting rewarded for them is very important. You all know this. Rewards are what drive some people."

"I understand that, Terry, "Frank said. "But we have to be careful and wise around rewarding people, especially around monetary rewards. I once heard about an Oxford professor who took six months off work to write an important paper. He decided to do it from home, from his apartment. On the first morning when he sat down to begin his work, he was distracted and disturbed by the shouts and squeals and laughter of children. His apartment overlooked a park and children came to play there every morning for a few hours. He tried to work but it was impossible. He realised that he would never get his paper done with such noisy distraction every day.

What could he do? He couldn't tell them to go away because they were entitled to be there. He couldn't complain to the park attendants because that's what parks were for. He couldn't complain to the parents either who were entitled to have their children there and very much wanted their children to play in the park. So what could he do?

So he went down to the park to the children, got them together and told them that he loved to see children playing. He asked them that if he were to give each of them £1 would they come back and play again the next day? They were delighted, gladly took the money and promised to come back and play again the following day.

The next day he went down again, got them together, thanked them for coming and gave them each 50p. They took the money and played away.

On Wednesday, he did the same, but this time only give them 20p each. Not pleased, they took the money and reluctantly went off to play but didn't play for as long.

On Thursday he went to them again, got them together and told them that he had no more money to pay them for playing but that he would still like them to continue playing. They were very unhappy, even annoyed, and went off saying they would not play again. Isn't that it, Teresa?"

"Exactly, Frank," Teresa answered, "he replaced one reward – playing and having fun – with another reward – money – and the money one superseded, took over and replaced the fun one. Very clever and very sad."

> "Rewards and punishments are the lowest form of education"
>
> **Zhuangzi**

"Yes, it is." Frank answered, "and it's something that we are very conscious about in our team or in our sport. There'll be gains for people from playing the game and being successful, but if whatever kind of gain takes over and becomes what really matters, we're gone. Not gone in the sense that we won't keep playing but the real spirit and fun and enjoyment of being a team and doing what we love doing, will be gone. Just like with the children in the park.

Making the shift in companies and organisations

"Yes, and very common," Mike intervened, "this is what money and financial rewards can do to activities. As Frank said, we see this all the time in sport, in nearly all sports, where the fun of playing and even the goal of winning are replaced with the reward of money. The extreme example is the journeyman in boxing who is paid to box... and lose. This is only the extreme example because others get paid to box or to play football or to run whether they win or lose, because money has become the key reward. And this is the norm in business organisations, where many people *only* work in order to earn money. It's that we need to correct and to find the right balance."

"And what would that mean?" Sally asked.

"What you think, everybody? Mike asked.

"I think it will be about getting our priorities right and helping people to get their priorities right." Terry came in. "Along the lines of what you did with Harry, whereby getting the job done, the garage tidied, was what mattered, and the financial reward followed on but was not the key driver. In our case, that would mean doing as we have been saying all along – getting people clear about and committed to the purpose and welfare of the company as being what really matters.

And, of course, giving them the confidence and guarantee that they'll be rewarded for the work that they do. But, that's the result and not the motivator or driver. That's how I see it. Does that make sense?"

"I think it makes a lot of sense," Teresa said, "this is very important for lots of reasons. A person called Alfie Kohn did extensive research on this and came to a very clear and categorical conclusion. He said that where good quality work is required over a period - as distinct from a quick once-off - there is zero correlation between money or rewards and good work. In other words, if we want quality work from our people on an ongoing basis, then he's saying that rewards or money will not deliver or guarantee that."

"But we would have to find a good way to give them the guarantee or confidence that they'll get fairly rewarded for their work, wouldn't we?" Tom asked.

"Yes, Tom, we would", Mike replied, "and to my mind, there has to be some correlation between how

"Happiness does not come from doing easy work but from the afterglow of satisfaction that comes after the achievement of a difficult task that demanded our best"

Theodore Isaac Rubin

well we do as a business and how people are rewarded. I cannot see or accept that there's no connection or correlation between how well we do as a business and what people get paid or rewarded."

"But how would that work?" Frank asked.

"I'm afraid to try to answer that, Frank," Mike said, "because unfortunately it is a source of conflict between me and some people at the moment. But, put quite simply, I think it's eminently possible and makes full sense to pay people wages or salaries based on acceptable rates for the job and then to pay people bonuses based on how we as a company perform financially and overall.

There are some good and safe overall models for doing this, such as Planned Sharing of Value Added, but we need not get into those right now, if that's okay. But is the principle okay with you and does it make sense?"

Mike sensed that there were some misgivings or doubt still, even if they seemed to understand and agree. But he weathered the silence. Eventually Natalie spoke.

"It all makes sense Mike, but what worries me a little is what great difference will it make? It seems to me that making this shift will require a lot of convincing and a lot of changing. I wonder if that makes any sense?"

"It does to me," Frank said, "I agree with what you're saying, at least in theory, but, a bit like Natalie, I wonder if it will make a great difference to anybody!"

Teresa then came in. "I think it will make a difference and it's a better way to work and to handle things. And, I accept, that it will involve considerable change in how we and others think."

"Well," Mike said, "there's no point in doing this if it isn't going to make a very big difference. I agree with that. I think it will make a big difference at every level, just like in the example I gave of my garage work with Harry. But I want us all to be very clear that it is worth the effort and that it will make a big difference. Unless we get our focus right and on the right things, things that really matter, then there will be little or no substance to all that we are trying to do.

If we do that and do it well, then everything will fall into place, including the rewards for doing good work. Something else that I would like us to talk about is the correlation between the highest paid and the lowest paid in the company. It's my view that there should be proportionality between these two because otherwise people will feel that they're working for *us* and not for their company as has been said here a few times in the past. But we can talk about that again."

"I'm okay with all that, Mike," Bernard said, "and even with that relationship between the highest and the lowest paid, without getting into detail, do you think that the bonus, where earned and where paid, should be the same across-the-board, or should it be based on individual performance?"

"I'm glad you asked that Bernard," Teresa said. "I have talked a bit about this with a friend of mine who works in this area. It's something we need to talk about, such as whether bonus payments would be monetary sums or a percentage of one's salary. And, whether they should be paid to everyone equally or related to people's individual performance."

"I can't see how it would be right to pay someone a bonus who is not performing satisfactorily, do you?" Tom asked. "I'm still not happy that we get this right. How can we handle people who are not performing well? It's ok to talk of giving bonuses to everyone, but will this make any difference to the poor performers? Maybe just don't pay them!"

"Maybe," Frank answered, "but are you sure that not paying them a bonus is the best way to deal with them? Or that it will work?"

"Maybe not," Tony came in, "but they can't be treated just like everyone else and ignored."

Mike and Teresa exchanged knowing glances and Teresa nodded assuringly.

"Ok," Mike said, "I know that we haven't agreed anything concrete about how we'll reward people and ourselves but I hope and believe that we agree on some key principles. Is that acceptable? We can return to this and with Teresa and Sally's help come up with good systems, based on these principles. As I said, I have some issues to deal with myself with corporate management on some of these matters. And thank you all for being so open-minded. As I said it's not easy, and it certainly is not easy for me at the moment," he laughed.

While he still felt convinced that what he was doing was the right thing, he decided to have another conversation with Brendan before taking the next steps. He was not sure if it was worthwhile getting into the detail of the questions around rewards until he received some kind of agreement on the overall situation with Brad and Martha on their visit.

Questions for reflection and action

1. Which powers do you use or favour using? How aware are you of these?
2. Can you identify with Harry's experience and reaction? Have you had similar experiences?
3. What part do individual financial rewards play in your organisation and for your people? Are you happy with how they are and how effective they are overall?
4. What drives or motivates your people? How important is it that this be really valuable?
5. Are there any things around rewards that you would like to look at or think about?
6. Are group or team or overall rewards or bonuses or sharing in the added value feasible for you in your organisation?

Chapter 20
Oh Not Performance Reviews Again!

A new paradigm approach to handling performance reviews

Several weeks had passed and several meetings were held and, in that time, all the members of the senior management team had had their own individual X meetings with Mike, and they had held ones with their own people. They all went well, although some said they could have handled them better. Some of this was just because of the new processes that were being introduced. Some people had to adjust to this new way of being together and, of course, they had to get over their cynicism or scepticism around visions and goals.

But they did, and they saw and felt from their managers that this time it was different and they saw that their managers truly believed in and were very convinced about and even passionate around their goals for their areas.

There was no doubt that something was different and was going to remain different. There was a new seriousness about things and about what was being said. But there was also a greater sense of meaning or warmth about everything. The link between the welfare of the company and people's own personal welfare was

> "We have to recognise that there cannot be relationships unless there is commitment, unless there is loyalty, unless there is love, patience, persistence."
>
> **Cornel West**

clear and indisputable. Some people tried to test the authenticity of what they had heard with their colleagues by making jokes about the road to Damascus but they really didn't work very well and quickly flittered out.

Notwithstanding how well things had gone and were going, Teresa knew the mood was not right when people arrived for the meeting she had called on Performance Reviews two weeks later. The issue of performance and under-performers had come up several times and she had assured Mike she would deal with it. She knew people might not welcome this particular way of carrying out their reviews.

Why they don't work

"What's wrong with everybody?" she asked. "Remember Mike said that we would need to give our people individual attention, as well as consultations in groups and teams? Remember we said we would be frank and honest with each other? Tom? What's going on?"

Tom spoke first. "Well, you know our views on Appraisals and Performance Reviews, Teresa. We do them but we don't like them and neither we nor our people get much out of them. You know how every year you have to keep after us to get them done? *Nobody* likes them. You know that! And I think, with all due respect, we could find more important things to talk about and work on! Sorry, but I'm just being honest as we said we would be."

"And why do you think Performance Reviews don't work and are you saying that this is a waste of time?" Teresa asked the group.

"I think it's because they're such uncomfortable meetings," Natalie said. "Nobody likes either giving or getting feedback or criticism and so you end up either upsetting somebody and maybe yourself as well, or avoiding saying things and ending up being dishonest, so that the meeting is at least trouble-free. That's just how I see it."

"Yes," Tony said, "and people hate them because they feel judged or that they will be criticised. I know my people definitely feel like that around my appraisals. And that's not all about me, so take that grin off your face, Bernard," he laughed.

"And then there are the ratings," Sally said. "It's such a job to get good performers to accept a three-rating, telling them that even if they have done a really good job, that it's only what is expected from them. I had such problems last year with a few of my staff who got all their reports and analyses done and in on time. After all that I had to tell them that they got a three, because they had merely done their job! And, of course, they'll find someone who got a higher rating to compare themselves with and feel aggrieved. It can be impossible to justify to people why one got a higher rating than another, and they do talk and compare."

"And it is even worse," Frank added, "when bonuses or increases are linked to ratings. I mean, how could anyone be honest about their performance or accept a rating if they know it will affect what they earn? I mean their new car or holiday, or new television could depend on what they say and on what gets said. Literally it wouldn't pay to be honest. It's expecting far too much."

"I have to agree with them, Teresa," Mike rowed in, "and I often wonder if people end up thinking more about their managers and how they are seen by their managers for all these reasons, than actually focusing on their jobs! I have so many people in my office, or trying to get into it, to tell me of some great thing they have done, hoping it will stand to them later in reviews when we talk to them. You know the people I mean."

> "Nothing in this world is harder than speaking the truth, nothing easier than flattery."
>
> **Fyodor Dostoevsky**

"That's enough," Teresa interrupted. "Thanks a million, Mike," she laughed. "You're a great help!"

"In actual fact," she told them, "I agree with everything you've said."

The group were amazed and looked at each other.

"Now I have bad and good news for you all. The bad news is that you, and we all, are going to carry out a form of Performance Reviews this year. Yes, we are. None of that rolling your eyes, Tom. And the good news is that it will be a different format and process that both you and your people will welcome and love. Believe me. The reason we're going to have Performance Reviews is because they are essential if we're going to achieve what we're after. Mike and I have spoken about this and agree that the good work in your X meetings will do no good unless it's followed up with and supported by good work at the individual level. Helping people, as we have repeatedly said, is our job.

Helping them to know what's expected from them and why, to want to do what is necessary and why and to be able to do and carry out what's required, as we learned from Mark. The Performance Review system we want to use, which we are calling "People and Performance Development System" (PPDS) will be vital in helping people to play their part in achieving what we all want. And, I assure you, it will work.

So Teresa explained the PPDS, to them and how it's a system based on self-assessment, with the manager acting as coach.

Self-assessment

"What do you mean by self-assessment, Teresa?" Sally asked, "Do you mean that people assess themselves rather than we do it?"

"Yes, that's exactly it, Sally."

"Why would we do that? Is it not *our* job to assess them? What if they say little or nothing?"

"In fact, that's not what happens Sally. In practice, using this approach actually means that far more gets discovered and said than using the traditional telling or appraising approach, because people know more about themselves and will often say things that a manager could never say without causing great offence. It works like this."

Then Teresa drew a red box on the flipchart to indicate what normally gets covered and said by the manager in the appraisal or performance review, only some of which understood and accepted by the person on the receiving end. And then she showed a far bigger green box to indicate what is shared and said when it is the person being reviewed who does the reviewing and the talking. "Is my model clear and making sense?" She asked.

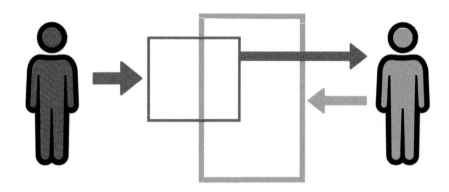

"Yes, I think I see it," Bernard answered. What you're saying is that if I give a whole lot of feedback to somebody in an appraisal, clear as it might be to me, they might *not understand* it and, secondly, even if they do understand it, they *might not agree* with it. Is that it?"

"Yes, that's exactly it. Why do you think that might happen and actually does happen, Bernard?"

"Because the red box represents *my* view of the world, based on what I've seen or on experiences I've had and, convinced and certain as I may be about these, I might not be at all right. It's just my view or perspective."

"I understand," Heather said, "and it becomes even more difficult when another person's view of the world is being imposed on you and you're expected to accept it. That's why, I think, that many people resent reviews because they're very often experienced or felt as unfair in that sense."

> "Ever tried. Ever failed. No matter. Try Again. Fail again. Fail better"
>
> **Samuel Beckett**

"Very good, and I agree with all that. Well said. And why would the green box be actually bigger?" Teresa asked the group.

"Because, as you said," Tony answered, "the person *knows* far more about themselves than the manager or appraiser does."

"Yes," Natalie added, "and because sometimes you can be afraid to say some things to people out of fear of offending or upsetting them, so it's so much easier and better when they say them. And, very often, they'll *say a lot more* than we might dare say, right?"

"I can confirm that," Frank said. When I talk to some players on the team, in confidence, and, more importantly listen to them, they're far more open and say far more things than I might ever dare to say to them. One of our top players told me recently, when I asked him how he was doing, that he felt he was performing very poorly because he was afraid of failing. I would never have known or believed that unless I had asked him."

"That's it exactly, Natalie and Frank" Teresa answered.

"I understand and agree with all of this," Bernard intervened, "but I already do this. I don't simply get the forms filled out and dish out an appraisal to people. I get them to fill out the forms beforehand to assess how they're doing. So I think I'm already doing this, Teresa."

"That's great, Bernard," Teresa answered, "and I'm very glad to hear that. But I hope you don't mind me asking about whether you are exactly following this process. What happens in the actual meeting, then, when they have filled out the form and, probably, given it to you? What happens next?"

Disagreements and differences of opinion

"Well, I go through what they have written or said and agree or disagree with some of it, and then I give them feedback and my assessment of how they have been doing. Is that not okay?"

"It might be, but it could also be that it's the same game that's being played. At the end of the day, they know that it is *your* opinion that ultimately matters and that will win the day. I could be wrong on this but I believe this approach, which is very common, is really a slightly different version of the same thing."

"May I ask, Bernard," Mike interjected, "what happens when there is a difference of opinion, when they don't agree with your assessment?"

"It very rarely happens. We always reach an agreement so there's no problem or conflict."

"And that might be great," Mike continued, "it might be there is no disagreement because there's a real meeting or coincidence of views. Or, it could be that they know that it's *your* view that really matters, and so they go along with it. I'm not saying that's the case, so that I'm putting it to you that it could be the case. Is that fair?"

> "I can grow as a leader only if I'm willing to accept feedback"
>
> **Jennifer Hyman**

"Yes, I think it is. I hear what you're saying and people might be afraid to disagree with me for one reason or another. Nice and agreeable as I am. And I am not saying that now because I am afraid of disagreeing with you Mike!"

"I think this is very important," Teresa said, "this approach is very common, as I said, but it is subtly, radically different from the approach I'm talking about, where you trust their review of things and of themselves. This faith or trust that you put in them and the respect you show for their honesty and integrity makes all the difference.

In your case, I think you're still being the final arbiter, Bernard, whereas in the approach I am recommending and proposing, there is no arbiter, because you're trusting and relying on their honest assessment and acting on it. In your case I can imagine – and I could be wrong – that people say and write what they think, but that they know what really matters is what *you* finally think and write. Is that accurate and fair, Bernard?"

"Yes, I think it is. I understand the difference. Thanks."

"Great. Now, is there anything else you think that's better about this approach, using self-assessment based on my poorly drawn boxes?"

"Well, it's green," Sally said, "meaning that it's the other person who's saying it all, so we can be sure it's both understood and accepted, which, as you said, is not the case with the red box, when we're doing all the appraising and talking. Very good. I like this Teresa and I think it fits with the approach we've been talking about and going after."

"I can see all that," Tony said, "but I still can't see it working. What if people are not honest? I can't see people owning up to things and admitting mistakes and accepting that they haven't done a good job. I've never seen it."

"I understand that, Tony," Teresa replied, "but I *have*! And the reason I have and you haven't, is not because I'm a finer person than you, about which there is no doubt, anyway, but because we are talking of and using different approaches.

Of course, if people know that they'll be assessed and judged by their manager, that the manager will have the final say, that no matter what they say, ultimately, it's the manager's call, then, of course, people will not be honest and will put up their best case. However, when you handle it differently like I'm suggesting, then all that changes.

> "It's up to God to do the judging. You haven't walked in my boots, so how are you going to judge me?"
>
> **Aaron Neville**

Really! People feel respected, trusted, cared for and important, and so they'll be very open and honest about their performance and everything else. Yes, naturally, some people will be cautious at the outset because they have been taught and have learned not to trust, but in a very short time space, they'll see that their views will not be superseded or ignored, trumped by the manager's view. We could argue this back and forth for a long time, Tony, but the only way to find out is to try it. What I drew about the red and green boxes earlier is not a theory but is my experience of what happens when I behave in a non-judgmental way. And I find the same is true with my friends and with my own children. Can we give it a try and see what happens?"

"Sure, Teresa. Why not?" Tony replied.

Then Teresa explained that there would be no ratings and the PPDS would not be directly linked to pay or rewards or bonuses. "If we have those, they'll be decided and agreed at a different time and in a different way." She told them.

Some had problems with dumping ratings. They liked categorising people. Teresa explained that this is part of the problem. She explained that it's much healthier if we let the natural law of things rule, meaning that there will probably always be some really exceptional performers who may need to be looked after some way. And, there will, unfortunately, probably be some who are not performing well enough in their roles. 'In their roles' she stressed, not 'compared to others. And these too need attention, albeit of a different kind. They saw the sense in this and felt relieved.

"What do you mean that we'll talk about pay increases and bonuses at a different time?" Heather asked.

"I want to separate or uncouple them," she said, "because I want people to see and use the PPDS as a means of finding out and committing to what they want and need to do better and not as a forum where they'll try to justify their case for an increase or bonus. Any increase or bonus will come from them performing better as a result of having learned and committed to doing so at the performance review session. Do you understand? It'll be a powerful mechanism or tool to help people perform better, so that they earn and justify getting an increase or a bonus. And, as we know, that will only be possible if we and the whole company are performing well.

But, I want a separate session on this whole question of rewards and bonuses as I want to move away from individual recognition to more group and team recognition, apart from those exceptional cases I mentioned. Is that acceptable?"

They all agreed with her.

Feedback for managers too

"Good. Another key part of the process is to help you as managers to get feedback from the people in the PPDS meeting around yourselves and to find out how you or the organisation are helping or getting in the way of people." She explained that this is a unique opportunity to ask for and get feedback. "It's easier to hear feedback when you *ask for it*, because otherwise people will not dare to give you feedback" she told them. "And we all need feedback".

"Hold on," Tony stopped her, "surely it is *we* who give the feedback not them? This is all about giving *them* feedback surely?"

"Well, it is, but it's really all about helping them to perform better and do more justice to themselves, surely? And, one of the best ways we can help people is to find out how *we* can best help them. We must create the conditions and environment that will help and enable people to be and perform better. That's the greatest contribution we can make to people's performance – developing a culture and the conditions where people thrive and perform in line with or close to their real potential. It would seem to me to be a huge opportunity missed if we didn't ask people this question. Don't you all want to be better managers? Well, this is one great way you can learn to do that. As I said, they won't – and very often wouldn't dare to – take the initiative and come forward with feedback for us. I'm very strongly, as you may notice, advising you to use this opportunity."

No one seemed to disagree, and Tony also looked convinced.

Teresa told them that the most important part of the PPDS was not review how the person did in the past which is over and gone, but to help and get them to be and *perform better in the future* and to believe in and expect great things from themselves.

"It's to help people get in touch with much more of the "P" of "Potential."

"We can be like this man," Teresa said, showing them the image below, "by judging, evaluating, being disappointed, criticising and not helping, not giving people the ladder. In fact we are blocking them from realising and reaching their real potential. We have to be ladder people"

"I recognise that,", Tom said. I'm afraid I do that very often."

"I'm afraid I do too," Frank joined in. No!

Things missed and blind spots

"I like all this," Bernard said, "and I think it will work. It's a much better and more human way to handle the process. But I have a concern or a question for you, Teresa. What happens if the person covers a lot of the right things about their performance, just as you've said, but misses

out on some important points? What should you do if this happens?"

"That's a very good question, Bernard," Teresa answered, "and an important one because people will undoubtedly sometimes miss out on things. We all have blind spots – things about ourselves that others see but that we don't see ourselves. So what do you all think?"

"I think you have to raise those points," Tony said. "We have to be honest and frank with people."

"But why do that if you have already got more than you had expected from the meeting?" Natalie differed.

"Surely it depends on how important the things are," Terry commented.

"Personally, I think I would leave them for another day," Heather said, "if I had heard a lot more than I expected. I would do that because I would be afraid that mentioning them might undo all the good work that was done and change the whole atmosphere."

"But sometimes there are things you simply can't pass up on," Tony said. "You would be cowardly or dishonest if you did."

"I think it all depends on how you say or handle them," Tom said. "You don't have to give the feedback as the absolute truth, as a judgment, but give it in a respectful way, as your opinion, just as feedback in fact."

"That makes all the difference, I think," Bernard said, "when my own boss talks to me, there's nothing ambiguous about it. His word is the final word and there's no talking to him. If I try to question anything he says to me, it only makes matters worse and he regards me as awkward, or defensive, or something. I think you're right, Tom, if you can be wise enough to give feedback as your opinion, which is all it ever is, then it makes for far better understanding and for a better relationship."

"I agree with that too," Terry added. "I try to use a similar approach when I'm talking to prospective clients and, by asking them questions, they become much more forthcoming and I learn a lot more. As a result, I'm better able to meet their needs. No, I think it makes great sense even if it will mean making some big changes in how we handle Performance Reviews, or whatever you now call them, Teresa."

"Well done everyone," Teresa said. "That's it. You're *all* right. No, I'm not being funny, I mean it. You're all right at the same time. How can that be? Huge differences but all right?"

Bernard laughed. "I bet it's Mike's elephant in the room again!"

Well spotted Bernard. We have to always watch for this, listen and try to find the greater overall truth. This is a really good example of it. But we need to practise elephantine thinking -talking and listening -, both here and everywhere.

Let me summarise what you've all said. In general, people will cover most of what you had in mind and a lot more, as I said, so the situation may not arise where they have missed much, or at least much that you know of. Do you all accept and agree on that?"

They all nodded and Teresa could see that they were convinced that much more would get raised and said through self-assessment than in the traditional way.

"But if they miss out on something you have in your own head and want to say to them, you should first of all decide how important is it. If it's not very important, then forget it and resist your tendency or habit of having to find fault with things always as a way to improve, which is very common for managers.

If it is important, then you have a choice: (a) Leave it for another time, as Heather said, in order not to undo all the good work that has been done and to recognise and affirm the person's openness, trust and honestly, or (b) Raise it now but do so as feedback, as your opinion, as Tom said, and try to make sense of it to the person. If you fail, leave it for then and come back to it later.

Are you all happy with that?"

They nodded in agreement.

> "Life is too short to waste any amount of time on wondering what other people think about you. In the first place, if they had better things going on in their lives, they wouldn't have the time to sit around and talk about you. What's important to me is not others' opinions of me, but what's important to me is my opinion of myself"
>
> C. JoyBell C.

"Good, "Teresa said, "and one way to avoid this happening in the first place is, as part of the process, is to ask people to ask some colleagues or friends of theirs to give them some feedback about how they're doing, not just in terms of performance but also in terms of relationships, and the effect they have on others. This will give them valuable additional information and help to ensure they don't miss anything in reviewing themselves."

"Ah, you mean 360 feedback?", Heather asked?

"No, I don't Heather. It's fundamentally different from the false, unfair, and anonymous 360 degree format. With 360 degree feedback, people often don't know who said what about them, why they said it and what real weight the things said had on their review. Do you understand the difference? With the PPDS the person is hearing feedback from a friend who can make sense out of the different opinions they've heard and merge them with their own. They don't have to ask for this feedback but you can encourage them to do so and most will, once they see it's safe. Just like we're asking for feedback because we want to be better managers, so our staff too should want to do the same.

The enormous difference to be made

The other very important part of the PPDS is the group or team review."

"What?" Sally asked, "is the PPDS not about individual reviews?"

"Yes, it is but nobody is only or purely an individual. Everyone is part of a team, contributes to it and is affected by it. It is the team that ultimately matters, so it's important to review how you're doing as a team or unit against your goals and objectives – what you're doing well and what not so well. Now of course in doing this in the team, each individual team member will be automatically reviewing themselves. And doing this will help and educate each person around their own individual review when it comes to it. We don't want people rating themselves as brilliant in a team that's not doing well, do we?

Are you all in agreement with that and convinced about how valuable, easy and comfortable the PPDS system is?"

They all nodded.

"But will you just do them now in future without me running after you?"

They all said they would but Teresa persisted "Why? Why will you do them now when you didn't do them … willingly I mean, in the past?"

> "It is an immutable law in business that words are words, explanations are explanations, promises are promises – but only performance is reality"
>
> **Harold S. Geneen**

"Well," Tom replied, because it's a much easier, comfortable and more effective system than the old traditional and judgmental way."

"Yes, and I think it will make a huge difference to the performance of individuals and so to the overall team," Bernard said. Imagine that if by giving people this kind of quality attention and coaching we got even a moderate 10 per cent improvement in people's performance, sure it would make an enormous difference to the area, to the organisation and to the happiness and welfare of the people themselves."

"I think we could get a 100 per cent improvement in some people who are not doing themselves justice at all", Tom added.

"And why do you think this little process or system brings about such an improvement, Tom?" Teresa continued to probe.

"Well, I think that if we only got people really clear about their goals, it would make an enormous difference. Many people, and some of them are my own people, are just drifting, and if I could get them fired up about their goals, our own goals as a company, our goals in the Operations Department, along with their own personal and professional goals, it would make a huge difference. I can definitely think of two or three people off the top of my head where this would bring about a significant improvement in performance."

"Yes, Sally added, "and just the very act of giving people attention will help enormously, I believe. In the Finance Department we're always running around and so busy that we never – and I mean never – take the time to just sit down with someone for an hour and focus on their issues. There is always an "end of month" and never a good month to give people time and attention. I think my own people will really welcome being given attention, being made to feel important and valued. I value them, but I need to not only *say* it but to actually show it by *giving them time*. And good time. Time when I'm listening to *them*, there for *them*."

"For me," Terry added, "getting feedback can make a big difference. I have some people in the Sales Department who think they're great and perfect. Some of them are very confident, and that's good, but they never get feedback and so don't address some areas where they could improve and be even better. I really like the approach to feedback that you explained, Teresa, where they ask for it and get it from their colleague and friends. I'm definitely going to encourage them to do that, and I believe it will bring about a significant improvement in our performance."

"Is there not a danger," Tom asked, "that we, or at least some people might limit feedback to people by way of these performance review sessions or moments? I remember a manager who kept a little notebook in which he kept notes of incidents and problems with people. "She'll be hearing about this again, I promise you." he would often say. I even heard of a company that had a very sophisticated computer programme for managers to capture every significant action or mistake of their people which would then churn out a report. They called it an objective feedback system. Can you imagine?"

I'm glad you raised that, Tom, Teresa replied. "That would be disastrous. I hope nobody thinks this is what the PPDS is about! It's about development. It's about the future. And it's about the overall, higher level performance of the person in their role rather than on detailed and specific points. These have to be addressed when they happen, when they're warm, live, real. This is about those two P's I mentioned and about helping people enjoy realising much more of their full and real potential. Isn't that a wonderful role for us to have and play as managers, as human beings? Are we all clear and in agreement on that?"

They all said they were.

"I like the whole idea of the group review, Tony said, "because it's a great way to make people aware that they are not just individuals, but are part of a group and depend on each other. I really believe that this is the case with everything, but it's easy to slip into individualism and thinking of ourselves. By understanding the needs of others and our overall needs, it will help people to appreciate that they depend on others and others depend on and look to them. I know this will make a big difference in the Logistics department."

"I agree with you, Tony," Frank said, "and I think this will also give people the feeling that they're being supported and will be supported. I liked what you said, Teresa, that the PPDS is also about us getting feedback from our people about how we might be failing to adequately support them or how we might be getting in their way sometimes.

I see it as a really natural and easy way to ask people for feedback without having to set up a special meeting. I'll definitely include that in all my reviews and I think that this alone will make a big difference."

"Well said," Mike added, applauding

"I like all you've been saying and I'm in no doubt that we'll receive enormous gains from this new process. And well done to you, Teresa. Great thinking and great work."

"I wonder if we'll need some more help with it," Heather said.

> "As you navigate through the rest of your life, be open to collaboration. Other people and other people's ideas are often better than your own. Find a group of people who challenge and inspire you, spend a lot of time with them, and it will change your life"
>
> **Amy Poehler**

"Yes, you will," Teresa said, "some simple forms, some training and some refreshing on coaching and I'll look after that bit once I'm happy I won't have to do any more chasing. After all, I hope it's clear you will be doing it for yourselves and your people and not for me."

"You're right" Tony said. "It's amazing what you can learn in an hour and how much you can change your mind!" They all laughed.

"I don't disagree with any of this," Tony came in again, "and I don't want to spoil the party. But I do want to keep you all honest! This all sounds very good and I believe it is. But aren't we forgetting something? I think it will be great if all this works and I think it will in the vast majority of cases. But, as always, there are exceptions. Now, don't look at me as if I had two heads. You all know what I'm talking about.

You know that we have people whose performance is just not good enough and, for all kinds of understandable reasons, we're not facing up to them. When we do, it becomes a major issue involving unions or legal people and it takes over and dominates everything. But, as a result, we're very loathe to challenge people and, most times, we turn a blind eye and leave well enough alone. Isn't that accurate and fair?"

"Yes, Tom, it is," Teresa answered, "and you're right that we need to deal with that issue. And we will. And you're right that we need a good way to deal with it and one that will not get us into all those legal fights that you accurately referred to. But I would like to separate that topic and discussion from this one. I assure you I'm not sidestepping or avoiding it. Can we do that, Tony?"

"Yes, I'm fine with that once we promise to come back to it."

"I agree with you Tony," Heather said, "and I definitely need a good way to deal with those situations too."

"And so do I" several others chorused.

"Okay, okay, I hear you and I promise we'll come back to it and I know that Mike is very keen that we do too. Is that okay with everybody?"

It was.

"Now, I know you're all happy with this and I can feel it from you. But we have to think of those who will carry out these reviews with their people. They'll need to be convinced too. Now we'll give them all the necessary forms and the training or familiarisation to be able to handle them well. But you will need to convince them too of its value as it will not sit comfortably with some of them. Do you know what I mean?"

They all said they did.

"Earlier Mike mentioned the value of this system and what we'll gain from it. I drew up a list of those gains for you to use to convince your people of the advantages – the real and concrete advantages of the PPDS.

Very simply, people will get great benefits and results from the People and Performance Development System because all of the following gets clarified, identified and highlighted.

G   **Goals** and expectations

A   **Attention** and interest

I   **Information,** inputs and feedback

N   **Needs** – organisational and managerial

S   **Support** and removal of blocks

G

People will improve because they are being invited, encouraged and challenged to set high goals and expectations for themselves.

One of the reasons why people do not realise their true potential and perform really well is that their expectations from themselves are too low – for a variety of reasons. The PPDS gets people upping their expectations, their goals, what they believe they can achieve and what they want to achieve.

People are encouraged to set higher standards for themselves and simply to expect more from themselves. This is bound to make a difference in most cases.

A

People need attention; we all do, as Sally said earlier. It is the most basic human need and it does not disappear when we become workers or professionals.

The People and Performance Development System ensures people receive attention and feel attended to, feel looked after, feel someone has an interest in them and that they are noticed, and that they matter.

This makes a huge difference at the critical subconscious and emotional level in people. Get this right and we are already half-way there to a big improvement in how people feel and how, as a result, they perform.

I

People will improve because they are better informed and get information and feedback on how they are currently doing.

People need feedback. We all do. We are not aware of many things around ourselves and so we need to see, hear and understand how others see us.

We as managers also need information and feedback ... about ourselves and about the organisation, and we need to provide the facility for our people to be able to give that input without having to ask for it.

Granted much of the feedback comes from themselves, but in time they will welcome feedback from you as their manager and from others. It is hard to believe that this will not make a big difference.

N

People will improve their performance if they truly understand what their organisation Needs from them and what the needs of the organisation are.

People in organisations do not operate in a vacuum, they are part of a larger whole and need to understand the needs of that greater whole and how they fit into it and what is required or needed from them. Feeling part of a team, of a larger group, or something greater than just my own little world is tremendously enlightening and inspiring. It can bring out the very best in people and get them out of themselves and their own insular interests.

And in all of this, you, as the manager and person responsible for many others as well as for the organisation, will also have needs that should be known and shared. And this is your big opportunity to share your needs in terms of realising the goal to which all subscribe. It is a great opportunity to remind people of our overall goal and to demonstrate your belief in it.

S

Finally, people need support.

Our staff will feel blocked in various ways, and we need to find out what may be blocking them. This may be something about us as their managers, about the organisation or about the individuals themselves. Uncovering these blocks and removing them will make a huge difference to how people perform, do you not think? Imagine if someone helped you in this way.

This might be helpful for you with your people to energise and support them in handling this in a really good way.

Questions for reflection and action

1. What is your own experience of appraisals or Performance Reviews? Can you understand the lack of enthusiasm of the team around Teresa's meeting?
2. With which of the concerns around appraisals or Performance Reviews would you most identify?
3. Have you had similar experiences in relation to self-assessment as Teresa had?
4. Would you see a system like the PPDS being:
   • Useful.
   • Very Important.
   • Essential for the welfare of your people and the organisation?
5. How competent, confident and comfortable are you handling Performance Reviews and people development in this way?
6. Why is self-assessment not only easier but more productive?

7. What about the things the person might miss or not raise? What would you do about these?

8. And, around rewards, increases, bonuses etc? Why is it wise to separate them from the review process?

9. What would you do if you get into an argument about some performance in the past?

10. Why are group Performance Reviews so important?

Chapter 21
You Can't Just Let Sleeping Dogs Lie

Handling unsatisfactory performance situations – and people

Teresa had two visitors after the session on Performance Reviews. She was not surprised. She had picked up some signs of unease or uncertainty in some people. And she was not too surprised that Natalie was one of them. She knew there were some issues in the Logistics Department and she and Natalie had touched on them a few times.

She also knew that confronting issues was not Natalie's favourite pastime. Natalie was easy to work with and rarely if ever got into conflict. She had good relationships with everybody or tried to have them. Some thought that she was too soft, but she believed that good relationships were crucial to getting things done. She also knew that Natalie was having some problems with one of her leaders, called Joe.

"Believe me, Teresa, I handled the meeting with Joe very much along the lines that you recommended and as we discussed. I definitely left it up to him to come forward and come clean about his perfor-mance – the green box process we talked about in Performance Reviews remember? But nothing happened. He wasn't forthcoming at all, no matter how hard I tried.

I applied the formula you gave us, namely to check which category he was in. What I mean is, is it a case that he simply didn't or doesn't know

> "I have said countless times high performance people are never satisfied with what they do or how they do it! Hence, I am always endeavouring to improve"
>
> **Dan Pena**

that there's an issue with his performance, or that he knows but doesn't want to do anything about it or to improve? Or, even more seriously, that he does know, does want, but simply isn't able to do the job, isn't up for it?"

"So you believe that he just doesn't *know* that his performance is unsatisfactory. Is that it?"

"Yes, exactly. He's oblivious to how unsatisfactory his performance is and, by coaching him I was never going to get there or will never get there."

"Okay, I understand, but before we get into that, can I remind you that sometimes people *say* that they don't know, for example, that their performance is unsatisfactory but, in reality they know very well but simply don't want to do anything differently. And, some may say that they don't want to change or improve, for whatever reason when, in actual fact, they are not able. But we'll come to that later on. So let me ask you, then, or coach you, what do you think you will do now or want to do?"

"I think I will simply have to tell him, upfront, that his performance isn't satisfactory. I have no choice."

"Alright, and are you happy with doing that?"

"I am, but I'm just afraid that that could damage relationships and not only with Joe but with others and that would set us back in terms of the kind of culture and company we're trying to be. Do you know what I mean?"

"I do, Natalie, but do you remember what we said about this kind of situation and why it's important to deal with it? But you still feel it might damage relationships because you fear that you might seem hard on Joe and not nice or fair to him? Is that it?"

"Yes, and I know what you're going to say and you're right. By doing what I'm doing, being honest with him around his unsatisfactory performance, I'm actually doing what is right and good for him as well as for the company. Is that what you're getting at?"

Two pillars attitude and process

Yes, it is. Exactly. You remember our two pillars – the pillar of the welfare of the business and the pillar of the welfare of the person – Joe's in this case.

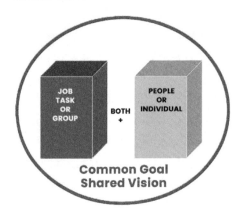

"When we go for what the overall good is – our red circle – we are actually being faithful to *both* at the same time. To be unfaithful to either one would damage the other. So in addressing this with Joe, you're really being caring around *him* and a very good friend to *him*, doing what's best for *him* and *his* welfare. Is that clear?"

"Yes, perfectly clear. So I'll meet Joe and tell him that his performance simply isn't satisfactory so that he, at least, knows that."

"Very good, and what do you think might happen when you do that? How do you think he'll respond?"

"I think he'll resent it, resist it, and argue that his performance is satisfactory. His word against mine. I have no idea where that discussion or argument will end up," Natalie laughed nervously.

"I think you're right, Natalie, and I can imagine an endless discussion about whether his performance *is* satisfactory or not. No amount of discussion, tribunal, enquiry, or court of justice, will ever absolutely establish whether his performance was or was not satisfactory.

> "Discussion is an exchange of knowledge; an argument an exchange of ignorance"
>
> **Robert Quillen**

But what's irrefutable is that *you're* not satisfied with it. It's your considered opinion that his performance is unsatisfactory and if you discuss this with him in that way, there's no need for endless argument and discussion. You, having considered the situation, have reached what you think is a good and fair conclusion that his performance is unacceptable. Of course, he can try to change your mind and we'll come to that, but for now, it's your honest and fair perception, as his manager, that we're talking about.

So, giving it as your considered and fair opinion or assessment, is different from saying that that's how it is in reality. It is still only a perception, an opinion, but you're entitled and, indeed you're obliged, to form such opinions so that you can take whatever action is required. Just like Frank is entitled and expected to form opinions about his individual players in the interests of the team and so in the interests of the individual. Are you clear on that and why it's important and why it will work?"

"Yes, I am, and I find your advice very useful. That's exactly how it is and I have no problem looking him in the eye and telling him that is my honest and fair assessment of his performance and that, in my opinion as his manager, I'm not satisfied with it. Isn't that it?"

"Yes, that's exactly it, and it may sound subtle or even theoretical, but it's very different when you give your opinion as *your opinion* rather than as reality. When you do that – talk as if it's simply the reality – you're imposing your view of reality on another person. This is unfair and is not even possible, because others will have their view of reality based on how they perceive it, and that is reality for them. So, when we impose our view on others as being the *reality*, we are doing violence to them. So this is a much more respectful and more accurate way of describing what's going on. Is that clear?

"Yes, I see the big difference and I think very often as managers, we do just that and people go along with it, even if they don't believe it at all and that can make them angry and feeling bullied. Yes, I think that's very good."

"Great, Natalie, so what do you think will happen when you discuss your opinion of his performance in this way with him?"

"Oh, I think he'll still deny it or refuse to accept it, whether he does this genuinely or disingenuously."

"Very good. And, if he does this, what will you do?"

"Well, I have some very clear examples, strong evidence where his performance has been far from satisfactory. I can give him those examples."

"Do you think that will work?"

"I don't see why not! I'll just give him the facts. He can't argue with that. Can he?"

From past to future

"I think he can and he might. But remember what we said – we think facts are facts, realities are realities. But, they're not. As the word says, facts are things that are made – literally. The Latin word is "facta"… means things made. So whatever you believe is a fact is still only your version of something that took place. It may be a very good and accurate version and it may be an acceptable version. But this isn't always so.

People have different versions of all kinds of things and believe they are "facts" – the way things are! So, when you select examples of Joe's unsatisfactory performance, there may be some that are absolute, in the sense that they can be measured; like for example if he said he would produce 100 and he only produced 80, just as an example. When things are measurable like that there isn't much of a problem, although there can be one. But most times things are not nearly so measurable. Is this how it is with him?"

"Yes, unfortunately it's very much like that. His unsatisfactory performance is not something that can be clearly and easily measured. It's more about his lack of responsibility, his lack of initiative, his judgement and decisions sometimes. It's often more about what he doesn't do more than what he actually does. And, you're right,

I could give him examples of this but I think he could argue the toss on many of them and have lots of explanations and excuses. But what do I do? I'm very clear about his performance being unsatisfactory. I can't live with it and you know that others can't live with it either. But what do you do?"

"It seems that you're clear about how you want him to be and how he should be. Isn't that so?"

"Yes, it is."

"So, suppose you made it clear to him that you are unhappy with his performance and you explain why this is so, why it's so important to you, to others, in general etcetera, etcetera, and that you want his performance to change and improve? And you handle it like we talked earlier, this being your considered opinion and your responsibility to form and act on such opinions. How would that be for a start?"

> "Our scientific age demands that we provide definitions, measurements, and statistics in order to be taken seriously. Yet most of the important things in life cannot be precisely defined or measured. Can we define or measure love, beauty, friendship, or decency, for example?"
>
> **Dennis Prager**

"I think I'm fine with all that. I think there may be resistance as we said, but I can deal with that along the lines we spoke of. But what do I do if we're still not in agreement about his unsatisfactory performance?"

"Yes, that's the challenge. And, as we've been saying, rather than giving examples from the past of where you saw this, which you could do but which might lead to endless arguments and excuses as you said, suppose you spoke about the future instead."

"What do you mean?"

"Well, seeing that we may not be able to get agreement about the past, which we can't change anyway, maybe we can agree about the future which we *can* change. Let's take just one of those areas that you mentioned, like initiative. Now, at present you're not agreeing that his performance here is unsatisfactory. So suppose, that instead of convincing that it has not been and is not good enough or attempting to do that, you identified what taking initiative would mean *in the future*. In other words, you could ask him what would good performance in terms of taking initiative would mean or look like. What would be happening if a person, like Joe, was taking the initiative? If you were able to agree on this then you would at least have a clear understanding of what taking an initiative would mean."

"So, you mean that I would ask him that question – what taking initiative in his role would involve and mean?"

"Yes, exactly, and by hearing it from him you would be clear that he understands exactly what it means. And, if he doesn't include everything in his list, you could suggest or add in some other important descriptions of what taking initiative means and check that they make sense to him. Is that okay?"

"Yes, that makes great sense. That way we would both be clear and know what this means in his case. And I could also ask him why this is so important, which would deal with the second area of 'wanting'. Yes, I think that would work very well."

"Great. That's what I mean by moving from past to future.

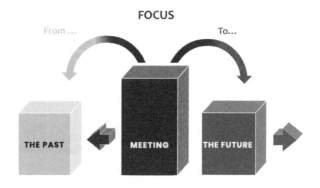

We don't need to argue or fall out about the past because we can agree about the future. And we can't change the past but we can change the future. This gives him an out too. And, it's the future we are interested in. And you could do the same for the other areas where you are dissatisfied with his performance. Is that feasible?"

"Yes, that's great. I can't see why the other way wouldn't work. I really like it."

"I'm delighted to hear that, Natalie, and may I ask when you might do this or how long might it take before you would know if there was a change or improvement or not?"

"Oh I want to have this meeting with him very soon, because it's been dragging on for a long time, as you know. And, I think there will be very concrete things that we'll come up with whereby I'll know in a very short timeframe if there has been a change or improvement or not."

"That's great. At least in this process we'll deal with the "know" element. There will be no doubt that at least he will know what is expected from him and why. It may not solve everything but it will certainly deal with one factor and it may be enough. As you said, it may also deal with or begin to deal with the second one – "want" – as well, but we'll see. You might come back to me and let me know how you get on. Is that okay?"

"Yes, it is and I'll come back to you. Thank you very much Teresa. That was great and I can think of some other situations both at work and at home where I could move from past to future. But I'll be back to you," she laughed.

But if NOTHING works?

And she was back, inside three weeks. She told Teresa about the meeting and how she had handled it and that, in fact, it all went very well.

"Yes, there was some resistance at the outset, but he accepted that I had

> "Whatever has happened to you in your past has no power over this present moment, because life is now"
>
> **Oprah Winfrey**

a problem and I successfully managed to avoid examples and defensiveness by moving to the future, as you suggested. That was fine too and he did quite a good job in identifying what taking more initiative, being more responsible, giving better leadership etcetera would mean.

I added a few more points in and he was fine with them too. It really was quite a good meeting but the problem is that I have seen little or no change or improvement in him. So now I have to take it to the next step. This hasn't worked, so I imagine it's time for discipline and we have a procedure that I can follow."

"Sorry to hear it didn't work but we're not finished yet, nor is it over, nor have you failed … not yet anyway! The question of discipline that you raise is important. Perhaps you think that maybe we could have gone this way from the beginning and saved a lot of time and effort?"

"I'm afraid that's exactly what I was thinking. It seems we'll have to go there now anyway, and we could have saved a lot of time, as you say."

"Maybe we would have, even though that's not my experience. But, even if we did, getting somebody to change their behaviour by force, using a threat of discipline or dismissal for me is not a good way to reach agreement or to get people to change. Very often it becomes an ongoing game of cat and mouse, with no winners and often a lot of losers. But even leaving that aside, and looking at it purely from the narrow view of time and effort, do you think it's effective purely from this point of view of time and effort?"

"I don't see why not. I would just get my facts together, explain the procedure to Joe or any other person involved, make clear again what I want and why, and that's it."

"But is it? That works very often even if the results aren't all that great as I just mentioned, but what happens when it doesn't work as well as that? Can you remember any instances from here or your past life where it didn't work out so well and what happened?"

"Yes, I can, very well. It went to a higher level and a higher level still and outside. And, you're right, it took an enormous amount of time and attention with everybody at every level involved."

"Exactly, that has been my experience too and, even after all that, it becomes a bit of a toss of the coin as to who wins. Legal people take over and we lose all control."

"I see, so what should I do, then?"

"It may well be that we'll end up with some kind of disciplinary situation here with Joe, but I hope we won't, and I believe we won't. I think you're trying to do the right thing here and to do what makes sense and is fair, and I still believe that will work. And even if it doesn't, you will have all the work done to go the legal disciplinary route and you'll be able to make great sense to anybody subsequently involved. But, as I say, let's hope that doesn't happen."

"Okay, I understand, so what should I do now?"

"Have another meeting with him and it's one that I like to call the "Last Resort Meeting". That is a very brief meeting, because you will not go over all the ground you have been through already. You'll simply repeat that you're unable to accept and unwilling to go along with this continued level of performance from Joe and that you require a change and big improvement as we have discussed. If he wants to go back over the same ground again you refuse to go there, because you've been over the case many times.

You make it clear that the only purpose of the meeting is to get a commitment from him that his performance will improve and that you need to see and be happy with this in the immediate or short-term."

"Okay, and what if he refuses, or resists, or becomes awkward?"

"You are right, he will. Or he may try all kinds of things. In that meeting you will be making it very clear to him about what you want, why you want it and when. When you do this, he'll feel confronted and cornered and will try all those things that you mentioned. He may again try to be defensive, to give excuses, to distract, to blame, to become personal with you, to become upset or evasive. Lots of things could happen."

> "If you tell the truth, you don't have to remember anything"
>
> **Mark Twain**

"Yes, I can see Joe doing a lot of such things and he is very clever and does them well, and you know I'm not very comfortable dealing with conflict and things like that."

"I know you're not comfortable dealing with these kinds of things and you won't have to. You ignore them and you bring him back to the sole purpose of the meeting, which is about your responsibility to get a commitment from him about what he is going to do to satisfy you about the level of performance you require from him. You remind him of what this means and why it's important, and you request a clear commitment from him to deliver on this. You stick with this position, don't move from it and insist on it. Is that clear?

"Yes, okay. I just hope it works."

"Well, if you're convinced that what you're after is right and good and fair and that you are being reasonable and respectful and caring around him, there's no reason why it won't work. It makes great sense to me, and I believe it will to him as well."

"Yes, that's fine. But suppose – and I don't want to be negative – that he agrees to change and improve, but then subsequently, fails to do so? What then? Time for discipline?

No, not yet. We still have one further chance which I call the "Last Last Resort" meeting. Believe me, the process we've been talking about does work and will work in 90 per cent of cases. There is or may still be 5 per cent or 10 per cent where it doesn't work and here we have to try once more to make the person aware of what's happening, why it is unacceptable, and what the consequences are of their continuing to work in that way. In this meeting, again, you don't go over any old ground except to repeat your unwillingness and inability to accept or live with this level of performance and then you make the person aware of the consequences for them if they fail to do so.

"You mean, discipline, or threaten them with discipline, termination of employment etcetera?"

"Yes, you make clear that these things may happen but not as a threat, not as something that *you* or we will do, but as a natural consequence of his unwillingness or inability to do what was required from him in his position. Things like 'Put your finger in a chainsaw and you'll lose it, continue to perform as you're doing and you'll lose your job. But it's you who will lose it. It's in your hands.'"

"I understand. I can do it, even though it's not a very nice meeting."

"No, it's not, but it can still be a very good meeting and it's important that you continue to think of his welfare and to care for him as well. You really want a change for everybody's sake, his included. It may fail because either he really doesn't want to for some reason, or he's not able to play the role. But let's not go there.

Let's give the process and the second meeting your very best shot. I think it will work."

"Maybe it will and I hope it will and I'll give it my best shot. I think Joe can do it. I really do."

"In all of this you have to be *you – Natalie*. You are not some functionary doing a job and a dirty one at that. But you are the real, soft, caring Natalie

> "I've learned that people will forget what you said, people will forget what you did, but people will never forget how you made them feel"
>
> **Maya Angelou**

with a genuine commitment to the company for everyone's welfare and benefit and a real and genuine commitment to Joe. You can do both and not sacrifice either one of them."

Believing in people

And Teresa was right. Just two weeks later Natalie told Teresa that there were definite signs of a change in Joe's attitude and behaviour. The message had got through. She told Teresa that she planned to continue to meet him on a regular basis to ensure it wasn't just a once-off wonder.

"That's great, Natalie, well done and I'm glad you don't have to use the "Last Last Resort" Meeting," Teresa laughed. "But, tell me, what do you think made the greatest difference? What did you do that brought about this big change?"

"I have to say that I'm surprised. When we began talking about this issue, and even during it, I had my doubts. I could very easily have gone down that disciplinary route and I can now see very clearly where that would have led. You know, I think the whole process worked but what eventually made the difference, I think, was my belief in him and his belief that I really cared for him. I think the relationship previously was very much parent to child and that was part of the problem."

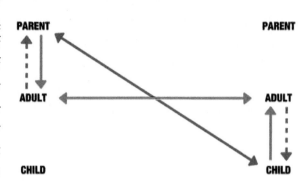

"I'm surprised to hear that you saw yourself behaving like a parent, Natalie."

"Yes, but not as a tough, punishing, hard parent but as a very soft overly-protective one. I can be like that. And I think that while he might have enjoyed and benefited from this in some way, he also resented it deep down. I think that's what was happening. It's very common, as you well know.

People project their early parent relationships onto future relationships with all the baggage it brings with it. You can see it everywhere, and managers pay the price for slipping into the Parent role. It all happens and does enormous damage unconsciously."

"Yes, I see that very clearly, which is why what we're doing here is so important at every level. Quite apart from employees, we all have to assume responsibility for our world and ourselves as adults – honest, brave, responsible adults. It's so much easier to play the role of Child and so difficult to get people to give up on it. So, what else do you think worked with Joe?"

"I think the process itself was built completely on an Adult – Adult relationship and eventually it worked. I think also that he realised that

I wasn't only focused on the welfare of the company or the business, on that pillar, but on the overall welfare of everybody, which included his own.

But, as I said, I want to meet him frequently to reaffirm and endorse that. Like all of those things, I'm sure he's addicted to his part of the Parent – Child dynamic between us. I'm determined to not let him slip back into that and I know it'll call for constant, ongoing work."

> "If you judge people, you have no time to love them"
>
> **Mother Teresa**

"That sounds just great, Natalie, well done."

"Thanks, and it calls for constant work on my part as well to behave as an adult and treat Joe as one. It's so easy to cop out from life and one's responsibility, so I hope I live up to my side of the bargain and I really appreciate your help on this, Teresa."

"That's okay, Natalie, and I do hope we can all continue to behave in this way for the welfare and betterment of everybody."

"I will really try as I see how well it works. But, you know, Teresa, I think all the team should be familiar with this process. Shouldn't we share all this in the full team meeting?"

"I agree, and you remember it came up very recently in a previous meetings. Let's do that. I hope you'll support me. I'll need it!"

"Don't worry, you have a converted disciple!"

Is it worth the trouble it will cause?

It was Tony who raised the topic of dealing with unsatisfactory performance again in a senior team meeting some weeks later.

"I know we've talked about this business of unsatisfactory performance in general but now we've a problem that we need to deal with" he told the group. "This has been going on for some time because we've lived with it and let it just continue. I think it's a fact that we try to avoid difficult situations and so we don't confront or challenge people nearly enough, or only do so in extreme cases. Is that fair?"

Most nodded in agreement with the exception of Terry. "I don't know. I think if you manage people well on a continuous basis, there won't be a need to have to challenge or confront them, surely?"

"Maybe so, but I think I manage people well but that doesn't mean there won't be problems. Remember that incident we had some months ago where we had considerable conflict over a disciplinary situation? It went on and on and on, and in the end we reached some form of compromise? Not only because of that, but partly so, I know that some of my managers are not challenging people on their behaviour or performance out of a fear of getting into that troublesome situation again. I think this is even more so now, because they want to support and promote this new culture we've been developing. I would like to do something about this situation, and at the same time avoid losing what we're trying to create around a better culture and workplace relations. We could be giving mixed messages. I wonder what others around the table think?"

Teresa exchanged looks with Natalie and both decided they would say nothing about Natalie's recent experience ... for then at least.

"I understand what Tony is saying, "Frank said. "I can see that our culture and relationships have improved enormously, and we're performing much better as well. So I can understand why people

wouldn't want to rock the boat. I often come across this, coming up to an important game if some trouble arises with some player. It can feel dangerous to bring it up in case it leads to more trouble. After all, it's only a minority and the vast majority of people are doing a good job and some doing an exceptional job. You get all three always, the Satisfactory, the Outstanding and, unfortunately, the Unsatisfactory"

"That's alright," Sally said, "but I wonder if that good performance will continue, because if people see that someone is getting away with murder, others will see it as unfair and become disheartened. What I mean is that these people, even if they're only a minority, can drag the rest down.

I saw two people in my department do that and, knowingly or unknowingly lower overall standards. We have to uphold standards because otherwise we could lose everything and staff could feel they can do what they like".

"Yes," Terry added, "and I don't think our really good performers are going to hang around if they see that they're working for an organisation that tolerates low standards. I know I wouldn't. And I can think of some members of my team who won't either. But it's not just about unsatisfactory performance, is it?

Don't we want to get to new levels of performance overall? To do that we need to be able to challenge people in a good way and help them to be even better. We need to be good at holding good mature and honest conversations all the time. Do you know what I mean?"

"I agree with all that," Tom said, "but how can we get people to face up to and confront these situations and these individuals without causing all the trouble that we had earlier this year that Teresa mentioned, and without undoing the really good work we've done over the past few months to get people on board?

"Folks are usually about as happy as they make their minds up to be"

Abraham Lincoln

I mean, since we began treating people with respect and in a more human way, people have changed and improved their performance and now we could lose all this if we 'come the heavy' on them! And, suppose it gets out of control! That Union kind of thing you mentioned Teresa and that I have heard talk of."

"Well said, Tom. So how could we continue to treat people well and with respect as human beings," Mike asked, "and, at the same time, challenge some on their performance if they've not delivering to the required standards? How could we do that?"

"I'm sorry," Teresa said, "but I don't see a problem! In fact, the way I see it is that, if we don't confront and challenge individuals on their performance, then we are not really respecting them. We owe it to them to be honest and to discuss things if we see their performance is unsatisfactory. If we don't, we're letting them down, I believe. I think we've talked about this before in a way."

"That's easy to say, Teresa," Tony said, "but people don't like or welcome us being honest with them when we challenge them and they feel that management is getting at them unfairly. And we appear to be going back on our promises to treat people differently, like we've been trying to do in the past few months."

Being truly fair to people and their welfare

"Yes, Tony," Teresa answered, "and what's wrong is that they don't see that they *are* the company. I think the mistake we've made in the past, and could make again, is to separate what's good for the people or the individual from what's good for the company and to see them as two distinct things, probably in conflict to some extent. So, what I see happening with your managers, Tom, is that they think or feel that if they challenge people for the welfare of the business, then they're not being good or faithful, or loyal to their people. Like they're letting them down or going against them.

"But, at times it's like that, Teresa," Tom interrupted. There are times when, quite simply, the good of the company and the business is more important and overrides what people want. That's just how it is!"

"Yes, Tom, I understand that, but it's not really like that. It's a bit like what we looked at before with two pillars. (Teresa drew two pillars on the flip-chart).

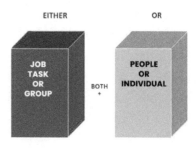

Two pillars – one pillar represents the business, or the work, or the project or task etc., and the second pillar represents the people, the human, the individual etc. Now, the mistake we make is that we think there is a dichotomy between these two, so that we either have to be faithful to one or the other.

If we respect people and the 'people pillar', then people think that means that we may have to sacrifice the business or the company at times.

If, like now, we decide that we need to look after the welfare of the company by insisting on high standards and high performance, then people believe this will mean we're not respecting people or treating them well. But I think this dichotomy is false! I believe that we need to be faithful to *both* of these pillars *all the time*.

And we do this by seeing that both pillars as part of something greater – all those things we said at the X meeting – what we want our company to do, and what we want our company to be, which we believe is good for everybody and for every aspect of people's lives as we said", (She drew a red circle around both of these pillars and wrote, 'Common Goal and Shared Vision' on the red circle.)

"This means that if we do not look after the pillar of the business or company then we're damaging our purpose and vision and so we're damaging the people pillar too. Equally, if we fail to respect our staff as people and treat them as rich human beings, then we're damaging the business, because we're not going to get the best out of the people working in the company. And, of course, we'll damage the overall vision, which is what we all want. Am I making sense?" she asked.

"Yes, you are," Bernard said, "and if you take the example of Mark's restaurant, you can see how this was so. If some of those waiters weren't doing their job or doing a good job, you could see that it would affect the whole restaurant and therefore affect each of the waiters and people who worked in the restaurant.

So, I agree with Teresa, and the way I see it also is that if Tom's people don't challenge these unsatisfactory performers, then they're doing them a disservice, not respecting them, and damaging their overall welfare."

"Touché," Mike said. "Wonderfully put. Do we all see this and agree with it?"

Tom spoke up, "Yes I do but I think we have to educate all our managers in this way of thinking and on how to handle these situations practically."

"What would that require?" Mike asked.

"I think we've to get across to them the philosophy of the two pillars that Teresa just talked about, and, if they comprehend that, it'll make a great difference to them in terms of their overall approach, as well as increasing their confidence and comfort in handling these meetings. But

"The most important kind of freedom is to be what you really are. You trade in your reality for a role. You trade in your sense for an act. You give up your ability to feel, and in exchange, put on a mask. There can't be any large-scale revolution until there's a personal revolution, on an individual level. It's got to happen inside first"

Jim Morrison

I think they need more. What I mean is some help on how they would handle a meeting like that."

"I understand," Teresa said, "and we can give them that support and give them training. Is it alright with you Natalie, if I talk about our recent conversation on this and about how well everything turned out and maybe you can share your own views and experience?

"Yes, I'm fine with that and delighted to be able to confirm how well some of these things work in practice."

Handling challenging meetings

Teresa then covered the different points she had discussed with Natalie over her case, things like the three approaches one can use in meetings like this.

A. **Coach the person** to an awareness around their performance and how it is not good enough. In other words, ask them how they think they are doing against the standards and the goal and get them to an awareness that what and how they are doing is not good enough.

B. Go in to the meeting simply to **find out what's going on** in the person's world, and, having done this, subsequently decide what to do in the light of that knowledge. Sometimes we simply need to find out what is going on rather than just jumping in. And, sometimes, we can be wrong.

C. Directly **tell the person** that you believe that their performance is not good enough and that you, as their manager or leader, are not happy with it.

"Yes, I think that's important," Heather interrupted, "I had a case like that second one you mentioned a while back with a customer relations person who had been quite curt and abrasive and downright unhelpful with some customers. I jumped on her, only to discover that she was waiting for the result of some medical tests on a growth that was discovered in a breast and she had been keeping it all to herself. I felt awful, and it would have been so much better, had I handled it that way, Teresa."

"The third one kind of deals with my earlier concern," Tony came in, "about what if they know but don't want to admit their performance is unsatisfactory. But I find that if you're holding regular review meetings with people, both individually and as a group, people will be aware their performance is unsatisfactory and will have no choice but to admit it."

"Maybe they will" Tom said, "but I think people will find this very useful. Some are not even aware that their performance is poor, while others are very aware of it but have no interest in doing anything about it."

"You're absolutely right, Tom" Teresa said, "remember the importance of identifying where anybody with any issue is? Remember what we said about this Natalie?"

"Yes, I do. In relation to the person I was dealing with, Teresa asked me what category the person was in, meaning one of the following three situations.

1. The person **knew** or **didn't know** that they had or was a problem, as Tom said.
2. The person knew but, for whatever reason, **didn't want** to do anything about it, as you said, Tony.
3. The person knew, wanted, but was **not able** to do anything about it or to perform to the required standard."

"And which was it in your case may I ask?", Heather enquired.

"It was really a mix of 1 and 2. He at least *claimed* not to know but he might have been using that to cover up for not wanting to do anything. This will often happen, I believe."

"Yes," Terry said, "I find that, more commonly and more importantly, people in category three – people who are simply not able to do something or do it well enough – may pretend to be in category one or two, because they don't want to admit that they are not able, that they are not up to it. I think I've had people in all three of these categories. Yes, I find that analysis very helpful."

"I agree. I think that's really enlightening," Tony said. "I can think of people in all three of these categories too. I have someone at present who may not be up to the job but is too afraid to admit it."

"And have you been talking to him about it?" Terry asked. "It's important to keep talking to people."

"I agree with all this," Tom said, deflecting Terry's question "and I think that training to be able to handle all of this would be very helpful. In particular, I think they could also do with some training in handling disagreements or conflict because this is bound to arise when you're trying to get somebody to accept that they haven't been performing well. Some people would argue that black is white and argue a hole through a bucket."

"I agree that people could do with training on this, Tom," Natalie said. "I had lots of conflict or potential conflict in the situation I was dealing with and it would have been really problematic if I hadn't had Teresa's help. She showed me how helping people to move from focusing on the past to focusing on the future is really important in dealing with such potentially endless arguments.

It can be very hard to get agreement on exactly what happened in the past, because people will be defensive and, because people see things in different ways, anyway. We were remarking, Frank, on how people can differ on things like football matches even though they've both seen the same game or reality.

> "You have brains in your head. You have feet in your shoes. You can steer yourself any direction you choose. You're on your own. And you know what you know. And YOU are the one who'll decide where to go..."
>
> **Dr Seuss**

They can have two completely different versions of a situation or of a referee! But I learned that we don't need to achieve agreement on exactly what happened *in the past* but rather move to what needs to happen *in the future*. If we can move away from conflict or arguments about what happened, before to agreeing what both sides accept *needs to happen*, then we can avoid a lot of trouble and potential conflict."

"Natalie, would you like to tell us how this worked in your experience?" Teresa said.

Natalie told them about how she and Joe had differed on whether what he was doing was satisfactory or not and about the problem with so-called 'facts' and how they had agreed on what good performance would mean in the future and how well this worked and how they had agreed on what that would be. "It just made all the difference", she told them.

When people don't change!

"I would welcome some support and training for my people too, especially on that issue," Sally said. "I believe that this will make a very big difference to how we handle and manage similar situations. I don't want to be negative, but as in a case which happened a few weeks ago, we also need to agree about how to deal with people who don't change, or who don't improve. This may be rare, but we still need to know how to handle people who refuse to change.

"I can answer that because that's exactly what happened in my case," Natalie came in again. She told them about the 'Last Resort Meeting' and how she had been so clear and determined not to become engaged in arguments or side shows or other evasive or distracting tactics by Joe. They were all impressed and convinced by her experience.

"That which does not kill us makes us stronger"

Friedrich Nietzsche

"I'm delighted to hear that, Natalie," Terry said, "and so assuring to hear that it worked in practice."

"Okay, "Tony said, "I can understand that, and it's good practice, but here I am, once again, being negative, but suppose that procedure doesn't work either, what then?"

Teresa saw Terry throw his eyes to heaven so she came in. "No, you're not being negative Tony. This will or may happen, so we need to be ready for it in case it does. What I propose, then, is that we have, what I call, a "Last Last Resort Meeting". Yes, I can understand why you all smile but, remember what I said earlier, that I'm hell bent on keeping people, not firing them or getting rid of them, and therefore I want to give everybody every possible chance."

"And what would happen at such a meeting?" Tony asked.

"It's very short and it's very simple," Teresa answered. "Your manager would again repeat what was said and offered to the individual at the last meeting - the "Last Resort Meeting", and then, give one final chance to reflect on their situation, pointing out that, if the person in question failed to do so adequately and appropriately, then there would be consequences. And, with full seriousness and full care for the person and attention to the person, leave it with them for a day."

"Well, that's really putting it up to them," Sally said, "it's no harm to threaten them with this."

"But this is not a threat," Natalie came in, "it's just pointing out what the consequence will be for them in not changing or making the necessary improvement, but it would not be a threat."

"Why not? You said to point out the consequences of them not changing! What's the difference between "consequences" and "threats?" Sally defended herself.

"What I think," Bernard commented, "is that a "threat" is saying what *I* will do to you if you do or don't do something. While a "consequence" is, what will happen to you if *you* do or don't do something. I can threaten somebody that if they don't do something I'll break their leg, but if I tell them that if they jump out from a third-floor window, they will break a leg.

That's different. So what I like about what you said Natalie, is that we're leaving the responsibility with the other person and then, if they don't respond appropriately, as night follows day, they'll end up out of work."

"That's exactly it," Teresa said.

"But I don't understand why they might change at that point if they haven't done so already!" Tony persisted.

> "It is never too late to be what you might have been"
>
> **George Eliot**

"I think that's a valid question, Tony," Teresa answered, "and sadly I think it's about people some-times needing a jolt to wake them up to reality. I see some disputes between individuals or between states that end up in some form of violence, and most times the eventual outcome is not far removed from what they could have, and indeed, should have, agreed or done in the first place. Like wars! It's sad but it's as if they didn't really see the seriousness of the situation until the violence woke them up. This is true in all of life and sometimes we need a jolt to shake us up or out of some malaise or hole we've been in."

"That makes sense to me, Teresa, but, tell me, do these meetings ever become emotional?" Frank asked. "I'm an emotional person myself and it can feel awkward when it seems a person is becoming emotional."

"Yes, they do," Teresa answered, "and it's important not to be surprised if this happens, if people get angry or cry. I take it you mean that kind of emotion, Frank? After all, everything we do is emotional, has some emotion in it, but I think I know what you mean."

"Yes, that's what I mean, and what happens if the emotion spills over? How do you handle such situations" Frank inquired. "They're not easy."

"No, but if you're not taken by surprise when it happens, it becomes much easier and there is nothing wrong with people losing the head a bit or losing some tears. Simply acknowledge their anger or tears and give them time to deal with it and they will. Just give them some space and say you are sorry they're upset and get things back on track as soon as possible. And actually, be and feel sorry for them."

"Well, I think we should organise this training for all managers," Tom said, "so that they can handle these situations just as we have talked about them here, but also how to handle emotions and anger and other problems that arise in the course of challenging and confronting people in this way."

"I agree," Teresa said, "and I have a programme in mind that will do just this."

"That was a great session," Mike said, "and well done Teresa, I love all of that and it's great to see that we now have a way of handling any kind of difficult situation in a good way, in line with our principles … in a human way. Well done."

Bernard looked worried. "I agree with all this, and with the necessity for and importance of training for our managers, but I think that more is needed. I think people, and I mean everybody, needs to have a similar understanding of how we're handling these situations. Remember our "two pillars" that Teresa spoke about. This message shone through to me in what Natalie told us and we have to find a way to get across to people that when we are confronting situations like this, it's not that we are taking the company side against them. We're all 'company', but you all know this. I just think that we need to find a way to get this understanding into people's minds and hearts."

"But isn't that what you have done or do in your X meetings," Mike asked.

"Yes, you're right," Bernard answered. "I suppose I was only thinking of some further and more general way to get this message out there."

"What about using your town hall or company-wide communication sessions, Mike?" Heather asked. "I know this is what you do anyway, to some extent, but it might help address Bernard's issue."

"I know what you mean, and I've been thinking about whether we should have a meeting or not before the forthcoming visit. I don't feel comfortable having one because there are so many uncertainties but, I suppose, there's never a good time. Let me think about it."

Questions for reflection and action

1. Why do many organisations avoid dealing with or addressing situations of unsatisfactory performance? Does your organisation do so or do you?
2. What is the main difficulty or challenge in dealing with these cases?
3. Why is it important to address issues of unsatisfactory performance? What happens when you don't? Is it not risky to culture and good relationships to challenge people?
4. What has the "Two Pillars" got to do with this? What is meant by a false dichotomy between what is good for people and good for the organisation?
5. What are three different ways you can handle these situations? Which would you prefer or use most often?
6. What does KWA (Know, Want, Able) mean? Why is it important? How would you handle people in each one of the categories – K. W. A.?
7. What happens or what do you do if you simply can't agree or get the other person to see that their performance is or has been unsatisfactory?
8. How does this approach differ from a traditional disciplinary approach?
9. How might or how do people often react when they are challenged?
10. Can you think of people who might react in this way and what would you do in those situations?
11. What is meant by 'The Last, Last Resort Meeting' How are 'consequences' different from 'threats'?
12. What would you do if people became emotional in a meeting like this?

Chapter 22
Cats and Dogs and Human Beings

How to handle difficult people – people "impossible to work with"

The following day, Teresa wasn't too surprised when Tony asked her if he could have a chat with her! She guessed what it was about, and she was right. For some time, she could see that Tony and Terry were not getting on and that Tony was very frustrated with Terry and had indirectly said so on many occasions. In fact, most people could see it. So she made it easy for him when they found time to meet.

"I can guess what this is about, Tony," she said, smiling.

"So *you*'ve noticed it too? You can see how difficult or impossible he has become?"

"Well, I can see that you two are not getting on, but I'd like to hear how *you* see the situation and the relationship."

"Oh come on, Teresa, you can see what's happening and how he is! Everyone does, you're not blind!", Tony said in frustration.

"Well, in order for me to help you, leave me out of it for now and tell me what you're finding so difficult."

"That's easy. I'm finding *him* difficult." Tony said in annoyance.

"Yes, I know that but what is it about him or that he is doing that you find difficult?"

"What everyone sees and finds difficult in him! You can see how awkward he is in our meetings. He agrees with nothing I say or with what anyone else says. He is most uncooperative. Whenever you go to him for help – and not just him, but his department people too – he gives excuses that he hasn't time for things I ask him to do, and yet I see him doing lots of other things. The things that he wants are the things that are good for *him*, his image and his self-importance.

When I challenged him one day on why he hadn't come back to me on an urgent request he was sitting on for days he got quite stroppy with me and more or less told me to mind my own business and my own department. And yet you see how he is at meetings and especially when we have visiting executives. He's brilliant. He puts on a wonderful show and I'm sure, they all think he's very special. Little do they know.

> "We are only as strong as we are united, as weak as we are divided"
>
> **J.K. Rowling**

He gets away with murder and it really annoys me. But he's so ambitious, so anxious to impress and get on. Do you really think he'll be loyal to and stick with this company? I mean, something has to be done. Mike or you or somebody has to do something about this. It's just not right. It's disruptive to the whole team. And we say we want to be a powerful and real team, don't we? Would you not agree something has to be done about him? "I'm talking to you because I can't really say these things in the full group."

Teresa listened to Tony for a long time and didn't contradict or challenge him on anything. A few times she said that she understood how he felt. Eventually, after a considerable silence, she said to him.

"If it's okay with you, Tony, in this meeting I would like to talk exclusively about *your* relationship with Terry, not Mike's not mine nor anybody else's."

"But *everybody* must see this. Everybody has a problem with him! It's not just me! Look at the mess he nearly got us into with our really important client and with Sharon! You saw how Tom felt. Everyone sees it, Teresa."

"I don't know that, and I don't know what kind of problem they have, if they have one, and I don't know if it's a similar one to yours. But today you and I are talking, and so I want us to talk about *your* relationship with Terry and nobody else's. That's important. Can we do that?"

"Okay." Tony agreed.

"Good. Well done. You see, I know you feel that there's nothing you can do about this situation because you've tried once or twice, but, difficult as it may feel, it is just your problem that I want to look at and bear with me on it please."

"Okay. I'll try."

Everything involves relationships

"What we're talking about here is not just a problem with Terry but a relationship problem, a relationship problem between you and Terry. It may be with others too but, as I said, it's only you and I in this room right now. So I'd like us to focus on it as a relationship problem which means that there are two parties, or two people in the relationship – you and Terry – and I'm not saying that he is blameless or that you are blameworthy. I think this is one of the most difficult challenges we meet in life. Let me show you this.

Teresa showed him a picture of a cat and a dog in which the cat had its back arched and was in a very aggressive and, probably, frightened state in front of the dog.

"You see Tony, no behaviour hap-  pens in a vacuum. In fact, nothing in the whole universe happens in a vacuum, outside of the independence of relationships with other planets or with other minute particles ... nothing! Relationships are at the heart of everything and, in a sense, more important than the objects themselves. The most minute or core particle of anything and everything is as it is, depending on the relationship it has with other particles. Here, in this example, this cat's behaviour has something to do with the presence of the dog, I'm sure you'll agree.

I'm not saying that the cat is a lovely creature and blameless, but only that its current behaviour in this scene is a result of, or something

357

to do with the fact that the dog is present and maybe with the dog's behaviour, wherever that is coming from. In fact, where it's most likely coming from is the presence and behaviour of the cat. And this is true of all of us. None of our behaviours happen in a vacuum, but always in relation to somebody else present in our lives.

"For this reason, we always have to take on board that we may have some responsibility for how the other person is behaving, which is not to say that we're to blame, but that we're a factor and will continue to be a factor in how they are and how they're behaving."

"I understand your example but I can't agree that it applies in this situation. Terry is Terry. He is as he is. That's a fact."

"Terry may be as he is but that's not to say that your version of Terry, *your* Terry, is the same as *my* version of him! No more than your version of "mother" is the same as mine but is based on your experience of your mother or of mothers, and mine on my mother. I hope you can understand this and take it on board because it's very important.

You only see Terry when he's with you, and how he then behaves with you. Just like the dog in my example only sees the cat as aggressive or upset or frightened or whatever, because she's always like that when he's around. It will be very hard to convince this dog that the cat is very different in other situations. Listen, I have a friend whose husband is a driving instructor and he believes that my friend, his wife, is a very bad driver! Why do you think this is so?"

> "The fault, dear Brutus, is not in our stars, but in ourselves"
>
> **William Shakespeare**

"Because he is judgemental and critical and has high standards around how people should drive, so he judges her against those standards, his standards."

"Yes, it's that, but it's even more. You see, he believes, he *knows* she's a bad driver. He's certain of it and can give evidence to support his position like you can with Terry. Why is he so certain?

"Because he only sees her when she's driving with him and so, when he's with her she's probably nervous that he may judge her or criticise her and so she drives badly."

"Exactly. He's quite justified in believing that she is a bad driver because that's all he ever sees and in fact he's wrong. In fact, she's a very good driver, has never had an accident of any kind and is very alert and aware and savvy. I know that. I've been with her and have seen her drive. Now I'm not saying that Terry is a saint when you're not around, but some of how he is and how he behaves when he's with you will have something to do with how he perceives you and because of the effect you have on him. Is that fair?"

"Yes, I can understand how that might be so."

Responsibility for the effects we have on people

"Good man. Well done. Now here comes the interesting and good part! Just as my driving instructor friend could change how he is and how he behaves when he's with his wife and so could seriously improve her driving, so too, I believe, *you* could change how you are and how you behave around Terry, helping and enabling him to behave differently. What are some things you could do or how could you behave differently that might make him feel different or better and so might, and I stress *might*, lead or help him to behave differently?"

"But why should I have to do this to get him to behave well? Shouldn't he behave cooperatively and well without me having to turn myself inside out trying to get him to do what he should do anyway. This is what we're supposed to be about in the team and what Mike is always telling us is important. This is not just about *me*, Teresa, and it's not fair to leave it up to me to deal with it."

"I know that Tony, but you can help him to change and be different."

"How?"

"By finding out what he needs. We all need different things and help"

"But why should all this fall on my shoulders to help him to change? This isn't just my problem. Mike must see it. You must see it."

"I know this is how you feel, Tony, and I could spend a lot of wasted time trying to convince you that you feel this more than others and so it might be more your problem than that of other people, or indeed a universally felt problem. I know you'd give me lots of examples of what he's doing and why it's so wrong. And, I'm sure that if I spoke to him, he would find lots of things about how you behave that are wrong.

But, let's not go there, please. Let me put it this way instead. I believe that you have more power to change this situation than I or Mike or anyone has. I believe that if you're able to change how you relate to Terry, then you will bring about big changes in him for the benefit of everyone, but especially for your own satisfaction and well-being. Now, I can understand very well why you might not feel like doing this, but how we feel should not always determine what we do or how we behave. So, can I ask you, what might you be doing that could, in fact, lead to Terry behaving as he does … in a bad way as you say? How could you be blocking Terry from behaving in a better way?"

> "You can't stay in your corner of the forest waiting for others to come to you. You have to go to them sometimes"
>
> **A.A. Milne**

"I understand. Well because we differ and he always goes against what I say, I do the same with him. I very often challenge what he says and, as you know, I'm very critical of how he handles Sales. Like with KEY Services. But, I think I'm justified in doing that. Am I not?"

"Maybe you are or maybe you're not, but for now this is a good example of something you do that may be bringing out the worst in Terry. How might that be true?"

"Well because he becomes defensive and exaggerates some of the good things they do in the Sales Department. And he attacks me, probably getting some revenge for my criticisms of things he puts forward. I can see that. That's true. I am definitely annoying the dog here very often."

"Well said and that's very honest and, I believe accurate. So that is one area where you could have a very positive effect on Terry and, who knows what may happen. Do you agree with me?

"Yes, that makes sense."

Helping people to change rather than demanding they change

"Now let's try to find ways in which you, by your behaviour – by how you relate to Terry – might help him to feel better about himself and so behave differently. Do you see what I'm getting at Tony?

"I see what you're saying and it's not easy but I do see how Terry feels I'm criticising him and judging him and that I'm against him, and some of that may be true. As well as that, I know he likes recognition, and that affirmation is important for him and I never give him that. In fact, I starve him of it. And I do that because it can be so annoying to see him going after and getting all that glory."

"Great, that's a good start. So you see that Terry has some needs – for recognition, appreciation or affirmation and things like that? We all have different kinds of needs, our own brands of needs. And far from trying to help satisfy those needs, however justified they are, you do the opposite. Right? And so what could you do, even if it involves a bit of an effort or struggle on your part, that will change that, and have Terry feeling less criticised and judged and more recognised and appreciated? You see, if you gave him more recognition, perhaps he mightn't need to go after it so much. So what could you do around that, do you think?"

"Well, I could refrain from having a go at him when the opportunity arises, and I could give him a "well done" because he does many things very well. Yes, I could do those things. Lots of scope there for change!", he laughed.

So Teresa and Tony continued talking and planning how Tony, by his behaviour, could have a very positive effect on Terry and on Terry's behaviour. Apart from feeling good about his plan, Tony told Teresa that, after it, he was feeling really good about himself and felt a load had lifted off his shoulders or off his heart.

"Well, I can only say you've been magnifi-cent," Teresa said. "As I mentioned earlier, this is one of the most difficult challenges we face in life and you've been great – honest, humble and fair. And, as I said many times, Terry is

> "Every saint has a past, and every sinner has a future"
>
> **Oscar Wilde**

not a saint, he's not perfect, no more than any of us, but we have to take people as they are and make the most of that reality. Giraffes have very long necks, bees sting, and we have to accept them as they are and it's in accepting people as they are, without any judgement or criticism, that we actually help and enable them to change and improve. Very often we expect or demand that people change instead of actually *helping* them to change. This is what I'm after here; that you will actually help Terry to change and possibly be less needy around recognition, affirmation and the like. And I hope you feel proud, Tony, that you have solved this or are going to – not Mike and not I. And if we had done so, we would have robbed you of the privilege and a justifiable pride or good feeling from having done so yourself. You see, in a sense, you were letting Terry decide and determine how you were behaving, which may not have been very Tony-like and may not have always felt good."

"No, you're absolutely right, Teresa, it didn't feel good at all, and I didn't feel good about myself. But, why am I the one to feel like this? What's wrong with me?"

"There's nothing wrong with you, Tony, or no more than there is with anyone else. We all have our own particular ways of behaving and relating and we're all different. I want to talk about this in the team some day soon because I think that we all need to be as aware of ourselves and our foibles and behaviours as you now are."

"That would be good, Teresa. I can assure you it didn't feel good at all to be in that tangle with Terry."

"I'm sure it didn't and now you're going to take control of how Terry's behaviour affects how you feel and what you do, and not hand that power over to Terry or anyone else. In my last job I used to get a lift from a colleague to work in the mornings and there was a short walk from the car park to the office. On the way to the office, he would stop at a kiosk and buy the morning paper from a man who was downright abrupt, unfriendly even discourteous.

> "I have decided to stick to love... Hate is too great a burden to bear"
>
> **Martin Luther King Jr.**

One day I heard my friend ask for his paper to be told: "What paper do you want? How do I know what paper you want?" I couldn't help asking him one day why he continued to buy his paper from the man in the kiosk who was so unfriendly towards him. He replied: "Why should I give that idiot the power to decide where I buy my paper?" And he was right and that's what you were doing to some extent by letting Terry dictate how you were behaving and how Tony behaved over the past while. Now that will stop and it's you, Tony, who will decide what Tony does and how he behaves, not Terry."

"I fully understand and thanks very much, Teresa," Tony said, "for how well you handled all of this. You really helped me and in fact empowered me, made me able, to do what I otherwise could not have done. If it's alright I'll let you know how I get on and I might even come to you if I'm not handling it well or if I make a dog's dinner of something."

"Well, I have every confidence you'll handle it well Tony. As I said earlier, don't take this personally. We all have issues with others. There's not one person in the team who doesn't find at least one other person difficult to work with. And not one person in the team who, in some sense, is not difficult to work with."

"But how can that be so, Teresa? Are we just a sick bunch?"

"No. not at all Tony. It's just that we're all different. And it's the same for every group and team. I've been meaning to talk to the team about this for some time. It's very important, I believe."

"Well, that's good to know that I'm not the only weirdo in the group or the only one with a problem," Tony laughed."

"Far from it, Tony, and you'll see that we're not all that weird but that we respond to people and things in different ways. What makes sense and is perfectly normal for one person might appear strange or "weird" as you say to someone else. But we can change how we respond, just like you're going to do in responding or relating to Terry."

"I fully see the wisdom in your approach now Teresa. It sounds interesting and fun. I can't wait. Thanks again for all that personal insight.

Questions for reflection and action

1. Do you understand how Tony feels? Have you ever felt like that?
2. Why is Tony having more problems with Terry than others are having … apparently? And why did Tony insist that everybody had a problem with Terry? Why do people very often do this? Do you?
3. Who has the power to change things in the cat and dog story? Can you think of "dogs" or "cats" in your world – people who rub you up the wrong way and to whom you react aggressively or negatively?
4. What will Tony have to do to change this situation? Why will Tony feel really good about this if he is able to do it?
5. Why does doing this change you, make you more powerful? Are there other people whom you can help using this approach, in or out of work?

Chapter 23
Managing Your Bear

How to get the best from your relationship with your manager – whoever and however they are

While Mike said it was alright to Martha to take a call and talk, it was far from it. He was nervous and he was suspicious about where things were really coming from. Maybe he was being paranoid, but he couldn't help feeling that this was further pressure from Brad to get even more control over him and what he was doing and to turn up the heat. And, it was so ironic in the context of the meetings he had just had, where he was encouraging his team to go in the exact opposite direction, the direction of letting go and trusting.

When the call from Martha came, none of his fears or suspicions were lessened. Okay, Martha was her usual friendly self and she tried to convince Mike that this was an across-the-board initiative. But Mike didn't believe her and Martha knew that. Mike did not try to argue or continue the discussion much longer. He reluctantly agreed to supply the additional information that Martha requested and equally reluctantly agreed to a fortnightly conference call prior to the visit, to explain what was being done and why, and to discuss anything else that needed explanation.

Of course, it meant hours of extra work in terms of preparing reports, but it also meant hours and days of work trying to get the message right, trying to choose the information that would attract least attention and further drilling down into detail. He wondered about all this. Did he have an option? It was exactly what had been going on with Tom in his area that wasted so much time and did so much damage. But it wasn't even this that most troubled Mike. It was the atmosphere, the environment, the relationship that underpinned this approach.

It ran counter to everything he believed in, counter to everything he was trying to bring about in his own company. He wondered if, in fact, he was misleading his people and leading them down a path to nowhere, leading them into a dead-end rather than to a promised land, and misleading them about what was really feasible around the business and how they managed it.

Should he put a stop to the direction he was trying to take his own team and the organisation?

> "Attitude is a choice. Happiness is a choice. Optimism is a choice. Kindness is a choice. Giving is a choice. Respect is a choice. Whatever choice you make makes you. Choose wisely"
>
> **Roy T. Bennett**

Should he be honest with his own team about his own environment and the challenges that he faced? Or should he try to play both sides as best he could? He found no answers on the way home from work. When the children had gone to bed, he explained to Joan why he might have appeared a bit down, and told her of his conversation with Martha.

Group work gives real control

Joan had no easy answers either. She just listened and understood and helped him to explore a little bit more of his options.

"I understand what you're saying, Mike, and I feel for you. I know what you're trying to do and how this development and the overall environment is so difficult for you. I don't think that there are any easy answers. Do you think that talking it over with someone, more skilled than me, like Brendan, might help? I find him always very helpful. I met him on Tuesday afternoon to talk over some things of my own and he was great."

Mike didn't pry into what Joan needed to talk about with Brendan "That's not a bad idea, providing he is not fed up of me by now. He always has a different angle on things, and it certainly wouldn't do any harm. Yes, I'll do that."

He felt a lot better after the conversation and he and Joan got onto other things, including some school topics that Joan was wrestling with. Very different topics from Mike's one and apparently not nearly so intractable.

"Maybe I'm better at solving my problems than you are." Joan joked.

"Sometimes I really think you are. And sometimes I can't help thinking that many of the problems we have are man-made ones, and by that I do mean "man" as distinct from "woman". I feel there's an inbuilt aggressiveness and competitiveness in men that women in general don't seem to have. As a matter of fact, I'm sad to say that many of the females I've met who have got on and progressed, did so precisely because they've become good at playing this man's game. When that happens it's even worse."

"I agree with you, Mike, and I see the same in the school. The difficulty isn't only with the male teachers. Some of my female colleagues can be just as difficult. It's hard to explain but it's like we're from different countries or galaxies.

> "I can't give you a sure-fire formula for success, but I can give you a formula for failure: try to please everybody all the time"
>
> **Herbert Bayard Swope**

Sometimes we can't make sense to each other. Some speak a completely different language and what we think and say appears to make no sense in that language. It's not that we're irrational but it's like as if it's a different kind of rationality. We had a situation two months ago where, because the combination of circumstances – additional work from being selected to pilot a new curriculum happening at the same time as three teachers had to take time off for health and other reasons – we needed to come up with a different roster and way of working, especially for us part-time teachers.

We spent two hours on it at a meeting which concluded with the proposal to set up a working group to come up with a temporary structure and roster. I saw where this was heading, and I very humbly and respectfully asked if a small group of us could have a look at it among ourselves.

They agreed, reluctantly I would have to say, but they agreed. We had a chat about it among ourselves, just four of us, and we came up with a way of making it work inside half an hour. Mind you, it wasn't all that easy to convince the others that it would work. However, reluctantly they agreed to give it a chance and it worked perfectly and so easily.

If we had not taken that initiative, it would have gone on for ages and with an outcome that few would have been happy with. It was the informality, the naturalness of how we worked that made the difference. It just happened. The right arrangement just emerged – fell out of our discussion."

"That's a great story and I understand it and how it worked. What I can also appreciate is the difficulty you had convincing others that it would work." Mike told her briefly about the meeting over the Quantum Logistic System and how good the outcome was and how some people initially were not too happy with it. "But, maybe I need to pay more attention to what Teresa, Sally and the other females are saying and thinking. Maybe there are or were situations where I very probably belonged to that other group that found it hard to come to grips with your proposal, Joan," he laughed.

Managing up!

First thing next morning he contacted Brendan and asked if they could meet. Luckily Brendan was free to meet that same evening.

Okay, it would mean being home a little late two evenings in succession but this time he felt it would be worth it.

Brendan did not need much background information on the issue that Mike wanted to talk about. He was very familiar with the tension between Mike and his boss, Martha, and even more so with her own boss, Brad. He updated Brendan about the recent meetings with the team and about their agreement and even enthusiasm around going after a very different way of working. He shared his concern about possibly leading them up the garden path or down a cul-de-sac. And, of course, he updated him on the latest news around the request for more meetings, more information and more control.

Brendan remained quiet as Mike explained again the situation. When he had finished, he smiled but said nothing for a few minutes.

"Bear with me on this, Mike. I'll make sense of it to you. I promise. Imagine," he asked, "you had found and bought your ideal, idyllic house, the house you've always dreamed of. And everything is done, and the deal is closed, and you go to the previous owner to pick up the keys of your new house. And, just as she hands them over to you, she says: "Oh, there's one thing I forgot to tell you.

Sorry. As you know that wood there is yours, all of it. But there's a bear in the wood, and you can't get rid of it or kill it because it's a protected species. Sorry I forgot to tell you that, but I hope you enjoy the house as much as we did!" And off she went. So, there you have it, Mike, your lovely house and a bear going with it! So, what do you do? Now I know you could cancel the deal, resell the house and forget the whole thing, but, for the sake of my story, at least, let's presume you don't want to do that. What would you do? Oh, and you can't get rid of the bear as she said."

"Well, I think the very first thing I'd do would be to make myself a cup of coffee or have a drink and come to terms with the reality of the fact that I have a neighbour I didn't know about and that surprise neighbour is a bear. And then realise that I'd just have to accept it and make the most of it! Sorry... maybe two drinks!"

"Very good. Good start, whatever about the drink. And what would you do to make the most of it?"

"I'm not sure. I suppose it would be no harm to find out about bears, and about my bear, and get to know it a little bit better so I know how to handle it and handle myself around it. I'm no expert on bears. But I could look on the internet or even go to the zoological gardens and ask someone about them. Maybe they're really lovely warm and friendly creatures and have just been getting a bad press. Fake news, you know! I'm only joking. I know how they are!"

"Very good. That makes sense. What else?"

"Let me see. Ah! I definitely think it would be wise to put up some kind of fence so that the bear knows where it can and can't go, and so that I know where I can and can't go!"

"Yes, that would seem wise. Anything else?"

"I could feed the bear, find out what it likes to eat and feed it that, so it doesn't need to feed on me! The internet and zoo could help with that too."

> "When you stop expecting people to be perfect, you can like them for who they are"
>
> **Donald Miller**

"That would make great sense to me too. Anything else?"

"I'm not sure. I imagine that bears are like other animals and don't like being frightened or surprised, so I would be careful around that. My neighbour had a dog once and it didn't like being frightened and just reacted. My bear might be the same."

"You're doing great! How are you feeling about your bear now?"

"A lot better. In fact, there would be an advantage to having a bear because it would be very unlikely that I would have many break-ins with my bear around. It would beat the neighbour's barking dog."

"That's great," Brendan said, "well done. You see, while managers, including your own manager, are not all like bears, some have the characteristics of bears! They have a lot of power, like to get their own way, can get upset and angry over all kinds of things, and are needy.

Recognise that, Mike? Because of that, it's important to know how to manage them and look after them. The mistake we make is that very often we believe that our managers should be perfect human beings, like us, and so we end up being disappointed and frustrated! We can sometimes feel our lives, our work-lives at least, are ruined because managers are not as we would like and expect them to be.

And while we feel some responsibility and right to manage people *below* us, we don't feel we have either the right, or the ability, or the responsibility to manage people who are *above* us hierarchically. So, Mike, can you work out how all those things you described around managing your bear might also apply to how you manage your own boss or bear … or both bears if you wish. But let's focus on Brad. He seems to be the big bad … bear. Let's go through them. What about the first one you mentioned, about not accepting your bear?"

Managing the more powerful

"Yes, I was just thinking about that as you were talking. I have to be honest; I never liked Brad and never saw him as a good manager. I think I always resisted him and hoped he would be changed or something. I'm not alone in this and we often talk about him when we get together among ourselves. Brad probably knows or senses this, I'm sure."

"Ok, Mike, so it might be a bit like your neighbour's dog. You could be making Brad nervous unconsciously.

How well do you know Brad and what makes him tick or thick, or what could you do to find that out? How could you get to know him better as you said you would do to find out about your bear? It was important with the bear, so it might be important with your manager too!"

"I don't know him at all except that he's not easy to work with. He is needy and demanding and is a control freak. And he can be so moody and volatile."

"Yes, I know this. You told me already. But do you know why he's like this, what makes him controlling and difficult? You see, if he's behaving like this, it makes sense to him to do so. For that reason, it would be good to understand him a bit more, rather than just putting labels on him. I understand how frustrated or annoyed you are with him. But that doesn't help in the long run. Just as you wanted to understand your bear more in order to be able to cope with him, it might be a prudent thing to do here too. You didn't just complain about your bear because he isn't a lamb or a dog. What else might you do around Brad, your bear?"

"Yes, I understand. I suppose, like all of us, he's a bit insecure and wants to show he's the boss. Maybe that's why he throws his weight around, as I was saying."

"Good. And if that were so, how could you actually help him to feel better about himself and his position?"

"Maybe give him clear messages that show I respect him as the boss. To be honest, I often do the exact opposite because he annoys me. Maybe if I made him feel better about himself, he would feel less need to impose himself and his authority on me."

"Great. I like it. What else could you do? You're doing great."

"Well, I said I would put up some fences to protect me against my bear in case it went wild and attacked me and it might be no harm to do something similar with Brad!"

"And what would that mean in Brad's case?"

"I'm not sure. I said that he's a bit of a control freak and wants endless information. What I'm thinking is that if I could establish and agree with him how much information he wants, how often he wants to meet, and propose some things around these, it might make him feel more comfortable. And, it would give me more space too to do what I want and need to do.

> "If you have some respect for people as they are, you can be more effective in helping them to become better than they are"
>
> **John W. Gardner**

Yes, I think that would be very helpful. I could do all that at these meetings I'm going to have with Martha, or during his visit in a while."

"Sounds good to me too," Brendan commented. "What else? You said you would feed your bear. What would this mean in Brad's case?"

"Oh yeah. Well, as I said, what Brad most needs is to feel confident and that things are under control. If this is some of the food this bear needs, then I see that I've been starving him! I feel he is insatiable and that nothing will satisfy him, so I only give him the minimum of information. I hate people who want full control, so I react against it when I see Brad wanting it. Maybe this is why I feel he comes after me so much and is never satisfied.

But, I can see that wanting to feel confident, in control and that all is alright, is fair enough. I can understand that. And I can see how I could feed him enough information and updates and plans to make him feel more assured. I created a hungry bear, voracious for information and control.

"Very good. Now, you mentioned that it might not be wise to surprise your bear. What about Brad?"

"Yes, Brad, like most managers, doesn't like surprises unless they're good ones. He hates that. You know, there are times when I take some delight when things don't go well, just from his reaction and the look I can see or imagine on his face! I know it's wrong but it's a fact. And, you're right. If I can help him to feel more secure by warning him of possible problems, I think it might be very helpful in preventing those moods or rash decisions that he can get into."

"Very good Mike, and, you know, while I know that Brad can be tough to work for, he's very strong and it's good to have a really strong manager. Maybe, behind the scenes he protects you and fights battles on your behalf. You won't find too many trying to take resources from your area with Brad around. Bears can provide great protection."

The true power we always have

"You're right, and Martha often tried to say that to me but I didn't want to listen to her or didn't believe her. You know, this is great, Brendan, I find it very helpful and I'm very clear about what I will do."

"That's good, Mike, but never forget that Brad is a bear and has a lot of power like all managers have, and so it's good to be aware and cognisant of this."

"What do you mean by that, Brendan?" Mike asked.

"Well, maybe I shouldn't say it at all, but managers have power and they can use and abuse it and we just have to be wary of that. We can forget it and see them as being on the same level as ourselves but they're not, because they have lots of things going on in their heads and all kinds of pressures on them. I had a manager once and people, on social nights out, having consumed considerable amounts of alcohol, would approach him to tell him the facts of life about the company and about himself. He would stop them and warn them. He would tell them to keep it for the next day or week and come to his office to tell him. He was just protecting people from their own naivety and from his power. I'm not saying we have to be afraid or too cautious, but we need to be aware of the person and the position of the person with whom we are talking. Does that make sense?"

"Yes, I have a problem looking up to or "kowtowing" to people. I like to maintain respect for myself and not let them feel they're superior. It's something I'm quite proud of, but I see how I might have been playing with fire … or worse still, with a bear. I need to think about that and work on it."

"I think that would be wise, Mike. I believe that if you work hard at building a relationship with Brad and stop wishing that he wasn't around, or getting into any game-playing with him, it will make a great difference in your life.

And, if you do all that, you'll find that you don't have to be so afraid or wary of your bear but will be able to differ with him, challenge him, and be honest with him on certain issues. Bears, like all animals, get nervous when they see people around them that are afraid, nervous and pandering. So if you're strong and confident with him, you'll find that he'll respect that too. You don't have to crawl or pander to him. Quite the opposite. How's that, Mike?"

> "Mastering others is strength. Mastering yourself is true power"
>
> **Tao Te Ching**

"It's great, Brendan," Mike said, "and I can really do virtually all those things and I think it will make a big difference to my life and to my effectiveness. You know, you can spend so much time and energy thinking about your bosses, trying to second-guess them, worrying about them, bitching about them, that you can become distracted from everything else. It can become a full-time job or your main one."

"You're right," Brendan answered, "and part of this "full-time job" can include a whole agenda to change your manager. I have seen managers plan and plot how to change or get the better of their managers and allow it to become the biggest or the only game in town. And I have seen many of these managers seriously lose out. Another pastime is to try to be smart and play games with your bear. I see this at times here and it's so stupid."

"I can see it too and I can spot it a mile away and it's both annoying and sad. I remarked on how some people always want my ear and they don't realise how I see through them. These games can end up being very dangerous. That's why I realise it's very important to take seriously the task of managing one's bear. It will avoid a huge loss of time and energy and will reap great benefits. Anyway, bears are good deep down. Like us all, they are just animals trying to look after themselves and not always doing it in the best way. Brad is one. I know! I am one!"

Brendan laughed. "So we have a lot of wild animals around, Mike? And many of them at senior levels."

The power to change the world!

"I know, Brendan, but why am I having to do all this? Just to help a large corporation become even larger! Surely there are better ways to use what I have in this world and make it a better place and, God knows, it needs to be a lot better than it is. But I'm not doing much to make it any better, am I?"

And he told Brendan of the dreams he had as a young man to make a real difference and do good things with his life and how now he finds himself a very long way from those dreams.

"Well, you're asking very big questions here, Mike, existential ones and ones that I often ask myself too. And, I think they're valid questions. Of course, it's far from being too late for you to take a completely different path or road at this stage.

It would, of course, have lots of repercussions for you and your family but that's not to say that they should not or could not be faced. I also think it would be good for you to consider the difference you are making or could make from your present position to, as you say, make the world a better place. In a sense, I think this is what you're doing with this whole project or journey you are undertaking.

You do have a lot of power to change many things and improve many things and I think it would be good for you to honestly and realistically assess not only what you're doing, but what you could do to genuinely believe and feel you're doing yourself and the world justice. Maybe you have more power to improve things and make the world a better place from this position than you would if you joined some NGO or social group. Maybe! I think that would be a worthwhile exercise for you to do before deciding to embark on a whole new path. "

"Yes, Brendan, it makes lots of sense and, you're right, that some of this has been behind what I have being and am trying to do. Maybe where I am is an ideal place from where to try to change things in society and in the world. Let me do that and come and talk to you again about it if that's alright."

"Sure. Do you think this might be a fairly universal issue?"

"What do you mean, Brendan?"

Brendan laughed again. "It's just that I wonder how senior teams in general perform given all these bears that are around. You see, what I believe in actual fact is...

And the two of them continued talking for another half an hour and finished with Mike looking a bit puzzled but smiling ruefully.

A very common problem

The very next day, Bernard asked Mike for help on an issue he was having resisting corporate interference in a quality change programme he was running.

While Bernard belonged to Mike's team, he reported directly to a manager in a different division of the company, the director of quality control.

Mike had seen, and indeed it was no secret, that Bernard and his boss did not get on and Mike and everyone knew that Bernard felt his boss made life very difficult for him.

They had had many conversations about this – about how his boss needed to always be in control of what Bernard was doing, needed a lot of information, was, allegedly, very volatile and unpredictable and could be dangerously moody, becoming quite ruthless around certain things and with certain people.

"Incredible change happens in your life when you decide to take control of what you do have power over instead of craving control over what you don't"

Steve Maraboli

On a few occasions, he insisted on Bernard taking disciplinary action against some of Bernard's employees, based on quick impressions – far too quick impressions according to Bernard. In a sense, Bernard did not feel in full control of quality in the company and was afraid to take a risk in case it turned out badly and his boss took advantage of it to bring him even more back in line.

Mike knew Bernard's boss and so was aware that not all of this was just in Bernard's head!

He decided to talk to Bernard about the relationship and to try out what he had learned in his conversation with Brendan.

He took Bernard through the same story of the idyllic house and the bear and asked him how he would handle it.

"Bernard, can you work out how all those things you described around managing your bear might also apply to how you manage your own boss or bear. Let's go through them. What about the first one you mentioned about not accepting your bear?"

"Yes, I was just thinking about that as you were talking. I have to be honest, I never liked Bill and never saw him as a good manager. I think I always resisted him and hoped he would be fired or promoted or something. I'm not alone in this and we often talk about him when we get together among ourselves. Bill probably knows or senses this, I'm sure."

Mike smiled to himself at how similar Bernard's thinking and behaviour was to his own. He continued to find out from Brendan what he could do to get a better response from his boss, along the same lines that Brendan had followed with him. Bernard had more similar reactions to Mike's own ones.

"Yes, I understand. I suppose, like all of us, he is a bit insecure and wants to show he's the boss. Maybe that's why he throws his weight around, as I was saying.

"Good. And if that was so, how could you actually help him to feel better about himself and his position?"

"Maybe give him clear messages that show I respect him as the boss. To be honest, I often do the opposite because he annoys me. Maybe if

I made him feel better about himself, he would feel less need to impose himself and his authority on me."

And so the conversation continued until Mike finally asked Bernard:

"What else could you do? Remember you said you would feed your bear. What would this mean in Bill's case?"

"Oh yeah. Well, as I said, what Bill most needs is to feel confident and that things are under control. If this is some of the food this bear needs, then I see that I have been starving him! I feel he is insatiable and that nothing will satisfy him so I only give him the minimum of information. I hate people who want full control so I react against it when I see Bill wanting it. Maybe this is why I feel he comes after me so much and is never satisfied. But, I can see that wanting to feel confident, in control, that all is working well, is fair enough. I can understand it. And I can see how I could feed him enough information and updates and plans to make him feel more assured. I created a hungry bear."

Mike smiled again at the similarities with his own relationship with Brad. "It seems Brendan was right," he thought, "it's a universal issue."

"Very good Bernard," Mike answered. And you know, while I realise that Bill can be tough to work for, he's very strong and it is good to have a really strong manager. I have often seen Bill fighting battles on behalf of all of you and he does it very well. You won't find too many trying to take resources from your area with Bill around. Bears can provide great protection."

1. Accept that you have a bear and that the bear is as he or she is. Don't be surprised. Very often it is a failure or inability to accept our managers as they are that causes us the greatest problems.
2. Get to know your bear, what they need, what they like and do not like. Spend time on this and make a list of their needs, characteristics, strengths and weaknesses. This will make them need you.
3. Feed your bear, look after them. Otherwise they may look after themselves. Plan this.

4. Be aware of your bear and the power they have. Learn to deal with this in your own way. Don't underestimate them. Look after yourself.

5. Don't frighten them or surprise them. Bears don't like to be surprised - unless it is with honey

6. Work hard at building a relationship with your bear - it will make life easier and allow you to do what you want and need to do.

7. Try to set realistic boundaries for yourself and get the bear comfortable with them. What meetings or information they want etc. so you know where the lines are and can operate within them.

8. Don't set out to take them on or change them as this can consume a lot of energy.

9. Be wise and your bear can be your biggest ally and will protect you.

10. Don't play games with your bear. They don't understand it and don't like it and you may get hurt.

11. Respect them and have confidence in yourself and you may get a relationship of mutual respect where you are able to face them and look them in the eye. Bears too have their fears.

12. Try to like them - like us they're OK deep down but are just animals who are looking after themselves and, like all of us, not always doing it in the best way.

"This is great, Mike. I find it very helpful and I'm very clear about what I'll do."

That's good, Bernard, but never forget that Bill is a bear and has a lot of power like all managers have and so it's good to be aware and cognisant of this." Mike knew this only too well in his own case, so he reminded Bernard of the power that bear managers can have."

"I understand what you're saying, Mike, and I'll keep it in mind.

"That's great, Bernard, and I believe that if you work hard at building a relationship with your manager, and stop wishing that he wasn't around, or getting into any game-playing with him, it will make a great difference in your life. If you do all that, you'll find that you'll no longer be so afraid or wary of your bear but will be able to differ with him, challenge him, and be honest with him on certain issues. Bears, like all animals, get nervous when they see people around them afraid, so if you're strong and confident with him, you will find that he'll respect that too. You don't have to crawl or pander to him. Quite the opposite. How's that, Bernard?"

Mike smiled at how quickly he sounded like or had become an expert on managing our managers.

"It's great, Mike," Bernard said, "and I can really do virtually all of those things and I think it'll make a big difference to my life and to my effectiveness. You know, you can spend so much time and energy thinking about your boss, trying to second-guess them, worrying about them, bitching about them, that you can become distracted from everything else. It can become a full-time job or your main one." Mike smiled, recalling the almost identical conversation he had had with Brendan!

> "We have to dare to be ourselves, however frightening or strange that self may prove to be"
>
> **May Sarton**

"I agree Bernard and I think it's very important to take seriously the task of managing one's bear. It will avoid a huge loss of time and energy and will reap great benefits". Then he found himself repeating what he had said to Brendan. "Anyway, bears are good deep down. Like us all, they are just animals trying to look after themselves and not always doing it in the best way. I know! I am one!"

"I think I can have a good go at managing my bear! Anyway, I can practise on you, Mike!"

"Don't you already?, said Mike with a wink."

Questions for reflection and action

1. Why do people not address problems with their bosses or managers? Why is it so important to do so?

2. Why are managers a bit like bears? Which bear qualities do you most identify in your manager(s)?
3. What, in your experience, is the most common mistake people make around their managers?
4. Which of these do you most need to look at or work on?
   - How well do you know your "bear"?
   - What does your bear need?
   - Do you have fences? How clear are they? Do they work?
   - Do you ever surprise your bear? Why is this so dangerous?
   - How aware are you of your bear's strength and power? Do they use it?
   - Do you know how to handle your bear's strength in a good way?
   - Why might it be wise to be a little careful, or wise, on social occasions or at parties when there are bears around?
   - Do you see this as being cowardly and fawning and trying to please?
   - What's wrong with trying to change your bear?
   - Why is playing games with bears dangerous?

Chapter 24
Gnothi Seauton (Delphic Oracle. "Know Yourself")

Really know who you are? Really know others?

Having spent time learning how to know and manage our bears, Teresa felt it was at least as important to get to know ourselves. It was for this reason that Teresa, having spoken to Mike, put the topic of "self-awareness" on the agenda for a meeting some weeks later.

Everybody, with the exception, that is, of Mike and Tony were a bit surprised and puzzled at what she meant and what she intended covering.

"Some weeks ago, Mike told us that he believed that we would only be able to bring about the kind of transformation of the company if we ourselves, as a senior management team, lived and practised what we wanted to see happening. A key part of that was how we communicate and relate among ourselves. We probably have different views on how well we work as a team, but would you all be in agreement that, however good or bad we are, we could be a lot better?"

They all agreed, even if there was some nervousness around where all of this might lead to. There were glances and furtive looks around the room as people did very quick audits of their relationships with their colleagues.

"I want to assure you at the outset," Teresa said, "that I'm not going to embarrass anybody or oblige anybody to get into public apologies, psychological introspection or forced commitments to change. What I would like to do is to explain some basic principles around human behaviour and self-awareness and simply invite you to look at some useful approaches and tools to improving our self-awareness. Is that acceptable? I imagine you all agree that there are few things more important than being aware of ourselves as the Delphic Oracle says 'Gnothi Seauton – Know Yourself.' Are you all happy with that?"

They nodded their satisfaction.

"So, first a few very basic principles. Let's see if we can agree on them and we can come back to them again and spend more time on them.

Would you agree that we all think we're normal? We do what we do because it seems the normal thing to us. And because of that, we take ourselves as the norm, as normal. And to confirm us in this, we share some of our normal views and behaviours with others, with other "normal" beings, who will agree with us. Is that true?"

It was, even if people still remained a little guarded.

"But, in actual fact, we're all different and no one has full claim on what's normal. People simply have different ways they have learned of being human, and ours is just *our* particular way of doing this and is far from being the only one, the right or normal one. Alright?"

"I understand that," Sally said, "but why is it significant or important?"

"Only because we can believe that our view of the world is the right and only one and has more validity than any other one. As a result, we can use our views and behaviours as the yardstick for how people should behave. In fact, like our friends around the elephant were certain it was a tree, or a hill, or a tube etcetera, we too can believe that our way of seeing things and handling them is the right one. This is not just a theory, it's true of all ten of us in this room and none of us have a complete grasp of what's right and best."

> "It is better to be hated for what you are than to be loved for what you are not"
>
> **Andre Gide, Autumn Leaves**

"I understand why this is important because it will affect how we relate, our relationships, how we get on," Frank said.

"Yes, Frank," Teresa said, "but it will also affect how well we actually perform as people. If we confine ourselves to a narrow range of what we think is right or good behaviour, then we're cutting ourselves off from enormous possibilities of different ways of seeing, thinking, and behaving. We're limiting ourselves to a very narrow range of what we think is appropriate and right. So, being aware of this will help us greatly in terms of broadening our range of responses to any situation. In a sense, because we see ourselves as a hammer, then all we see around us are nails. We limit ourselves."

Learned responses to cope with life

"And why do we do this, may I ask?" Tom asked.

"A very good and important question, Tom. At a very early age, before 6 or 7, we develop coping mechanisms to deal with our environment, because we can't understand or articulate what is going on and then these ways we use to cope with whatever happens become our standard ways of responding. Because they work for us, we tend to use them all the time, whether they are the right or most appropriate response or not. For example, a brother of mine when he was young, felt left out of things and not included in what others were doing.

He learned to cope with or handle this by withdrawing into his own world. This, then, became a frequent or common pattern for handling situations like that. It seemed a good one and worked for him and protected him and so it became his typical, usual, normal way of responding. So, it became normal for him, a very effective way of dealing with all kinds of situations like this. He still does it.

This might sound awful but really it's good news because it means that these are simply learned behaviours, patterns, templates he has learned and uses. But that's all they are. They are not how we *are* but describe how we *behave*. And, because of that, we can work on these behavioural patterns and develop alternative and better ones."

> "Imperfection is beauty, madness is genius and it's better to be absolutely ridiculous than absolutely boring"
>
> **Marilyn Monroe**

"What are you saying, Teresa?" Bernard asked, "that we are not who or what we think we are?"

"Well, what I'm saying is that we use the verb "to be" when we talk about ourselves and our behaviours, or about others" behaviours, and we say they are ambitious or selfish, or cautious etcetera, as if that's the way that they are. I'm saying that there is an alternative view which says that these are simply learned behaviours and, because they are learned, we can unlearn them and learn and practise new ones. The system I'm talking about here and going to use is called the "Enneagram".

I won't go into it here but it's a very old system that was rediscovered about two centuries ago. It differs from other so-called profiling systems in just that – it doesn't say that we are a certain way but that we've learned to behave in particular ways and we can change that behaviour. So it's very good news," she laughed.

"I think I understand that," Bernard answered, "so what would you like us to do?"

"Yes, Bernard, I would like you to do something and it will only be an exercise and far from ideal. This approach I am talking about, the "Enneagram", describes nine different personalities or nine different ways in which we respond in our own particular way to situations in our lives. What I would like to do, if it's acceptable to you, is to explain, very briefly, what each of these are and how they differ, and then see if you can identify with any of them, or with some more than others. So I will describe, very briefly, as I said, what each one is and what I would like you to do is three things in fact:

1. Firstly, see if you think it describes to some extent how you are or how you behave.
2. Secondly, see if you think it's a good description of how somebody else you know, like somebody in this room, behaves.
3. And thirdly, I want you to get into pairs in order to get anotherperson's help in identifying which of these nine types you are closest to."

They all seemed a little lost or puzzled, still but were interested and happy to go along with it.

"We will do the first two parts, namely, thinking about yourself and about possible others as we are, individually, and then I will get you into pairs for your discussion work. So, I will read a very brief description of each one, from one to nine and pause and give you a chance to think about each one as I go through them.

"Enneagram" types or personalities

I will call these "Types" so **Type One** is someone who wants a more perfect world and continually looks for flaws and mistakes as if nothing seems quite good enough. They can be highly self-controlled and structured and strive for excellence. They believe that there's almost always a right way to do everything, and *they* know it. As a result, they try to fix people and situations. They can experience feelings of dissatisfaction with how things are and get irritated, but even if they are angry, they'll try to not show their anger. That's Type one."

People looked around at possible suspects, but Tony kept his head down.

"**Type Two** want to be liked and try to meet the needs of others and attempt to orchestrate the people and events in their lives. They try to feel worthy and valued by offering gifts, attention, resources and advice and help to others, especially those who are in need, or important people, or those who are important to them.

> "We delight in the beauty of the butterfly, but rarely admit the changes it has gone through to achieve that beauty"
>
> **Maya Angelou**

They focus on what others are feeling and in doing this they very often lose connection with what they themselves truly want and deeply need. They can get angry, then, if they feel unappreciated or undervalued by others because their value comes from others. That's Type Two"

Type Three. Type three people want respect from others and they go after this through being successful and worthy of admiration. And so they focus intensely on specific goals and plans and they do all this with a self-assured and confident demeanour and image. In doing this they can become out of touch with their truest self and innermost heart's desire.

I would ask you to be careful about this type because as managers we can be expected to have goals and plans etcetera. So be careful, don't assume that because you have goals and plans that you are necessarily a Type Three. So take your time again and don't worry if you're not able to identify with any of these."

"**Type Four** want a deep, unbreakable and authentic relationship with themselves and others. They feel most alive when they authentically express their personal experiences and feelings. They search for deep experiences and emotional connection and avoid rejection or feeling not good enough. They think about what is missing and how they are different and disconnected from others. They consciously or unconsciously compare themselves to others and can feel deficient or superior. They are often sensitive and fine-tuned and can be moody and self- reflective and self-referencing. Lovely people … if there are any among us.

Type Five individuals want to absorb knowledge in the areas they perceive as important and intriguing. They can be highly cerebral, emotionally detached and self-contained. Being a five can be extraordinarily private. They look for ways to guard against intrusion and the experience of feeling energetically depleted. They can guard themselves against feelings by intellectualising them and can have difficulty differentiating thoughts from feelings. They can be calm in a crisis, self-reliant, private and independent but can be easily drained energetically, so they go inside their own heads and find peace and "being ok" there. I can give you some very good examples of how Type Fives react!

Type Six. These people have insightful minds and create anticipatory or worst-case scenarios to help themselves feel prepared in case something goes wrong. They can be tentative, and some can engage in high-risk behaviour to prove that they are fearless and some do both – fear dangers and take risks. They search for meaning, certainty and trust and the avoidance of negative scenarios from occurring is important for them. They can have continuous thoughts of doubt, concern, or worry and can suffer from anxiety, dread and vexation that the worst may occur. They are often problem-solvers, sceptics, and they seek loyal and trustworthy individuals and teams. They can be ambivalent about authority figures sometimes. I hope you're recognising some of these either in yourself or in others! We probably have some sixes in our group.

Type Seven. Sevens want to experience everything possible that is new, stimulating, exciting, and pleasurable, while rebelling against limits or restraints. They relish the stimulation of new ideas, people, and experiences, and avoid pain and discomfort, creating elaborate plans that will allow them to always keep all of their options open. There can be a constant search for pleasure and stimulation and the avoidance of pain and discomfort. They can have a hyperactive mind that

> "A life spent making mistakes is not only more honourable, but more useful than a life spent doing nothing"
>
> **George Bernard Shaw**

emphasises the positive and constantly moves from one idea to the next in rapid succession. They have a continuous thirst for new stimulation of all kinds. Exciting people!

Type Eight. Eights pursue the truth, like to keep situations under control and want to make important things happen and some of this to hide their vulnerability. They can continuously experience deep, quick, intense anger that propels them to take immediate action. They may feel but rarely show sadness, fear or other vulnerable feelings. They can act big and bold and have an impulse to take immediate action, particularly strategic action. They can be direct and confronting and can intimidate intentionally or unintentionally. They can also want to protect others as the way to show their own strength and lack of vulnerability. Type eights are great strong people.

And finally **Type Nine**. These people want peace, harmony, and mutual, positive regard. They avoid conflict, and don't readily access or express their own points of view but embrace multiple perspectives. They prefer a relaxed demeanour to get along, rather than potentially creating tension between themselves and others. They can diffuse their attention and this can make them forget what's important to them as a way to not cause tension or conflict. They can be inattentive to their own feelings and needs and appear mellow, low-key, even-tempered. They keep their own anger subliminal and out of awareness. They are often affirming, affable, agreeable, and approachable and blend easily with others. They can be non-assertive but equally passive aggressive when feeling pressured. Lovely people and loved by people.

The search

So how did you all do? I can see some of you are clear enough and others look a bit puzzled. You don't look too happy, Tom, but don't worry. We'll get there. And, even if we don't, it's not so much about getting your type exactly right as about improving your overall self-awareness. So don't worry.

> "We have to dare to be ourselves, however frightening or strange that self may prove to be"
>
> **May Sarton**

Now I want to get you working in pairs, as I said, and I have matched you up in a particular way.

I would like you, Tony, to work with Frank.

And I would like you, Terry, to work with Natalie.

I would like you, Bernard, to work with Heather and vice versa of course in all cases.

And then, Sally, Tom, and I will work in a threesome.

What I'd like you to do is to work with the other person to try to find out which type you most belong to. You can take it in turns or handle it any way you wish. Let's give about twenty minutes to it, if that's alright."

They went off in their pairs and had their discussions. When they came back, Teresa said:

"I'm going to get the ball rolling to give good example if that's acceptable. Sally and Tom were both very much in agreement with me that I have a lot of the Two in me and that's not just because I'm in Human Resources. Being appreciated is really important for me and my self-worth is very dependent on how others behave and respond to me. I can see that I try to find my self-worth externally, from helping others.

That's probably why I chose or ended up in Human Resources or people management. These can all sound like very nice qualities and people can like Twos, but we're not nearly as generous and good as we think and our work to become accepted comes at a great price. And nice as we are or as we appear, we can be highly manipulative. I think this is where I am. Can we stay with our own group and hear from you, Sally, or Tom?"

"As you know, Teresa," Sally spoke, "I ended up fairly clear also. I don't think it will come as a great surprise to many that I have a lot of Six in me. I'm very good at identifying what might go wrong, as you all know, and this can appear negative, but it comes from a desire to avoid bad scenarios occurring. I like rules and regulations and protocol, because quite honestly, I can find it difficult to trust people. Being reliable and consistent and predictable are all important to me and I like regular, agreed and prescribed ways of doing things. I think we should all follow the rules and what we agreed in the group or team."

"And tell us what you were thinking and saying, Tom."

"Yes, well, as you know, Teresa, I ended up not very clear. There are some things in some of these categories that I could recognise, but I found it hard to confine myself to any one of them. There are some that I don't believe I belong to like Nine or maybe Six, but there are also a few where I see bits of myself. Maybe I don't like fitting in or being labelled or boxed. I would like to think some more about it, if that's alright."

"Sure, Tom, I understand and we can come back to it whenever you want and if you want. How did you and Natalie get on, Terry?"

"A bit like Tom, I ended up a little unclear also." Natalie said. "I would identify with many of the things that Tom said about getting things done. But I do it in a different way and, for me, good relationships are very important. I don't like conflict. I like peace and harmony and things being fairly comfortable. I could be accused of being a Nine because I can appear easy-going and not too pushy, but I think we can get things done without rubbing people up the wrong way. I'm prepared to look a bit more at how I might be a Nine. Is that okay Teresa?"

"Absolutely. What I would most like is that we all continue to observe ourselves so we're more aware of how we are and to work to better understand other people rather than labelling them like I mentioned earlier and as Tom also mentioned. And you, Terry?"

"I found it difficult. Maybe it's because of what you said earlier, Teresa, around what being a good manager means. I just happen to think that success is important and is, to a great extent, the name of the game. Natalie thought that I might be a Three, but I'm not sure. After all, organising and planning and making things happen are core to my job.

"In the depth of winter, I finally learned that within me there lay an invincible summer"

Albert Camus

And I want to give a message of being a good leader and this means appearing confident and successful and not showing weaknesses or flaws too much. I think I can be like you, at times, Teresa, in that I really want to help people. I'm not sure."

"Okay, that's fine, Terry, and we can look more at this if you want, and, the important thing is to continue to be alert and aware of yourself."

"Yes, that's fine, Teresa."

"How did you two get on, Frank and Tony?"

"I think we ended up fairly clear about where I am and you'll all probably agree with Frank that perfection in getting things right is very important for me," Tony said. "I put it down to my being an engineer but I can see that I can overdo it in terms of wanting control and being intolerant of mistakes.

And I can see fairly clearly how I like things done *my* way. I've learned a lot about myself over the past few months and I can now see why my people might feel put down or subdued by me and want to do what I want. I really want to make things better, whether this comes from being an engineer or being a One. You all know how good I am at spotting what is wrong or flawed and I can see from this how I can be a nuisance at times. Yes, I'm convinced I am a One."

"I didn't end up nearly as clear," Frank said, "I don't think things are as simple as this and we are all quite complicated. I did find the whole thing quite difficult and I'm not sure that I'm any clearer about where I am. There are some things about being a Four that I could identify with, like being creative and not like being just ordinary. I think a lot about myself and I've had a more complex history than most people in this room and that's a fact. I can feel at times that some of you see me as a weirdo but, believe me, it's far worse from the inside!"

"That's great honesty, Frank," Teresa said. And like I said to others, we can continue looking at this if you wish."

"Absolutely, Teresa, wherever that might take us ... if anywhere!"

"Finally, how did you and Bernard do, Heather?"

"Very good, I think. We had great fun and I think we agreed where we both were, isn't that so, Bernard?"

"Absolutely, Heather," Bernard answered. "I found it a little difficult to realise I was a Five, but I can see that. I want to understand things better and, as any of you who have visited my house will know, I love books. I also like to think things out on my own and, where possible, try to find a new angle on things. I suppose I must drive some people mad sometimes, always having an answer or some angle on things. I have to say, I like being like this, even though I recognise how frustrated and annoyed I can be when people take my time or waste it."

"I'm fairly clear also that I'm a Seven," Heather said. I think you all know how I love to try things and get involved in new things. I can get bored easily and I like to move on. That's why I've had a few career changes in my life – I just wanted something new. I think I'm optimistic and positive and I like being like this. I think I might work harder at being persistent and uncomfortable with things.

> "Sometimes I can hear my bones straining under the weight of all the lives I'm not living"
>
> **Jonathan Safran Foer**

But I find all we're doing here is very helpful. This is a good place to be and I no longer see greener grass elsewhere. Seems you are going to have to stick with me for a while. I don't feel like going anywhere for a change. I don't really know what I would change. I like how I am but I'm sure many of you have ideas on things I might do differently and better," she laughed.

"Thanks Heather, I'm glad that you're clear and happy enough about things and about how you are," Teresa laughed.

The search continues and will continue

"And well done to all of you. This has been very rushed, a bit unsatisfactory and maybe not comfortable for all of you, but I think it's important that we're all aware of ourselves and of each other. I left you out of this, Mike at this time, because you and I have talked about it already. Mike believes he is a Two, in case you're all interested, which explains why he's such an attentive and caring human being! Are you all okay with that? Does anybody want to say anything?"

They had a lot to say and everybody seemed delighted with the greater awareness they enjoyed of each other. Some joked with others about how they were, and some made fun of themselves.

"As I said, if any of you want to get deeper into this, let me know, let me know and I can get more information and help for you. What I would ask is that we each make an effort to continue to learn more about ourselves and to learn and appreciate others and how they think and behave. I think that would be very helpful."

"I agree completely," Mike said, "since Teresa worked with me on this I have learned a lot about myself and how addicted I am to certain behaviours. Believe me, It's not easy to change, but I make an effort to catch myself slipping into my typical patterns. I look forward to you all helping me with my efforts to be more self-aware! Thanks for doing that, Teresa, and I know it was risky for you but I believe we will all gain from it and it will make us a more united, better, and stronger team."

They all seemed to be in complete agreement. "Thanks Mike, and, apart from the on-going work at improving awareness of ourselves and others, there's a wealth of information available to anyone who would like to deepen their understanding of the "Enneagram" and themselves. So, please come to me if you would like that."

She felt sure that some would do just that. She hadn't long to wait. Tony followed her to her office. He told her how helpful he had found his meeting with her over his relationship with Terry.

"I'm making a big effort to be more aware of myself and how I react to Terry. I can see now how much of a pain I must have been. I don't find Terry or his way of handling things easy, as you know, but I have to say the cat and dog process seems to be working. I'm now seeing Terry in a different light and I believe he's changing too."

"That's great to hear, Tony. As I said when we spoke, this is one of the most difficult things we face in life. People annoy us because of how they are and how we are and we blame them for it. That's great work you're doing."

"Thanks but I know I'm only at the beginning of this. I found today's session very helpful. I got a glimpse of how I am and how I can give the impression that I'm always right and my way is the right way. I now realise I have been paying a huge price for this way of thinking and operating, and I would love to change it. You see – and you probably know this very well – that we can get blinding glimpses of how we are, but then these fade and we go back to how we were. I think how I handle things is generally good and this is important.

The desire to reach high standards and all that. So, it's not easy to give up on things that have served me well all my life. It's for that reason that I'd like you to find me a coach – someone who would be strong and demanding and even tough. I want to change and I believe I'll need help and support to do so."

"I understand that perfectly, Tony, and I'll arrange for that help to be made available. I think I know who would be ideal for you in that role. I'll get back to you when I talk to that person. Ok?"

"Sure, that would be great, Teresa. As I said, this has been an eye-opening experience for me and even my wife and family have remarked on the change … already! You're a magician, a miracle worker, Teresa," he said, laughing.

"Well, that's great news, Tony … grist for the mill for me as a Two. Helping and being appreciated is lifeblood to me," she laughed.

Questions for reflection and action

1. Do you understand and agree with the philosophy of the "Enneagram" that we develop ways of coping early on in life that stay with us and we with them?
2. Have you any idea, based on this brief information, which type seems closest to you?
3. And people around you and close to you? Do you recognise any … without labelling them?
4. Are there some people you find particularly difficult that you might want to improve?
5. Is there any area where, based on this knowledge, you need to be more aware of and watchful of how you behave and relate? Do you need any help from someone?

Chapter 25
Why Managers are Bullies

We're all bears! And our own bears need managing

Many changes had been made since Tom had met with the group after the Quantum Logistic System problem had been resolved. All was well and everybody was feeling good about what had been achieved. It was a real test of their ability to introduce serious change and do so in a constructive way. The change was an on-going process, with lots of revisions along the way. All seemed well until Tom arrived in Teresa's office one morning, asking her to initiate an investigation into a claim of bullying against one of his managers. Tom was visibly shocked and upset.

Not only because everything had seemed to go so well, but also because it was Albert who was involved, someone he had learned to trust and in whom he had great confidence. Teresa listened to him and was sympathetic. But then she told him that she would not be initiating any investigation into the accusation of bullying against Albert.

"The hardest challenge is to be yourself in a world where everyone is trying to make you be someone else"

E.E. Cummings

"But why not, Teresa," Tom argued, "isn't this the procedure and one that we should respect and honour? Isn't this person entitled to have her case of bullying investigated by us in management, and especially by you, as head of Human Resources?"

"Maybe she is and maybe we'll do that, but at the appropriate time. I assure you that we'll resolve this in a constructive way that is acceptable for everyone."

"Are you saying that we're going to compromise on this or come up with some fudge arrangement that will save Albert and all of us from losing face? Is that what you mean, Teresa?"

"Not at all, and I hope you know me better than to think I would do that Tom. The problem is that once we initiate some kind of formal investigation, then Albert is already accused and to some extent already guilty. Even if the investigation found him blameless, it's still on his record and there'll be comments and feelings of 'no smoke without a fire'"!

"But that's always how things are in these situations and, for that matter, in all kinds of legal situations. Surely you recognise and have to accept that? And you know that I, more than anybody else, want to look after Albert in this matter. But I also want to handle it well and do what's right and what this person is entitled to."

"Yes, I recognise that this is what happens in these kinds of situations and in most legal forums, but I don't agree with them and I'm not happy with handling things in that way. Quite apart for the serious and long-term effects on Albert and his reputation, I don't think that this is the best way to come at truth and what is right."

Forums to get at truth

"But why not? Isn't this the way to get at the truth? By hearing both sides, arguing both sides and then adjudicating on what happened is the right way to deal with it. Surely that's standard and well tried practice?"

"It may be well tried practice but I don't believe it's best practice. What happens and what would happen in this case too, is that both sides would prepare their strongest argument and dig out all of the possible evidence that would support their side. In doing this, they would ignore and turn a blind eye to anything that might go against them, even if it's valid and true.

Equally, they would exaggerate and over-emphasise points that support their argument and position. Whatever about us, there's no doubt that for them what's true and right ceases to matter and only *winning* becomes what matters and is most sought after. It becomes impossible to get at truth and people become very emotionally attached to the picture of the world they have created and with which they identify. Do you know what I'm saying?"

"Yes I do, but I don't know any other way and it'll be up to us to eventually decide who is right. Isn't this how all major disputes get handled? Isn't this how things work in society in general?"

"It may well be, but I believe it's a very unsatisfactory way of dealing with things and I would argue that in society in general it doesn't work there either. In courts of law, it's often the best performer that wins, rather than what's true and right."

"So what is the alternative, then? How would you handle this or like us to handle it? Do you have some better way?"

"In the end we are always rewarded for our good will, our patience, fair-mindedness, and gentleness with what is strange"

Friedrich Nietzsche

"Yes, I do, Tom. I believe that rather than Albert or this girl being right or wrong, the real truth may lie elsewhere. I don't mean in a compromise or fudge, but there can be two very different and perfectly valid versions of the the same situation, both of them true, even if they appear quite contradictory on the surface. I believe that there is always a deeper and more complete truth behind everything and it's that which I would like to find, or rather I would like *you* to find."

The buck stops with you

"So you're passing the buck or the problem over to me now? Getting it off your desk or agenda? Very neat Teresa!," Tom laughed.

"Maybe that's what I'm doing, but I'm not doing it to get rid of it and I'm not asking you to deal with it because I don't want to. It's because I think you're the right person to deal with it."

"Thank you very much, Teresa, I'm honoured!"

"Well I'm very glad that you're so honoured and happy, Tom but it's not just because of your undoubted skills but also because they both work for you and therefore it is, in a sense, your issue and should stay there, at that level. If I take it on as a formal investigation, that raises it to a new level and takes the power away from you and from them, just like when two people in a dispute in normal life escalate it to lawyers and the legal forum. They lose all or most of their power."

"Yes I understand that, but what do you want me to do?"

"What I would like you to do is to talk to both of them separately and, even more importantly, listen to both of them separately. You may have to do this once or twice in order to get to that real and deeper truth that I spoke about. I could speculate or conjecture what that might be, but I could be all wrong and we won't know until you've listened to both of them. Does that make sense, Tom?"

"Yes, it does, even though I have no idea what will happen or how it will work in practice!"

"I know that, Tom, but I think that when you've listened to both of them and challenged them in an interested and supportive way to describe and tell you what happened and how they're feeling, I believe you will know what to do and how to handle it. That will come down to the quality of your listening and the quality of your presence to both of them."

"Yes, Teresa, I understand what you're saying but what do you mean by the quality of my presence to them?"

"What I mean is that you must be genuinely attentive to and interested in *them* and in *their* welfare, so please make sure that they understand and feel that. But it's not just about caring for them, you are also listening with interest to what is the real truth about what happened in this situation. This may mean that, at some point, you'll need to challenge either one or both of them on some things they are saying or feeling, but you must always do so in a caring, attentive and respectful way. If you handle it in that sensitive way they will feel reassured when you challenge them."

"I think I understand that, Teresa, even though I've no idea how it'll work or if it will work."

"I understand that, Tom, but I'm convinced that it will work and that you'll make it work if you handle it in such a way. I think the real, full and rich truth will emerge and you'll be able to get both of them to see that truth, whatever it is. If you ever want to talk to me about it then please feel free to do so, but I don't think you'll need to. I think you'll find it or it will find you on your own."

> "Let others see their own greatness when looking in your eyes"
>
> **Mollie Marti**

"Okay, Teresa, I'll do that and, for some strange reason, I think it will work and I prefer this way of going after it rather than the formal investigation route, even if I have no idea what the outcome here will be."

"Well done, Tom, and I admire you for what you're doing in taking this on. It's never easy to go into something completely blind or unclear about what the outcome may be and that, as we know, is especially true for us managers. So, thanks for doing this."

Another miracle!

Teresa received no more information about this matter in the following weeks and didn't make any inquiries, but she had told Mike about it.

"Is this your revenge for my appointing Albert, Teresa?," he laughed.

"Ha ha, not at all Mike. You know I trusted your decision and, who knows, Albert may be perfectly happy about this issue. He's been doing very well and shown great courage so I hope it's resolved in an acceptable way for him too. He's ruffled some feathers, so he's not popular with everyone and that's why it's important that it's dealt with in an agreeable way."

She heard nothing more about the change either, so it seemed to have continued to be successful. Then, one evening when she was about to leave the office, Tom asked if he could have a few minutes with her. He seemed relaxed and happy.

"So, what news have you for me, and by the looks of you it seems it's all good news!"

"Yes, you're right and I'm glad to say that it is. All done, all over, and all happy."

"Pray tell me more!"

"I really have nothing new to tell you and nothing that will be of any great surprise to *you*. You're a wizard. It turned out exactly like you said! I did exactly as you suggested and we had two individual meetings and one joint one. Strangely, Albert ended up apologising to her!"

"Really? That doesn't sound too good."

"No, on the contrary, it was *very* good. He didn't apologise for what he had done but because he said he believed that he hadn't understood her or her situation adequately. He had no doubts that what he did was the right thing but he underestimated the effect he had had on her. Indeed it was because he was so convinced and felt so right that he mishandled the situation just a little bit because he didn't make enough effort to really understand her problem and where she was coming from. What had happened was that she felt cornered and panicked.

She had serious doubts, both conscious and unconscious ones, about her ability to cope with her new responsibilities, so she went into resistance mode about the whole change. She felt or she claimed that Albert's passion and conviction was overpowering and she felt defenceless. She knew or suspected that Albert was making sense and being fair, but he sounded just the same as other managers she had known and worked for. It was this that she called bullying.

A typical and easy call. He admitted that what made it worse was the fact that what he was saying made so much sense and she couldn't argue back about anything. Her only port of call was to go after how he was handling things, which she labelled as bullying. Albert understood the effect he had on her, even if that was not at all his intention. He was apologetic for not understanding how she was feeling and why. He also realised that he has some things to do that will help her greatly and he can change some things quite easily. They both ended up in a great place and, in fact, were *both* apologetic about how they had handled the whole thing."

"And, do you mind telling me, how you achieved that happy outcome? You seem to have done magical work!"

"Not at all, it happened exactly as you described and worked for the reasons that you mentioned. I did very little and, actually, doing very little and saying very little was what made the difference. Yes, that was new for me but it felt great. I listened to both of them and was, as you said, really present to them, concerned only for *their* individual well-being and the answer just popped out or became very evident. I had to give just a little bit of help to both of them to take the risk out of being honest about all that they did, but it was very little."

"Well, I'm thrilled to hear all that and just imagine, Tom, all the trouble and time that would have been wasted if we had begun that formal investigation!"

"I was thinking the very same myself but also I was thinking about how unsatisfactory the result would have been compared to what we have come up with. One of them would have won and the other lost, or maybe both lost in some sense and the repercussions would have remained for a long time."

> "Let your creative and imaginative mind run freely; it will take you places you never dreamed of and provide breakthroughs that others once thought were impossible"
>
> **Idowu Koyenikan**

"Yes, and as I said, Tom, they would both have been given a bad name, which might have gone against them for a long time to come."

"You're absolutely right, Teresa, and I see this as a really big learning experience about how we need to handle all kinds of situations. I am especially happy about what I learned around my own role as a manager and how differently I was in this situation compared to how I normally would have been. It was very powerful but in a very different way, a very different form of power."

Me a bear?

Mike asked Bernard if he would be agreeable to share his story about "managing your bear" at the next meeting and he said he had no problem doing that.

When Bernard had finished his explanation and told the group how useful it was for him in managing his manager, Tom said:

"So you want us to use this process in managing Mike?"

They all laughed.

"You already do it very well, all of you," Mike said. "I know your tricks," he said laughing. "But what you may not know and that I know, is that each of you has to manage the bear within yourself."

"What you mean?" Heather asked. "*You*'re the bear here!" "Yes, I am, but you›re all bears too, with your own people and with other people in the organisation and you might forget this."

"Oh, I see", Heather said, "I never thought of it like this before. Imagine! My lovely customer service people see me as a bear. Me! So what does managing the bear in yourself mean or involve?"

"What do you all think?" Mike asked. Tom was smiling but said nothing. He knew very well what Mike was talking about.

"The first thing, I think," Teresa said, "is, like Heather has just commented – to realise that we are bears. I'm sure, like Heather, none of us saw ourselves like that and we could be oblivious to the effects we have on people who see us as being very powerful. We might say something very lightly or casually and not be aware of the effects it could have on other people. I think this is very important."

"I agree," Natalie said, "and we could have people who are afraid of us and we mightn't realise that at all."

"You can be sure of that," Mike said, "I know that's a fact in some of your cases anyway."

> "He who controls others may be powerful, but he who has mastered himself is mightier still"
>
> **Lao Tzu**

"I can vouch for that," Terry said. "I had a meeting on a project two weeks ago, and I became frustrated at it and barked at a person who was new to the meeting, and I heard afterwards they were very upset. Luckily, somebody told me that, or otherwise I would never have known, would never have realised that she saw me as a bear. It's really important to know we have power and to use it well."

"And you see that clearly now? Terry" Teresa asked.

"Yes, very. I've learned a lot of late and I've done some thinking since our self-awareness or "Enneagram" session. At the time I wasn't clear about where I stood in terms of my personality type, but I'm much clearer now. And I have a lot of work to do, so don't let anyone think I've had an overnight conversion." Terry laughed.

"Delighted to hear that Terry", Teresa added, "And, like Terry says, we can be unaware of our strength and what we do, and think we are operating in good faith. It's for that reason that very often we managers are accused of bullying without ever being aware of it ourselves. We're just not conscious of our own strength. But when we hear that someone has accused us of bullying, we're shocked. We can be very nice people but just underestimate who we are and of the power we have."

Why we bully so often

"Yes," Mike said, "but remember what we said and agreed some weeks back – that if we, or any of our managers ask people to do things without giving them the rationale for doing those things, then we're being violent and, in fact, bullying. Do you remember that? Apart from being unwise as a management approach, it's actually wrong to ask or expect somebody to do something just because *we* say it. If we do that, we're asking and expecting them to go against or ignore their own rationality and so their own humanity."

"I think that's very important," Sally said, "but I was also struck by what Bernard said about boundaries. Everyone needs some boundaries within which they can operate comfortably, but we can be the biggest offenders in ignoring such boundaries. I'm a major offender in that regard. I can call meetings at the drop of a hat and people drop hats or down tools irrespective of what they might have on. After all, the Finance Department is what ultimately matters!" she said, laughing. "But people feel they can't say no.

It has just become normal now. When we do this, apart from making people feel insecure, we're robbing them of their rightful ownership and accountability for things. Setting up good and clear boundaries will help *us* too, because it means that we trust people to get things done and so they'll be freed up from worrying and following up and checking and wondering what *we* are thinking. I have really learned that in the past few months and learned a lot about myself. Trust and finance are not good bedfellows! As Galbraith said: "There is nothing as cowardly as money". I know that. I have been managing my department and my people in quite a cowardly and cautious way."

"Well I know that story very well," Bernard followed on, "from my own manager as I explained at the beginning of this meeting but, what's shocking me is that I do the very same. And I do it for what I thought were good reasons – my need to know what's going on, so I feel in control. Quality is even more important than Finance Sally! I interfere, get involved, ask for reports and reviews and respect no boundaries. And nobody ever tells me that. They wouldn't dare! I would maul them!" he said laughing.

Mike stole a glance at Tom who was still smiling quietly.

"What I now realise," Tom said, "is how dismissive I am of ideas and suggestions that people make. I do it so often. I do treat them like children and as if I know best always. And, of course they are afraid to push back or challenge me."

"I understand that." Frank said. "We can think that fear is a good thing to have and a good power to use, but fear is never good. It's a very easy and indeed cowardly way to get things done as you say, Sally. I've seen so many managers use it and it gave them great control. But they never got really good performance from their people, either, as they were more focused on not upsetting or angering their managers, than they were about doing the right thing. They became too cautious and became afraid to take any risks. When people are afraid and act out of fear, they don't do anything wrong but don't do very much right either.

By behaving as very strong managers and probably unconsciously mistreating our people, we can block them and so we lose their support and never get the best from them. Remember all those blocks we talked about months ago. This is it! People can go into their shells, become overly careful, play the game and end up making a relatively poor contribution overall. It's a price we pay that's invisible but enormous, because we take it as how things and people are, without realising that it's *we* who made them like that – cautious, lacking initiative, following and not leading … just mediocre.

Very different from the people Mark seems to have found!"

Doing permanent damage to people

"The trouble is," Natalie added, "that it's easy to do damage and lose people's trust forever. It doesn't seem fair but we can mark and harm people by just one attack or outburst or unfair treatment. People don't forget or, even if they try, the wound can remain. It's a bit like a dog that bites you once and forever more, even if they're nice and friendly and wag their tails, you always have that fear that they might do it again.

I made a relatively small mistake with a supplier improvement campaign we were running in my last job and my manager, who was normally supportive and courteous, savaged me.

I never forgot it and was always on my guard ever after, in case he did it again. I know it's silly but that's how I am and probably how most people are."

"Well I can understand that," Teresa said, "we're responsible for the effects we have on people. Good intentions are not good enough. It's not only how things leave our mouths but also about how they arrive to the other person and how they affect them that matters. Getting things off your chest can be great for you but not for the other person who has to receive them! We need to be aware of the effects we're having on people.

> "There is no greatness where there is not simplicity, goodness, and truth"
>
> **Leo Tolstoy**

And, remember too that just as Bernard needs to feed his bear, our people need feeding too and they need to be looked after. And if you all don't do this, they end up at my door looking to be fed, and very unhappy at the same time. They're not all the same, they will have different needs, so we must be attentive and intelligent around spotting what their needs are."

"I agree," Tom said, "and we need to protect them and stand up for them as well. Some people can feel insecure and be afraid and we can help them by giving them assurances and, without being in any way paternalistic, we can defend and protect them when that's justified. Some people need that reassurance and perform better when they feel more confident. We're not all the same and we can think that everyone else believes we are.

Remember all Teresa told us about the "Enneagram"? The interesting thing about it for me is that we can take ourselves as "normal" with everyone else slightly off kilter. But we all have our different ways of seeing and handling things and we can be very blind to how we are. Now stop laughing under your breaths please! Things that I see as normal, others may not see them like that at all. So I can expect people to respond to situations and events as I would, forgetting that everyone responds in a different way. But because of my position I can insist on it. But you all know all this."

"Oh, we never saw you as normal, Tom. Have no fears. Haha. But, I'd like to go back to what Terry said," Sally commented, "and, maybe I'm speaking for myself, but sometimes I fear I take things out on people! I can be cranky and in bad form sometimes and looking for a cat to kick or someone to blame for something being wrong, and in my job, something will always be wrong. I need to cop myself on and be more aware of myself, so this is a very important message for me."

"And do it MY way"

"I can identify with that," Tony said, "but I think my biggest weakness is wanting things done *my* way always, like throwing my weight around. Okay, I can see you're smiling because you've all seen it in me anyway, but, seriously, it's something I'm looking at because it doesn't do me or anybody else any good. As you say, Mike, it's a form of bullying. Terry and I have spoken about this a few days ago.

I'm an engineer and precision and ensuring everything is done correctly is very important for me. That is one reason why I was so critical of Terry when we had that problem with Sharon and KEY Services. I wanted things done my way, correctly. While that's fine, "correctly" may be just my own version of what is correct or how something should be done. But my people, unlike you lot, take it from me and go along with it. They have no choice. And I'm learning, no, stop laughing, I'm learning, that their ways will very often be even better than mine, hard as that is to believe ... for me!" he joked.

"I have to come clean here on this," Teresa said, "This has probably been the greatest and most difficult learning that I have experienced since we began this search or whatever it is. And, you may be surprised to hear, that it was

> "The unexamined life is not worth living"
>
> **Socrates**

409

not about work at all! It was about my own two children who, as you all know, have not been the easiest to manage in the past few years. But I learned that I was very much part of the problem by how I was acting as a parent. Unknowingly I was a very strong bear with them. As a result, they reacted in all kinds of ways to protect their own spaces and freedoms and, I suppose, their dignity. As some of you know, there has been a huge change or transformation in them and they're taking great responsibility for their lives and taking themselves very seriously. This has been a greater transformation for me than we have achieved here."

"And what did you do differently?" Tony asked.

"It's hard to sum up in a few words, but I changed how I related to them. I got some help from a friend on this, on how to handle them better. So, I became present to them as a mother but to help them think through where *they* were at and what *they* wanted. In essence, I coached them and trusted them that they would work out what to do if I let them, and helped them to do so. It was very difficult at times and felt very risky. It still does, to be honest.

They came up with many things that I was not too convinced about, but I went with them and eventually it all turned out so well. I don't agree with everything they say or do and I don't have to. But, not only are they much better and doing well but now we're all good friends and they come to me with things that they want to talk about, which is great."

"And why do you think they're doing that now, Teresa?" Natalie asked.

"I think – and indeed I'm sure – it's because they now know I'll listen to them and not give out to them, neither correcting nor even advising them. I just listen and remain present to them, talking them through things until they're happy that they know what to do. The kinds of things that we're beginning to do here now with our own people. But, enough of me and my private life. I just had to share that with you because I now know that this approach really works."

"Well said Teresa. Thanks for that. And well done everybody," Mike said. "As you can see we all have a lot of work to do on ourselves, myself included. You all did very well and, as each of you was talking about the areas that you need to look at, I kept saying to myself: "me too, me too". And can I hear some big lessons from this about how we all need to manage and behave?"

Principles and practices

Everybody then contributed ideas on what they needed to do differently in the future and Mike summarised them in the following list.

1. Understand that you are a bear or are perceived to be one. This might help you understand people's behaviours around you.
2. Understand that people, at least some people, are or may be afraid of you.
3. Don't underestimate the power you have – to do good things and to damage people.
4. If you once maul people they will find it hard to trust you in future.
5. Understand people's barriers and respect them as much as you can.
6. Look after people and they will feed you and look after you.
7. Protect your people and use your power to do so. They will respect you for this.
8. Be aware of what annoys or upsets you and that this may be more about you than about the actual situation. Bears too should occasionally take a look at themselves!
9. Beware of throwing your weight around, bullying and getting your own way always. It is not always good for you or for anyone else.
10. Clever and powerful as you are, you have a lot of other clever people around you. Make the most of them and they will make life much easier for you.

"Thank you all. That's a great list. And we can help each other on all these behavioural issues. We have spoken before about getting feedback from others and I think it would be appropriate if we each did that within this team as well, because, as we said some time ago, we're unaware of our blind spots.

And, in case you may be thinking that we're now going to become all nice and soft, it's not like that at all. In actual fact, being aware of ourselves and our strengths will allow us to be much more honest with our people and to be very frank with them. Others will have much more respect for us if we work in this way. Nobody really respects a bully and it's very easy to be a bully as a manager without even being aware of it. Let's work on it and help each other. Suppose you all had a word with Teresa to find out who you would like to act as a coach for you to give you feedback about yourself and your behaviour. Would you all be up for that?"

> "Better a cruel truth than a comfortable delusion"
>
> **Edward Abbey**

They all nodded their agreement.

"Now I'm not enforcing this, so don't accuse me of acting like a bear, but I think it would be a help to us all. Teresa knows I have my own coach and people who give me feedback. That's why I'm so perfect." he joked.

Questions for reflection and action

1. In what way are managers bears and why are they not aware that they are bears? What is the very first step required to deal with this?
2. Why does Teresa say that managing and bullying often go hand in hand? Why are managers often surprised and even shocked when they are accused of bullying?

3. What boundaries do you have with your own people? Are they clear ones and well understood? What are the major challenges to respecting boundaries with people?

4. What is wrong with fear as a motivator and driver of performance?

5. What does Teresa mean when she says that we are responsible for the effects of what we do and say?

6. Why do managers need to be especially aware of and careful around their moods and emotions?

Chapter 26
Circling Wagons Often Makes Sense

The risks and rewards from being courageous, open and honest, town hall meeting

Mike thought of cancelling a planned Town Hall session prior to the visit of the company's corporate executives. He felt nervous about standing in front of people and giving them a message and inviting them to commit to a new effort to improve the company while he was unsure about even being around to lead that initiative. He could not be entirely open with people. That would be irresponsible. This was a matter he had to face alone to a great extent. He talked it over with Teresa but, in the end, decided to go ahead with it. They reckoned that not holding it might cause more concern than facing up to the challenges as honestly as he could.

At the meeting, as usual, Terry and Tom and Sally shared the expected information and, as usual, there were no questions. Then Mike spoke for a few minutes about the overall situation and talked about the forthcoming visit.

"I think everybody here is aware that we have an executive visit in two weeks' time and this will be nothing new for most of you. I know you'll do your usual good job in presenting our company in the best possible light. I never cease to be impressed with the quality of the explanations and help you give to visitors like these on their plant tours.

It's easy to take these visits for granted and it's equally dangerous to do so. Corporate executives make these visits in order to get a good feel for our different operations and I know they use this information in their decision-making around the business and which sites or locations should be developed and which phased out or closed down.

I believe this forthcoming visit could be a bit different from other visits in that it's the express purpose of this visit, as part of a tour of various sites, to assess which sites are core to the overall strategy and which can be dispensed with."

Mike could sense some change in the atmosphere in the canteen but he also knew that some would hear what he was saying as sabre rattling.

"That said, I wouldn't like you to do anything different this time from what you normally do. And you all know by now, that I like us being open and honest with all our visitors and showing and telling them as it is. I would hope that you're all able be honest in reflecting the efforts that we've been making to transform this into a very special place to work. We're only beginning. We have a long way to go. But I hope that you'll have sensed the beginning, at least, of a programme of work to make this a very special company and entity – a place where you're proud to work and where you're equally proud of the contribution you're making and that you genuinely feel recognised for that. We have done fairly well in terms of recognising the efforts you make, and there's more to be done.

You've all heard me say many times that your individual rewards and overall welfare rest on the overall performance of our company. However, it's equally important to ensure that the translation of improvements and results into rewards for those who ultimately make those results happen needs to be fair and equitable. That's always a challenge, and it's one that I personally am taking on, without any guarantees that I can deliver on that challenge."

While there was some little more interest in what Mike was saying, the message and soundbites seemed the same as usual and people's level of interest remained at the usual low level.

"It's the possibility of having a dream come true that makes life interesting"

Paulo Coelho, The Alchemist

Responsible, yes, but to whom?

"I believe we all have a responsibility to each other, to those who come after us, to our community, to our suppliers and partners and to ourselves to make it very difficult for the corporation to decide against this site. I think we're all doing very well in this regard, and we have successfully dealt with some serious challenges over the past few months which will stand in our favour, I hope. I say, 'I hope' because my lords and masters – and I can't add "mistresses" – are not always happy with how I or we handle things here. But, I'm proud to say that we have consistently delivered on our commitments and met our targets."

While there was some increase in interest, much of it sounded the same message as usual.

Mike continued. "I would like you all to understand that defending or promoting the standing and status of this company is of great importance to me. I say that, not because doing so will further my cause, get me a bonus or improve my standing in the management hierarchy or ladder. None of those have any great interest for me. I tell you this because I would like you to understand that this is what I will be doing during the executive visit in two weeks' time.

I want you all to know that my loyalty is to *this* company and to *you* and not to my career or some other agenda. I believe that doing that, developing this site, this operation, and working to make it as good and successful as possible is the way I can make the best contribution to you and the corporation. I wouldn't like any one of you here to think that I'll be in the boardroom in two weeks' time looking after either the exclusive welfare of the corporation or my own. I assure you I will do nothing that will advance my own career or standing at the expense of this company or anyone in it. I would like you all to know that as long as I'm here, I will be loyal to this company and to you who work in it."

Mike could see that the atmosphere in the room had changed.

"I hope everybody here understands that both I and my management team are very clear, convinced and at one, that the welfare of this company plays or should play a key part in the welfare of every-body who works here. We don't see any conflict between your personal welfare and the welfare of this company. Your own managers have, I'm sure, already shared their own belief with you that by working to develop this company and improve it – and we do need to do that and need your help to do it – we are

> "Be who you are and say what you feel, because those who mind don't matter, and those who matter don't mind"
>
> **Bernard M. Baruch**

promoting and adding to the welfare of every individual. This doesn't mean that there won't be times when we have to take tough decisions. But, when we do this we will be equally clear that we're doing it for the welfare of your company and so for *your* welfare. That is our responsibility, not only to our company or the corporation, but to you. I would like nobody here to be in any doubt about that. I'll honour that commitment for as long as I'm here. That doesn't mean that I'm in full control of the destiny of this company and so of your destiny.

Nobody is. I don't have the wherewithal to be able to guarantee you absolute security. Nobody has. But I'll do my best to maximise that security and optimise your welfare in the process. Who knows what will happen during this forthcoming visit? It would be remiss and irresponsible of me not to share the challenges we face.

You know that sometimes we differ on things, you and I and my management team. Sometimes, I challenge you on things and we disagree. I do that always, not because it's good for the corporation only, or for me, but because I believe it's the right and best thing for *everybody*. Equally, I challenge my corporate masters and, again, we differ and disagree. I also do so not because it's good for us, for our company here or for you, but because I believe it's what is right and best for everybody.

I say this because I would like you to understand that not every-thing is in my hands or in our hands, but there is a lot that we *can* do to promote the security and welfare of our company. I assure you that that is a very clear goal or objective of mine, not only for this forthcoming visit, but for everything we do. I want to thank you for the very good work you do and for your generosity in doing it and in devoting a considerable part of your lives to this company. I don't think we, as management, have always adequately recognised that. I don't think that we, as management, have always managed and led as we might have. But, we're committed to doing that as well as we can and to continue to improve the leadership we give you.

Terry and Heather try to look after our customers on behalf of everybody. Frank and Natalie work hard to make sure our suppliers look after us because it's also in their own best interests to do so. We have responsibilities to our corporation and Sally looks after ensuring that we do that well and that corporate management see and understand that we do it well. She also does a wonderful job, which I'm sure none of you know anything about, in ensuring that as a company we're making our contribution to the welfare of society and this country and doing so in a fair and honest way. It gets her into trouble now and again but she's up for that.

It's not Bernard's job to be concerned about the community, but I'm so happy that he took on the challenge of working to make sure we're always seen as a really valued member of this community, as truly good citizens. Many of you are very aware of that. I think it's more apparent to you what Tony and Teresa and Tom and Bernard do every day to keep this place operating and functioning really well. Again, on all our behalf I hope all of this is clear and thank you for your attention.

More importantly, I thank you for your continued efforts every day to make this a really good company for all our benefits. It can appear, like I have just outlined, that the big players and shakers and makers are up here, but really we produce nothing, not a thing. It is *you* who do it and I appreciate and thank you for that. Thanks again."

For a few moments there was silence, with people wondering if that was the end of what Mike had to say. Then, somewhere, somebody began to clap and then everybody did. Mike felt stupid that he had to hold back tears, but he consoled himself with the thought that the effort to bring about the cultural change he wanted over the previous months had been wearing on him and had taken its toll on him, not to mention the enormous challenge he faced in two weeks' time.

There was a buzz in the room and among his own team. Some said 'Well done'. Some looked bemused or confused. Many people thanked him and congratulated him and wished him well as he made his way back to his office. It was as if he was leaving or that they sensed it was possibly the end of something.

Visit from the "trouble makers"

An hour later he received a request for a meeting with some people. He recognised the names. They were all members of the so-called "staff committee". "What have I done or said wrong now?" he thought. "Whose toes have I managed to step on?"

> "If you want to know what a man's like, take a good look at how he treats his inferiors, not his equals"
>
> **J.K. Rowling**

Matt and Alice and Larry looked serious and sullen when they came in. He greeted them warmly and they sat around the meeting table.

"You may or may not know why we three are here. We've been involved over the past nine months in trying to establish a form of staff committee." Matt said.

"Yes," Mike smiled, "I knew that, and I guessed that's why you three are here. Thanks for coming in, but how can I help you?"

Alice answered. "I'm not sure what you know about us, Mike, and what we've been doing in this past year. I won't try to explain it all, but essentially, we felt that as staff and as workers, we needed to have more of a say in things, rather than being on the receiving end of decisions from management on everything.

You could say it was a question of rights. Decisions, and what happened as a result of them, were all one-way and we and our colleagues were always on the receiving end. It was what management in their wisdom decided that only mattered and we were expected to take their word for the merit and validity of such decisions and go along with them. This was so, irrespective if the decision was something we welcomed or not.

We were never consulted, except on relatively minor matters such as the layout of the canteen, sports and social club activities, safety committees and things like that. Some of them were important and valuable, but none of them had much impact on the things that were done here and how they were done. We weren't trying to be a trade union, negotiating terms and conditions and pay etcetera – though that too might have happened. It was more about being treated with respect and having some kind of voice in what was decided.

That's why we got together and persuaded many others to join us. We felt that management were doing what they liked with us and we didn't like what we saw them doing. I'm saying all this because we never had the opportunity to say it before. It seems that you were very definite about not wanting to recognise us.

"Yes, that's so, and I'm very happy to explain why I refused to recognise you as a group."

Mike was going to continue but Larry interrupted him.

"Sorry to interrupt you or cut across you, Mike, but I don't think you need to explain to us why you took that stance. There were times when we didn't understand why you were so adamant and closed about it, but we do now."

Mike smiled, "I'm delighted to hear that and curious as to why you now understand my apparent close mindedness."

Matt came in. "Well, there were times, Mike, when we were very angry with you for refusing to talk to us. We couldn't understand it because you always seemed reasonable and open-minded.

But over the past months we have seen an enormous change in how things are done and in how management relate to us and take decisions. At first we thought it was a ploy, a tactic to get around us and undermine us. Then we saw that it was genuine. There were more and more situations where managers changed their minds from listening to people, from engaging with people, and not only on operating issues.

On one occasion, my own line manager, Albert, completely reversed a direction he wanted to take when he met with our team. Not that what he had intended doing was stupid or very wrong, or even that he was completely convinced that what we were saying was right. But he trusted us and was willing to go with what *we* wanted and *our* rationale and was prepared to give it a chance. But it worked and worked very well. What made it even better was that he recognised this and told us that our plan was actually a better one than what he had in mind. But that's just one example of the change that we have been seeing over the past few months. We don't always get our way when we differ, but it's always 'what makes most sense' that rules and we find that respectful and wise."

> "There are only two ways to influence human behaviour: you can manipulate it or you can inspire it. Very few people or companies can clearly articulate WHY they do WHAT they do. By WHY I mean your purpose, cause or belief – WHY does your company exist? WHY do you get out of bed every morning? And WHY should anyone care?"
>
> **Simon Sinek**

"I'm so pleased to hear all that. We've been trying to change and there is more changing we have to do. It isn't always easy, believe me."

Whose side are you on?

"We know that," Alice said, "we can see the efforts that everybody is making. But, Mike, it was your message this afternoon that made it all very clear to us. We met as a small group after your talk and spoke to a few others and we agreed that we would disband whatever identity or structure we had as a staff committee.

We've been mostly inactive because there has been no need to be active but we wanted to formally let you know that we don't exist anymore as a committee. We think it's important that you know that, and that it's generally known before the visit takes place in a few weeks' time. We know that word has reached the corporation about the unrest that people felt and now we want to make it clear that it no longer exists.

It was unavoidable that word would reach people in corporate management because of the many contacts we have with colleagues there. It was not what we wanted but we're aware that it could have a negative effect and be counter to what you want to achieve during this visit."

"I'm glad to hear that," Mike answered, "because, you're right, it caused quite a stir in corporate circles when they were told of this. I always assured them that it was nothing serious, but I'm not sure whether they always believed me or not. But may I ask, what has now brought this to a head so that you are ceasing to exist as a group?"

It was Matt who answered. "It was what you said at the meeting, Mike. It became very clear to us and to everybody that you are very much on *our* side as are your entire team. We always took it that as manager, you had a responsibility to the corporation and that was over and above or against what might be good for our company here and for us as members of the company. We now see very clearly that you're on our side.

Now we are under no illusions that you can always deliver on what's best for us here, but it dawned on us that it was absurd to think that we needed to organise against somebody who was actually *on our side*, fighting on our behalf. To be honest, I think we slipped into traditional management–workers thinking, presuming that management, by virtue of being management, were on the side of the overall business and therefore we needed to be organised to defend ourselves."

"Yes, that's exactly how I saw it, Matt," Mike answered, "and that's why I refused to let management or myself be portrayed as fighting against the welfare of staff here. I knew that if I did or allowed that, I would have created two completely artificial sides and I couldn't go along with that. But I want to pick up on one thing that you said about me being on the side of this company as against the side of the corporation. It's not exactly like that. It's that I believe that the best contribution I can make to the corporation is to make this company here the very best it can be in every sense. That's my responsibility and as the general manager here, it's the best way I can serve the corporation in my role. Now, not everyone always understands this or even sees it like this." He laughed.

"Well," Alice said, "we're sorry for any trouble that we caused but I hope you understand where we were coming from. We only wanted to be respected and involved. Because we had no other way to make an impact, we formed the association. Now we have involvement, real involvement, so we don't need the association anymore. There has been a real change. We and many others have been involved in different meetings and forums on big strategic issues. This is a huge change and I hope you understand that, Mike?"

"I certainly do. And I say that because as a management team, we have often failed badly in how we manage people. We are all stuck in old traditional ways and it can be difficult to get away from them. We're still struggling with that as you can see. But we're trying to follow a very different management paradigm and I'm glad to hear that that is being noticed and felt."

"There are only two ways to live your life. One is as though nothing is a miracle. The other is as though everything is a miracle"

Albert Einstein

"It certainly is," Larry said, "and we'll play our part to make sure that your efforts and those of management are recognised and reciprocated."

In view of all that he had struggled with and in view of the forthcoming visit, for the first time Mike felt that maybe, just maybe everything might be alright. He dared to imagine how welcome this would be for Joan, for his team, for the people in general and for himself and the struggle he'd been engaged in.

"I want to be honest with you, as always, and thank you for coming to meet me today. You could have just slipped away quietly and disappeared, and nobody would have minded. It took some courage and honesty on your part to come and say this to me. I'm very grateful and it does make a big difference to me. As you have heard me say, I cannot guarantee anything. I am not in full control. It can feel a lonely place at times, but, this kind of support makes a huge difference to me and actually helps me to be stronger and better in representing this company and all who work here. Thanks again."

They all shook hands with Mike and left.

When they had left, Mike sat and marvelled at what had just happened. Could this be one of those miracles that happened to Moses in the desert as Sally had mentioned? "I hope so," he thought, "and I think I'm going to need a lot more of them in the next two weeks!" he smiled to himself.

Questions for reflection and action

1. Does the change of heart on the part of the committee make sense? If so, why?
2. Do you think they are unwise to give up all of their 'power' and trust management?
3. Why might they not see it like this?
4. What was the most important thing that Mike did or said that made all the difference?
5. What relevance has this for you, even if you have no union or staff committee?

Chapter 27
"OK Corral" Time. The Set-up

Planning and being ready is everything... or IS it?

Mike's boss, Martha, asked him if he needed any help preparing for the visit of Brad, the corporate VP, but Mike said it would not be necessary. He was clear about what was on the agenda, the main topics being

- The usual performance topics
- The corporate-local relationship
- Relationships and issues with government authorities
- Future, forecasts and plans
- Heather's status as a director
- Corporate local culture and style

Mike knew the extent and seriousness of what lay behind many of these topics. What was hidden and overt was what most worried him.

Martha continued to offer support. They should prepare and go through the different topics and presentations before the trip, she insisted. And then, when she arrived, they could spend an hour or two going over everything to make sure they get it right.

"I know him well, Mike," she said, "and I know the corporation well. And this is a very important meeting for all of us, you included. We'll only have one chance at it."

Mike listened but, despite much pressure from Martha, refused all help of any kind.

"Thanks for your offer, Martha and I understand what you're saying. I appreciate your offer, but this time I want to handle it differently, whatever the consequences. I think it'll go fine, whatever happens."

"Ok, Mike. If that's what you want, there's little more I can do to help. I have tried. By the way, do you think there might be a chance for me to meet Joan as usual? We always have great discussions, and I would like to hear where she's at and what she's been thinking."

Mike wondered if this might be their last meeting but said nothing of that. The visit was to take place over two days with dinner on the night of the first day, as usual, which would be in Mark's House of Harmony restaurant.

"Sure Martha. There will be an hour or two before dinner on our first day and, if you're not too tired, Joan could come to your hotel."

"That would be great, Mike, and I'll be fine to meet Joan at one of those times."

Dry, very dry runs are out

But it wasn't only Martha who asked about preparation for the visit. It was raised and discussed at their senior team meeting and Mike made it clear that there was no need for any special preparation.

"I only want everybody to be honest and completely open. You all have whatever information will be required and, if something special is needed, we'll get it during the visit. Is that clear and are you all happy with that?"

They weren't happy and they all asked various questions and struggled with the idea of doing no preparation, having no dry runs of presentations.

> "Don't bend; don't water it down; don't try to make it logical; don't edit your own soul according to the fashion. Rather, follow your most intense obsessions mercilessly"
>
> **Franz Kafka**

Mike persisted and insisted he wanted no special preparatory work done.

"Some of you will face serious challenges during this visit. You know what I mean, Sally? And so do you Tom and Teresa. But, you'll all be challenged in different ways. I assure you, this will not be an easy meeting, but it will be a good one, once we're honest and courageous about what we're doing and why. Teresa knows that I face special challenges, But I'm ready for these in the sense that I knew I would have to face them at some stage. I hope you're all okay with that."

Despite his clarity on the matter, he had several individual visits in the following days from people asking if he wanted this or that covered. His answer was always the same. "You cover and do whatever you think is best and right and I trust you'll handle that well, as usual."

He chose not to mention to Heather that her status was on the agenda. He thought it was better to leave it with the other things that needed to be resolved.

Welcoming a real bear

Mike had arranged for a car to pick up Martha and Brad from the airport and met them at reception when they arrived, getting them signed in and organised.

All of Mike's team joined them for coffee and were introduced to Brad, none of whom had previously met him, though some of them had spoken with him. Most of them knew Martha, whom they warmly greeted and welcomed. You could touch the apprehension in the room.

When coffee was finished, Mike got everybody seated and explained how he would like to handle the visit.

He outlined and ensured the objectives for the visit as Martha had explained them, checked these with Brad and asked his own team to do everything in their power to help achieve Brad's objectives.

He explained to Brad and Martha that they had had no prior meetings on what to cover or how to handle things as he wanted his team to feel free to share anything they wanted and to answer all Brad's questions and needs as openly and honestly as possible.

"I hope you're in agreement with this, Brad. It's just that I've seen too many visits like this turn into shows for the visitor, hiding what we don't want them to see and showcasing for them what we do want them to see. All of the information that you will require, Brad, is readily available anyway. I know everybody is aware of how important this meeting is. We have some big issues to discuss and equally big decisions to take, especially you, Brad, and I want to help you in every way I can to take those decisions and to help you make the right ones."

> "There's nothing more efficient than honesty and nothing more powerful than vulnerability, because vulnerability reveals everyone in your life who will abuse power immediately and almost irrevocably.
> Be vulnerable. Be honest.
> Be open and show your heart. That's the best way of telling your heart that the tigers are no longer in the grass"
>
> **Stefan Molyneux**

Mike was very relaxed in saying all of this, but you could sense the tension and sense of expectation in the room. Everybody knew it was a very different way of handling a visit like this and nobody was at all sure how it would go. Everyone felt uncomfortable.

"I'm fine with that, Mike," Brad replied in an apparently relaxed way, "do you have some kind of time-plan for the two days? Do we have one Martha? I would like to feel sure we can get through everything in the time," he asked.

"Yes, Mike and I have talked about this, and he said he would prepare a suitable time plan."

"Yes Brad, while I know in general what you'd like, rather than have things orchestrated for you, I felt it might be better to hear how you would like to handle things in order for you to make the most of your time with us. I can guess at most of these, but what are some critical things that you would like to do?"

"Well, I'm familiar with what's happening, performance, results, etcetera but it would be good to go through these so that I can get behind some of the words and numbers. As usual, I would like to spend a lot of time having a look around and talking to some people, so I can get my own feel for things. You and I, Mike have some topics we need to discuss and we'll definitely need time for that, a lot of time. And, I would like to have the opportunity to spend some time with some or most of your own team to get to know them and to hear how they see things. We have some issues, Sally, that we need to discuss about some government changes that you have raised.

Is that okay?"

"Yes that's great," Mike answered. "Suppose you and I and Martha spend an hour or so first off, to begin a discussion on some of those crucial points. Then we could spend some of the afternoon going through the overall business – our performance, results, and our plans and projects for the future. We could break that up with a short walk around just to give you a feel for the operation and to help you decide where you would like to spend more time tomorrow. You and Martha and I could then spend some more time to discuss those areas of concern that you have.

"You'll want a fairly early night so we might meet at 6.30 for aperitifs and we could use that and dinner for you to spend some time with the other members of the team. Again, you might need to spend more time with some than with others and I have an office for you where you could meet some people tomorrow.

What I suggest, then, is that you and Martha decide how you would most like to spend tomorrow. As I said, I would imagine you'll want to look at some selected areas and meet some members of this team. Then we can decide that in the morning and continue our discussions and decision-making. How does that sound?"

"It sounds fine," Brad replied. "Quite different, I would say. I'm accustomed to a more organised and rigid timetable, but I'm satisfied with it once we have time for those essential discussions, Mike."

"Don't worry. I think there's plenty of time for that Brad. I promise you, you'll not go away without having had the opportunity to get into and deal with whatever you wish. That's what I want too."

Cards on the table

The others left and Martha, Brad and Mike sat down for their first meeting.

"I won't beat around the bush," Brad said, "you know that there are many things that concern us and that we must resolve. I know that Martha has kept you informed, and you and I have had our different exchanges as well."

> "To be yourself in a world that is constantly trying to make you something else is the greatest accomplishment"
>
> **Ralph Waldo Emerson**

There was little doubt about how serious his tone was and little doubt in anybody's mind how difficult the meeting was going to be.

"Yes Brad, I'm very aware of that and very aware of your issues and concerns and I really hope we can address them. As you know, this is important for me too, and my life, so I'll make every effort to resolve all relevant issues. Am I right in thinking that the main ones are:

A. You, or the corporation, have a problem with my, or our, management style and approach. You see it as being too loose and that I'm not sufficiently in control. I know that sometimes you have been upset or annoyed when I didn't have detailed answers for some of your questions nor detailed plans for what we were going to do. And I know you weren't happy with my leaving things up to people to resolve. And part of that would be a possible impression that we do just what *we* want to do and don't always follow corporate standards, protocols, procedures etcetera. It's my impression that you think that I only consider the welfare of this company here rather than the overall corporate welfare and you know that I disagree with that perception, but we can talk about that.

B. There are some issues with Teresa around Human Resources, around appointments, and around some of the directions that corporate HR want to take. Teresa will lead out on those discussions.

C. There is also the specific but very important topic of discussions we have been having with our own government authorities here and Sally has been handling those and should be involved in them. But, are they the main issues? I know we need to look at the whole area of performance, but I think that should be satisfactory, even though I would very much like to get your ideas on where you think we need to do better. So, are they the main areas that we need to lock horns on Brad?"

Brad looked somewhat taken aback at Mike's forthrightness but answered normally. "Yes, I think you've captured fairly well the main areas where I and others are unhappy. It's good that you see them so clearly, but I'm not sure I share your confidence about our ability to resolve them, without some serious changes Mike. You and I have had our personal clashes and differences but I wouldn't like this to be positioned as a problem between you and me only.

I came here with a very clear agenda and brief from my own peers and bosses and there's no way I can go back to them empty-handed. Like you, I want this to be a good meeting but that will only happen if we agree on those fundamental changes I mentioned, changes you need to make. Is that clear, Mike? Anything you want to add, Martha?"

"No Brad, I think that's very clear and I think Mike is clear about it too. He and I have spoken about it on a few occasions. This may be included

> "If there had been no troublemakers, no Dissenters, we should still be living in caves"
>
> A. J. P. Taylor

in what you listed, Mike, but there was the issue with that major client that caused all of us a lot of concern. We felt we should have been more involved and it all seemed very risky to us."

"Oh yes, Martha," Brad commented, "Yes, we were, and indeed are quite unhappy about that and how it was handled."

"I understand," Mike answered, "yes, that's important, and we can and will cover that incident."

Martha came back in. "I think I've been very honest with Mike, Brad, in the run-up to this meeting, that I didn't see any clear way out, or easy solution to all of this. I think some pain is unavoidable – breaking eggs to make omelettes etcetera."

Mike looked unperturbed about this discussion.

"Yes, Martha is right, she and I have had many conversations and I'm perfectly clear on how difficult this meeting will be. Very challenging. But I believe there's an acceptable way forward if we can find it. And I believe that if the three of us work honestly, respectfully and coura-geously together we'll find that solution. If we manage to do that, we'll be able to make sense of it to others. I can see that neither of you is too convinced of this, but I believe it's possible to achieve our goals fully." And, he was right, they didn't look at all convinced but nevertheless there was an air of expectation in the room.

"Are you both still happy to start off on the topic of performance, results, plans etcetera as I explained earlier?", asked Mike.

Brad looked worried and a bit impatient, but Martha said:

"Yes, I think that would be a good place to start. You said that you want the team involved in this, Mike? So maybe you should get them in."

Locking horns around customers

When they had all assembled, Mike turned to Brad and Martha and asked them where they would like to start.

They began with Sales and then moved to the other areas of Marketing, Operations and Finance.

Each area was covered by the respective manager.

The presentations were open and honest and difficulties and challenges and mistakes were shared in a very transparent way.

After they had made their presentation and shared their information, they asked Brad and Martha if they had any questions and they dealt with those.

They also asked if Brad or Martha had any concerns or ideas on what could be improved. There was no shortage of these and they were all noted, with the managers agreeing to consider them. Recommendations on which people in the corporation should be involved were made and commitments to follow up with them agreed.

There was some tension and uncertainty around plans and forecasts because some of them required agreement and support from the corporation. Some of the discussions were left up in the air for later resolution and it was apparent that everybody understood the background tension around the relationship between the company and the corporation. When Terry had covered the Sales situation and plan, Brad came in.

"Thanks for that, Terry, and well done. That all looks good. One of the things that Rick, our corporate Sales executive asked me to check up on was how we're doing in general on our client relationships. I gather at the time we had that issue with, was it KEY Services Limited? you weren't too happy with how you were dealing with their need. Isn't that so? Are you confident that you'll have enough support in the future and that we won't get into those kinds of risks again? That would have been serious had it gone wrong … and it nearly did, I understood."

"Yes, I'm very confident and I keep telling Rick that I am, and that we're in good shape."

"I think it's important that everyone is totally clear about this. Our customers are everything to us and without them

> "Insanity is doing the same thing, over and over again, but expecting different results"
>
> **Narcotics Anonymous**

we have nothing. Quite simply, the customer must always come first and I wasn't sure that such a clear understanding existed at that time. I picked up that there was a lot of talking, a lot of discussion, and a lot of negotiating. I think that's dangerous and I know that Rick does too. Is that clear Terry?"

"Yes, it is, but I feel very happy about how we handled that. Yes, Mike or myself could have simply mandated Tom and the Operations Department and others to simply make it happen at whatever cost. But had we done that, and even if we were able to do it, the cost in terms of relationships, performance, and actual delivery would have been huge."

"I understand that but there's a cost to everything and there are times when we have to take that hit out of interest in and care for our customers. That's our job and our responsibility as managers, isn't it? This is fundamental for me."

"If I may say something," Heather came in, "I think we actually ended up with *better* relationships with KEY Services Limited and with Sharon than we had previously enjoyed. She is in no doubt around our care for them. I think Sharon realised that she was being a bit unfair. She was afraid we might try to get out of it and so was very demanding. Not only did we get a solution that helped us and avoided a lot of cost and trouble, but she and Terry now have a much better relationship and she trusts us much more. Isn't that so Terry?"

"Yes, absolutely Heather. I think we have much better relationships and much more trust. I know that now, if or when she has a problem, she'll come to me or to us. And she does. Recently, she informed me that a big contract was coming up for negotiation and she would very much like *us* to secure it. And she said she wanted that, not to do us a favour, but because she genuinely has more confidence in us than she has in other suppliers.

In fact, she made reference to that situation you referred to, Brad, and discussed the mess she was in through the fault of her own company and herself and how impressed she was with the way we handled the crisis. Yes it turned out very well and I'm very happy with how we're relating to and dealing with all our customers. They really trust us and see us as valued and critical partners. If we get this new contract, it will be great and I'm sure Rick will be delighted too."

"I'm glad to hear that, but it all sounds a little messy to me", said Brad. "I mean if every customer situation requires this amount of discussion, it means we're going to be very slow in responding. I think this is what managing is about – being able to take quick decisions and then make those decisions work, by making things happen. Mike and I have had these conversations and he knows that I would like him and all of your managers to have and be more in control. That's one key message I would like to give you all."

"Yes, you and I and Martha have had these conversations and we differ on the kind of control that we want to have." Mike said, "To me it's more about power and the kind of power we have. I would maintain that Terry and ourselves now have more power with KEY Services Limited than we ever had in the past and certainly more that we would ever have had if we had simply gone ahead and delivered the order as she originally demanded. Strangely, I don't think that she or they are any less powerful either as a result of this new relationship that, I have to say, Terry and Heather handled quite brilliantly.

We're both more powerful, and able to achieve more this way than we were in the past. I know we differ strongly on this episode and I'm not trying to win an argument, nor am I trying to pretend that everything is easy and smooth between us. I'm only pointing out how well this approach works in our opinion. I'm not trying to impose my view on you or simply going along with yours, Martha, but see if we can come up with what is the best way to handle things which will meet both our needs."

"I understand what you are saying, Mike," Martha said, "but, as Brad has said, it can seem very messy and loose and not the kind of strong management that we need. But we can talk about this later today or tomorrow, because we certainly need to."

"Yes, Martha" an obviously irritated Brad said, "we definitely need to have that talk. There is no way we can run a successful business and meet our commitments unless *we* are in control. To me it's as simple as that."

It seemed a good time to take a break and everybody was relieved when Mike suggested that.

"After the break, you might like to take a quick walk around, as we suggested earlier Brad, and that will give you a better feel for what you would like to look at in more detail tomorrow. Is that acceptable?"

Brad agreed and they broke for coffee.

Questions for reflection and action

1. Do you understand Mike's wish and plan to handle this visit differently from how they were normally handled? Why might, this be a better way to handle it?
2. What are the pluses and downsides of being fully open as Mike wanted his team to be?
3. Do you recognise the dynamics between the corporate visitors and Mike and his team? What is going on? How common and how important is this issue?
4. Any ideas how this will get resolved or how you would resolve it if you were in this situation?
5. Do you agree with Brad on the importance of and need to be in control?

Chapter 28
Staking Out "The OK Corral"

Handling serious difficulties with honesty, respect and courage

After coffee Mike asked Tom to take Brad around and introduce him to different people and to selected areas as he wished. "I think 40 or 45 minutes should be enough to give you an overview of all that's going on and, as I said, you can get into more detail on particular areas tomorrow, based on what you see today. Is that alright?"

"Yes, that's fine. Are you coming with me Martha?"

"No Brad, I'm pretty familiar with the operation and it might be better for you to do your own thing. I can chat with Mike in the meantime, if that's good with you, Mike?"

"Yes, I'm fine with that," Mike replied.

Very brave or very foolish?

When they had left, Martha turned to Mike.

"I know this isn't easy, Mike, but I have to be honest with you about your attitude. I don't think it's helpful and I can see that Brad is not at all happy with how things are going. We have to be careful here. You have to be more conciliatory, Mike. There's a lot at stake. You know that. Be careful, Mike."

"Of course, I will, and of course I realise how much is at stake. But not just for me, for everybody concerned. I have to think of the people and their lives who work here and I have to be faithful to them too. I'm not going to give up on them and on what I think is right and best for them just to please Brad in order to protect myself and my own career."

"I understand how you think about this, Mike, but you also have an obligation to the company and the corporation to which you belong. You work for them and you also have responsibilities. You must understand that."

"I fully understand that, and I have responsibilities to you, to Brad and to the corporation to make this company here the very best company it can be. But part of that responsibility is about being courageous and honest and challenging, helping the corporation to be true to its own values and principles. This is where you and I and Brad disagree and, I'm afraid, we'll keep coming back to this point. How can we find a way that's good for everybody, and I mean everybody? I believe it's possible and I intend to keep striving to make that possibility a reality, wherever that takes us."

> "I'll take fifty percent efficiency to get one hundred per cent loyalty"
>
> **Samuel Goldwyn**

"That all sounds fine and well-intentioned, but it seems to me you ignore the reality of your situation. It's like you yourself said, it's all about power. You work for this corporation and in practice for Brad and it seems to me that you don't respect his power. You don't seem to realise that ultimately, he has the power to decide and he'll do what he wants and you have to respect that power and go along with it, just as you expect your own people to respect your power to decide things."

"I understand what you're saying Martha but I'm afraid you're missing the point that I'm making around power. Just like in the example we gave around KEY Services Limited, when they and we ended up, not losing any power, but actually both ending up more powerful. We achieved that by coming to a decision and agreement that wasn't just good for them and wasn't just good for us but was good for both of us.

That's what I mean by power and the kind of power I want and the kind of power that I use with my own people. I don't want, and I don't impose what I think, just for the sake of it, but because I believe it's right and best. And I find out what's right and best, most times, by listening to and respecting other people. That's what happened in that instance and what happens every day here. People here are not going around obeying others but doing what they *want* to do because it makes sense to them. Of course, there are times when not everybody agrees and so somebody has to make a call, but nobody has a problem with that when it happens."

"I do, even if it sounds a bit idealistic to me. I don't know if that approach will work in practice."

"I understand your problem and that it sounds very different to you. I'm afraid this is one of those concepts that only makes sense when it's tried in practice. It's a bit like riding a bicycle. The theory that a little narrow wheel will stay upright is odd and there's no way you can convince a child that it will. The only way they'll believe it is when they try it and see for themselves. The same is true with this concept and, believe me, it works and is already working. I think you have seen it work yourself. But I'm not sure this will make sense to Brad. And God knows what he may come back with after his short plant tour," he laughed.

Martha laughed too. "You're right. Who knows? On a different topic, you know we have to deal with that issue around Heather and her promotion to the position of Customer Relations Director and to being part of your senior team. You can imagine the eyebrows that will be raised when somebody who has been missing from work for long periods for maternity leave is promoted over the heads of ambitious people who have not missed out on those two to three years when Heather was out.

Now, you know I'm not suggesting or even thinking that we should change our policies around maternity leave, but we need to be realistic about things like career decisions and promotions. Of course, we must look after Heather, but we also have to think about the overall business and about other people with

"Whenever you see a successful woman, look out for three men who are going out of their way to try to block her"

Bruce Mars

legitimate aspirations. I know you realise there were lots of people who were not happy that you went ahead with this decision in which Teresa was also very heavily involved.

Now, there's no one who is a stronger defender and promoter of women's rights and welfare than I am. You know that and some people in corporate management fear me."

"Yes, I fully understand that, Martha, and it's probably better that you have this discussion with Teresa herself. She has been handling this and I happen to agree with what she has done, but it's better that you talk to her about it. Is that alright? If you need to talk further to me, just let me know."

"Sure, I'm happy to do that, oh here comes Brad - round two," she laughed nervously.

Out of control

"I hope you had a good tour even if it was very brief," Mike asked, but Brad's face suggested the opposite and Tom, following behind, threw his eyes to heaven in a warning look at Mike.

"Yes," Brad answered, "it's an interesting process and quite different from our own and others that I've seen. I have to say I was impressed with how confident the leaders were in each area, even if I wasn't happy with the level of control they seemed to have. The team-leads appeared to understand the process very well but didn't seem to know much about what was actually going on. They had to ask their own people on several occasions. In other companies and sites, the team-lead would have all the details at their finger-tips and be completely on top of everything. Quite frankly, that would worry me, Mike!"

"Well why don't we have a chat about that now as part of our overall agenda because I think it touches on some of the major issues that we need to resolve. Maybe it would help, for this part of the discussion, if Tom was present. Would that be acceptable?"

"Sure, sure, whatever!"

So they sat down – Brad, Mike, Martha and Tom.

"So what's going on Tom," Mike asked with a smile, "your people don't seem to know what's going on and I take it that, if *they* don't know, *you* know even less!," he joked.

"I think you're being a little facetious, Mike," a visibly annoyed Brad interjected. "This is a serious matter. It's not a joke."

"I agree completely," Mike answered pleasantly, "believe me it's very serious for me too. Be in no doubt about that. My question to Tom was a serious and realistic one because if his team leads are not in control, then he is not in control and I am not in control either and you, Brad, are right to be concerned. So, that's why I am asking you, Tom, what's going on and how do you feel about it? I could give an answer, but I want to hear it from you as you and I have had many conversations about this."

"Yes we have, Mike," Tom answered, "and as you and Curt in corporate management know, being in control is very important to me. But, what I want to be in control of is not precisely what everybody does, but of what they deliver, the outcome. I want to be in control, in as much as that's possible, but in control of *results, outcomes.*

It's those that I have to answer to you and Curt and everybody about. For many years – too many to be honest – I tried to achieve these

> "A wealth of information creates poverty of attention"
>
> **Herbert A. Simon**

results by controlling everything. If this visit, Brad, had happened a year or two ago, things would have been very different. Not only would my team leaders know everything that was happening and be able to explain it in detail, but they wouldn't even have to do so, because I would do the talking for them.

We would have had days and weeks of preparation for this meeting, going over every possible question you might raise and making sure we had the right answers. It was such a waste of time, and you would never really know if what we told you was true or not or if you were seeing things as they really are. But you would have felt I was in control! The very same thing was happening in my area. People would spend endless time getting information ready for meetings with me and giving me the answers I wanted, and doing the things. I wanted done, became what mattered – far more important than doing what was right and best.

Mike and I have had many conversations about this and we can see the enormous difference it made when we stopped all this reporting and game-playing. Once my people, know what's to be done, know what's happening, and really want to do it, then I let them get on with it. Of course we spend time ensuring that everybody is able to do what is required, that's essential. But the rest is relatively easy once that's established. But, tell me, Brad, what kind of things did the leaders in the areas not know and have to ask their people?"

"They were familiar with the operation but when I asked them for some figures and details they didn't know. People back home would have that information on the tips of their fingers. I also asked a few of them about absenteeism figures and they looked completely lost. I still have no idea what your absenteeism looks like. That to me doesn't look like you or other managers are on top of things, Tom."

Tom laughed. "Believe me all that information and data and figures is there, but it is with the people who need it to make decisions. It is not much good if I have lots of data and information. It has to be with the people who need it to make decisions, to adjust, correct etc. And *they* do have all that detail. Regarding absenteeism, probably the reason why they couldn't give you percentages for absenteeism is that they don't keep them. They don't have any. Or, if they do, it's minimal. People don't want or like to be absent, because they know that it will affect things and make life difficult for their colleagues. The same is true if somebody is late. Occasionally I have seen people arrive late and on every occasion two things happen.

The person who arrives late is very apologetic and can't wait to get going and catch up with what has been happening, and the manager or team leader welcomes them and is delighted that they've arrived. It's good news for everybody. They believe that if they start keeping records of things like absenteeism or even individual efficiency, then they will, in a sense, be accepting absenteeism as a reality and so making it acceptable.

Trying, then, to get it down from 5% to 3% or 2% becomes a separate exercise, a game. I don't want to go down that old road. But, this is exactly what happens at our own level. I'm sure Mike has no idea or keeps no records of when we're absent, if we ever are. But, if he did, I think he'd inadvertently be legitimising us being absent. Why should it be any different from anybody else? A great boss I had once used joke about what would happen if statistics and data were kept in maternity wards in hospitals for new-born babies let fall by nurses."

"So are you telling me that you keep no figures or records or hold information on anything?"

"Yes, of course we do. I need to know what's going on and to be able to give Mike and the others the information that he and they need to manage. But what matters is that the people have the information they need to do the job. My people know what I need to know and I don't have to ask for it. If there's a problem they'll come and tell me about it.

If I see a problem that they haven't mentioned then I'll bring it to their attention and we'll talk about it and get into it. But I don't use information as a stick to beat them with and, if I did, all kinds of games would be played to mislead and side-track me. Just like we used to do with visitors like you in the past Brad," Tom laughed.

> "The purpose of collecting so much information can only be power"
>
> **Nick Drake**

"Well, it looks very haphazard and loose to me. As managers, we need to be in control of things and this smacks to me of a complete lack of control."

"This is not meant to be disrespectful, Brad, or to appear smart, but which would you prefer, a manager or team lead like Curt has, who keeps and monitors figures and percentages on absenteeism, knows with great accuracy and reliability that absenteeism is over 5% and has a goal to bring it down to 2 or 3%. Or, a team-lead here who is not exactly sure if absenteeism is below or marginally above 1% and doesn't care too much because it makes no difference. Or, if I could put it differently and, again, I want to be respectful, which manager is doing the better job for the company or corporation? That's a rhetorical question really."

"Well, maybe they're not mutually exclusive and you could have both."

Different paradigms and real control

"This is part of a fundamental difference between us, Brad," Mike came in, "that we need to address urgently. I don't happen to think they're mutually exclusive. I think it's Tom's approach that's very influential in making absenteeism a non-issue for us. And absenteeism is just one example we're taking to make the point. The same holds true for efficiency, quality, safety, housekeeping etcetera etcetera.

And, staying with Tom's area for the moment, if you were to ask any of those people how they feel about this way of working compared to the previous one, you'll be in no doubt about how much they enjoy and prefer this way of working. It's made a huge positive difference to them and to everybody."

"But we're not in the business of making people feel well, nice and good as that is. We're in the business of delivering results."

"Yes," Mike answered, "but we say that it's a corporate value to treat our people with respect and we try to respect that value and make it a reality here. And we don't do it just to be nice to people but because it is a much better way of managing them as people, as rich human beings for the benefit of everybody. And in terms of results these teams who have switched to a new way of working are achieving results way in excess of what was previously achieved – on every score. And it means that Tom and others are freed up to do what they should be doing, rather than doing other people's jobs for them.

And Tom and the others can now get their work done during the day rather than staying on late into the evening or bringing work home with them. In practice there's much more control than before. Everyone is in control of their area and Tom has the time and space to be really in control of Operations overall. I know you don't find this easy, Brad, and I can assure you that Tom didn't find it easy either.

He loved the cut and thrust of morning meetings, weekly meetings, review meetings of all kinds. It was his work, every day, his life and he was very good at it. But it was a waste of his real talents and a failure to fulfil his real role as Operations Director. That's why I say that he now has far more real control, than he had in the past which was for the most part illusory. Because his people are now taking ownership and responsibility. They are better able to handle everything and anything that arises because they do it together, as one team, with collective thinking and those 100+ heads thinking and working together are way superior to anything that Tom, with all due respect, could come up with on his own.

You and I might differ a little on what we mean by control and how we can best achieve it, but at the end of the day, it's not control that you and I or the corporation are after, but rather performance and results. Achieving those on every score, every target and value is the best way I can serve you, Brad, and the corporation."

"That's okay, Mike and Tom, but it all still sounds very laissez-faire, idealistic and haphazard to me. I can't see how a company, and even less a corporation, could be managed along these lines. I just can't see it and, quite frankly, I can't see how I or this corporation could live with it."

Martha intervened, mercifully. "It seems we have a lot more work and a lot more talking to do. I think it's time that we went back to our hotel. Brad and I could do with a little break and rest. Is that okay, Mike?"

> "We are living in a world that is beyond controllability"
>
> **Urich Beck**

"Yes, that's fine Martha. We can pick you up around 7.30 and take you to the restaurant, if that's alright. As I said earlier, it will give both of you a chance to have some informal conversations with some of the team as well. So let's do that."

Mike couldn't help feeling that there was a change in Martha and a smile she couldn't quite keep off her face!

Breaking bread instead of hearts or heads

Things were much more relaxed when Mike arrived to The House of Harmony with Brad and Martha. Joan had met Martha in the hotel and seemingly had a great chat. While Mike was waiting for Brad to come to reception, Martha took advantage of the moment to talk to him and she was obviously excited.

"That's some lady of yours, Mike. I love the way she thinks. And she has given me some things to think about around my own life. I hope it all works out for her."

Mike wasn't sure at all what Martha was talking about but he was pleased and relieved that they had a good chat and were apparently excited by some things, whatever they were. He could do with good news. Wherever it came from!

When they arrived to the restaurant, all of the team were there, with the exception of Heather, who would join them a little later.

Mike left Brad and Martha so they could have their own informal chats as drinks were offered and served. The restaurant had prepared a special cocktail called Harmony and everyone sampled a glass and some had more than one.

Brad had some longer chats with Bernard and Heather and Tony and with Natalie and Terry and then dinner was served.

For some reason Mike felt like calling it 'The Last Supper' and joked about this to Martha who didn't find it too funny.

A few unusual incidents occurred during dinner.

Brad, who was left-handed, saw his cutlery re-arranged to suit him without having said anything. He looked surprised.

Martha was given special information about the menu because it was remembered that she had certain minor allergies. She was impressed. When the waiters had withdrawn, she mentioned this to Mike and the others and thanked Mike for remembering.

"I assure you I had nothing to do with this, nor would Mark, the restaurant owner. It's just how they are here. It's always a wonderful example to me of what can be achieved when people are given owner-ship and responsibility."

Brad told the table about what had happened with his cutlery and how they couldn't have known beforehand that he was left-handed, but they must have simply observed it. He was surprised and showed it.!

When the main meal was finished, Mike proposed a toast.

"I want to toast Brad and Martha and thank them for being here. Nobody around this table is under any illusions about how important and challenging this visit is for all of us, but I don't want to get into that now. I just want to say thanks to Brad and Martha for the effort they made in coming here and for the interest they have in us and for their determination to find and do what is right and best.

> "Next to excellence is the appreciation of it"
>
> **William Makepeace Thackeray**

In thanking them, I'm also thanking the corporation. We owe a lot to them also. Somebody, a long time ago, had a vision and courage to go after their dream, and we should be very grateful to them for that. We have to be grateful to many people since then who equally showed vision and courage and I want to remember them too. I want to also remember all of our people on whom we depend, but who don't share all of the benefits from the company that we do. I want to thank every one of them here tonight.

We also have some excellent and very loyal and reliable suppliers on whom we depend and who are, in a sense, part of our operation and our success. I want to remember all of them, Frank, and would like to pass on my thanks to them through you. And, Terry, I would like our very happy customers to be with us in spirit tonight and I hope that they're smiling and feeling pleased about the great job that you and Heather and Bernard and Tom and everybody do to add value to them and their world.

So, whatever happens tomorrow in our discussions, let us be grateful tonight for what we have and trust that we have the wherewithal to resolve anything that needs solving. As I said yesterday, one of my clear goals is that Brad and Martha can go away tomorrow feeling very good about their visit and very good about the future and I thank them again for their interest and support for us."

Brad was visibly taken aback and impressed with Mike's words.

"Thank you for all that, Mike. I truly appreciate all you said and that's not to turn a blind eye to certain issues. Tonight has been a lovely night. I had some great conversations with Terry and Bernard and others that I would like to continue tomorrow.

And I've heard of your great achievements with your football team, Frank, and good luck in the final. It seems you have achieved some miracles with those lads. And it was a wonderful meal. I have a custom of always saying thanks to the restaurant manager on occasions like this so I wonder if he or she is around so I can do that?"

"I don't know," Mike answered, "you never see too many managers around here, but let me ask."

He asked one of the waiters who told him that, in fact, Mark was on the premises and Mike thought, who better for Brad to talk to than the owner and manager.

> "The best way to find out if you can trust somebody is to trust them"
>
> **Ernest Hemingway**

When Mark appeared, Brad praised him for the quality of the food and service and thanked him for it all. "I eat in a lot of restaurants and I can honestly say that not many would match the quality of food, atmosphere, attention and friendliness of your restaurant, Mark. Well done."

"Thank you Brad but I have to honestly say that it's down to the staff. I'm not even sure if Sarah, the restaurant manager, was here tonight or not. It doesn't matter. As Mike and the gang know, my people know what to do and they really want to do it and do it well and they're good at it. We leave it to them and they see and spot things that *we* would never see. I know it's very different for you in charge of a large corporation but, in a sense, we're both faced with a similar challenge in that we cannot be on top of everything that happens and we have to trust people. You trust people thousands of miles away, I trust people just a few doors away. We have no choice but I never cease to be so agreeably surprised at how people respond to being trusted. So I'm very glad to hear again that you enjoyed your dinner Brad."

Brad smiled and looked at Mike. "Believe me Brad, I had nothing to do with this," Mike laughed, "I wasn't sure that Mark would even be here. Honestly."

"Yes, I know that," Martha smiled, "I have been here before and I've had the very same experience. Thanks Mark and nice to see you again."

"And, I would like to take this opportunity Brad," Mark said, "to compliment you on the contribution you're making to our community here. Bernard is a household name around here and your company is seen in a very different light from any other company in the area, or in the country, I would say. Most companies sponsor different things and one always feel that it's more of a mere Public Relations exercise than a genuine desire to contribute to and be part of the community.

Not so with your company. It's a real part of the community but not in a paternalistic way. As a result, people in the community respect the company and don't take advantage or abuse the generosity of the company. They are right behind it and very grateful to have you in our community."

Questions for reflection and action

1. Do you agree with Martha that Tom is being too bold and risky? And that he should change his attitude? Where do diplomacy and 'healthy politicking' come in?
2. Do you understand Brad's shock at the lack of control? Do you need this kind of control?
3. Why does Mike – or Tom – no longer want this level of control?
4. Are Mike and Teresa really being fair to the corporation and the company in being so tolerant and loose around Heather and taking risks given her circumstances? Is this really "good for business"?
5. Is Mike really looking after the interests of the corporation and of Brad? Do you think he is being too insular in his approach? How will this be resolved, do you think, if it can?
6. Why did Mike mix 'business and pleasure' over dinner do you think? Risky? Do you think it worked?

Chapter 29
"More High Noon" than "OK Corral"

Finding the elusive breakthrough that is always there to be found

The next morning, Brad, Martha and Mike met to plan and discuss the day ahead.

"Many thanks for last night, Mike, it was a most enjoyable night and a great experience. And I heard and appreciated all that you said. I'm not saying that it takes us too far forward and I think Mark is right when he said that my job in managing different companies within a corporation is different from his, even if there are similarities. I have a job to do and I cannot and will not let anything get in the way of my doing that job. I'm sure you understand that."

"Yes I do, Brad, and I meant what I said last night about making this visit a success for you. I really want that and I want to find a way to do so. I also want to do that in a way that's compatible with my own principles, values and approaches."

"I hear that, Mike, and, while I would like that too, it may just not be possible. Our two approaches may not be compatible and I think I've been trying to make it clear to you from the outset that neither I nor the corporation will be willing to continue as we are with you as general manager of this company. I'm not sure you appreciate just how serious the situation is for you, Mike, as Martha very well knows. Is what I'm saying clear, or are you not clear about the consequences of continuing to manage as you do, in direct conflict with what I and corporate want?"

> "I'm telling you there is hope. I have seen it, but it does not come from the governments or corporations. It comes from the people"
>
> **Greta Thunburg**

451

"I think I'm very clear about all that, Brad, but there are two things that, with great respect, I want to make clear to you. The first one is that I believe in what I and we are doing here. I think it's the right and best thing for us and, in fact for the corporation and for you too.

I think it's perfectly aligned with the mission and principles of the corporation and that what we're doing will contribute to the welfare of the corporation and everybody involved in every way. I believe that, even though you and others may not be in agreement with it.

The second point is that I have no choice but to do what I think is right. I won't and I can't renege on that. Should all of this end up with my leaving the company, so be it.

I'm ready for that but I don't want you to hear that as a threat or that I'm putting a gun to your head, or to my own. I'm simply saying that I cannot give up on what I believe is right for everybody. Leaving this company where I have spent these last fifteen years is not what I want, but it may come to that. You can imagine the consequences from this for my family and friends, not to mention for all the people here who look to me. I'm sure this will not come as a shock to you and you may have come here with lots of alternatives in your head. I'm sure you're not stuck." He laughed.

Brad smiled. "Yes, that's very clear, and I think it's fair and respectful. I will be equally fair and I have to say that I have learned some things on this visit. If it's alright with you, Mike, I would like to have another look around. Yesterday I met a chap called Albert whom I found interesting and I'd like to ask him some questions. I'd also like a meeting with Terry and with Bernard on some corporate associated issues. Is that agreeable? I also need a little time with Sally on the discussions she's been having with your government.

"Yes, that's perfect, and maybe we can allow a few hours for that."

"I'd like a little time with Teresa also," Martha said. "I want to go over the handling and arrangements around Heather which, as you know, HR and myself find unusual and a little unsettling. And there are some things she's talking about around rewards that I also need to address."

"Okay, let's do all that and meet back here again around 12." Mike said.

Company and community

"Before we go, Mike," Brad said, "there's one thing that more puzzled me than bothered me from last night and it was what Mark was saying about Bernard and the company's work in the community. What was all that about?"

Mike laughed. "Yes, I thought you looked a little lost, Brad. Bernard has been leading out on this and he sees it very clearly. Most times people are grateful to companies like ours for the contribution we make to the economy, jobs, suppliers and others. And this is completely valid. It's the same here too, but Bernard has managed to integrate us into the community in a special way so that people really appreciate us and admire what we do. We work with people in the community on all kinds of things.

So, for example, you'll not see any homeless people or beggars on our streets. It's not that we pay for what gets done, but we help with it and encourage the local community to deal with issues like this as any other important member of the community would do."

"Well, that's nice to hear but I don't think that's our role. We're a business, not a social centre."

"Yes, we're a business, but the way we see it is that, above all, we are a 'company' and by that we mean as the word literally means – sharing bread – 'com pan', with bread. Business is what we do but what we are about is making a contribution and making a difference in the world. And we do that in five different areas.

For our customers, of course in terms of the very important products and services we provide for them. For our suppliers, whom we see as partners of ours in business as we rely and depend on them and they on us to some extent. For our people, without whom we would not be able to do what we do. For our community, of which we are a part and with whom we share resources, meaning everything in our environment of which we are all also a part. And, of course for our corporation, who made and continue to enable it all to happen and without which we wouldn't be here at all. So, it's much broader than just profit or the share price, and that makes an enormous difference to how everyone feels and works."

"I understand that but I'm not sure everybody else does or will, Mike. It sounds paternalistic and playing a role that's not the one we exist for."

"I understand that thinking, Brad, and I recognise that it's different, but I believe this way of thinking is a much healthier and overall better one and a more sustainable one in the long term, than seeing us purely as a stand-alone business parachuted into this area. Working as part of larger entity or community helps and improves every one of the players."

> "And the day came when the risk to remain tight in a bud was more painful than the risk it took to blossom"
>
> **Anais Nin**

"How does it help *us*, apart from generating goodwill?"

"Well, the way we see it is that we're all interdependent, and so is everything in the whole world. It's a different view of the world from simply seeing everything and everyone as resources that we pay for and use for our benefit. With that there's no connectivity or relationship. You pay your money and you get what you get, and that's the end of it.

We see it differently. I believe in being mutually inter-dependent. We all gain. For example, we needed planning permission for the extension we built last year. Everyone told us we wouldn't get it as it impinged on a large number of people, residents etc. We were warned by politicians, local councillors, legal people etc. that it simply wouldn't happen. But it did. And it happened because we – Bernard in fact – met local people and explained what we were doing and asked them what they thought and how it might be problematic for them.

He took a risk, because they could have said no. But they didn't. They discussed it in small groups and finally everyone agreed that it made sense and would be good for everyone. People were astounded and you may have heard some of the surprise at corporate level too. It was worth millions to us and the corporation. Now, I want to be clear, that's not why we relate as we do. It's not manipulative in order to get our way. We simply want to be good and responsible and helpful citizens of this area."

"It's certainly very different and new. It may need some talking about, but I hear what you say. Let's get moving."

Promotions, women, meritocracy and solidarity

Before Brad came back, Martha came in and told Mike of her meeting with Teresa.

"So, how did you get on Martha. You look pleased enough!"

"Well, yes, I am actually. I learned a lot. Quite apart from the danger of creating a precedent, I was worried about how this would be seen by others and if they saw that it was fair for somebody to be out of circulation for over three years out of ten and still end up in a senior management position. I know how good Heather is and what you think of her, but I was worried about how others perceived it and the precedent it might cause."

"Oh my God ... precedents. Not a very much valued or used word around here! Anyway, now, you seem satisfied with the outcome?"

"Yes, I have to say I am. Teresa assured me that not only are people in agreement with this promotion, even those who may have had an expectation and missed out, but they're actually fully in agreement with what was done and why it was done. And, it's not only because everybody respects Heather and has confidence in her, but they like the principle of this as well. Of course, they see that there's some inconvenience and catching up to be done, but they like the sense of family or community or togetherness in all of this.

That's what most surprised and impressed me – that everyone was prepared to make sacrifices to make this work. I heard lots of examples of people filling in for Heather, supporting her whole area to make sure it works well, making allowances etc. This won't come as any big surprise to you, but it's like as if productivity, important as it is, is not everything. There are other things that matter in a company.

And, as Teresa says, people are adamant that this approach and attitude actually helps productivity in the longer term. She asked me to have a chat with this Albert chap and I learned a lot from him. I can see how very different but very good a way of working this is. He gave me example after example of how well it worked in terms of productivity alone. Apparently, Heather asked his help on a few occasions when she was not available and he filled in brilliantly. As a result Albert became much more aware of Customers and a wonderful synergy between Customer Service and Operations developed. It's hard to explain, but I'm sure I don't need to explain it to you." she laughed.

> "A bad system will beat a good person every time"
>
> **W. Edwards Deming**

"That's fine. I think Teresa is right but what's important is that we treat people in a good and human way, irrespective of whether it will lead to improved productivity or not. It's not why we handled Heather's situation this way, even if Teresa is right that it probably will lead to an overall improvement in performance and results as well. We just believe that treating people well, as full human beings, is the right thing to do anyway and we trust that principle and that it will work for us. So I'm delighted, Martha, that you see it like this and I understand that there are complications to it and it needs to be well handled. But, that's true of everything, isn't it?"

"Yes, it's different, and it can appear much easier to handle things in a bureaucratic way, with rules and regulations for everything. I can live with this and I think I can get others to do so also."

"Thanks for that Martha and for being open. May I then confirm her appointment to the position? I think it would mean a lot to her."

"Yes, you may, Mike, I'll stick my neck out on this one."

Can't get away from "rewards" and pay

"Thanks, and did you and Teresa talk about her thinking on rewards?"

"We certainly did. I can't say we reached an agreement on it, but we'll continue to talk about it. She told me about your wishes to achieve greater proportionality in how people overall are rewarded and she feels that all your team would be happy with that too. Remarkable. I'll be very interested in the system of "Planned Sharing" she's investigating. I can see how giving everyone a stake in how well the company is doing makes sense and using a bonus system for that also makes sense to me. It means that if you have a bad year, people will not get their bonus. I just wonder if people will accept that, should it occur."

"I think that's a valid concern. Teresa, and I think it depends on the level of openness and transparency there is around financial performance. We plan to educate people on some of the basics, so they truly understand the financial situation and we'll keep them up-to-date, then, on an ongoing basis. There are now some very good and committed people from staff who could help us get this right. Just to make sure we're doing what makes real sense and not what just makes sense to *us*. But, you're right. It's something that has to be carefully handled."

"That's good to hear. Good luck with it. I think I can explain it to the Human Resources and Finance people back home and we can continue to look at it together. I'm not so sure I can do the same

with Brad, or that we'll be able to scratch all those itches he has."
She laughed.

Corporate and government and respectful relationships

Brad was in much better form when he arrived a few minutes later.
Mike and Martha were relieved.

"How did all that go, Brad." Mike asked.

"It went very well in fact. I learned a lot and I must admit there are
some good things happening, even if they might not be what I would
do. That chap Albert is very good and has a lot of experience. He was
comparing working here with working in some
other very large and successful corporations
with which I would be very familiar and why
he's so much happier here.

Happier because he's able to do a lot more
and make things happen easier and better here.
He does seem to have huge respect for and trust

> "Too many of us are not living our dreams because we are living our fears"
>
> **Les Brown**

in his own people and you could see that in his people as well. I'm not
sure that what he does would work everywhere, but it certainly works for
him. And he seems to get on well with and be trusted by Tom as well,
which is important. I also had good meetings with Terry and Bernard."

"That's all good to hear. How did your conversation with Sally go?
I have been heavily involved in those discussions with government but
left it to her to update you and hopefully get across what we believe is
the right way to go."

"Yes, she was very clear and convincing. Ultimately the final decision
is not mine and I'll need to go back to Rick and see if he agrees. It could
be quite a major change, but Sally sees that it's the only and right way to
go and everybody respects Sally and her thinking. It may probably have
a substantial effect on our bottom line, and so we'll suffer somewhat
in the short-term. But she believes that this will happen eventually

anyway and that we should give the lead on it. She argues that we're doing very well and will continue to do very well anyway and that we should be appreciative of that.

I think she believes that we should not grow this business any more than its present size and level. That's interesting. I know it's a big ask, but strategically she's quite adamant that this is the way to go. As I said, I'll have to talk to Rick about it but I'm in a much better position now to do that."

Getting beyond the rock and the hard place

"I'm very glad to hear that and well done to both you and to Sally. Maybe that's one topic where we can make your visit a success, Brad, and send you away happy!" Mike laughed. "I would like to find others too and I've been thinking a bit about it. I'm not trying to get my own way or to presume that what I'm going to say will resolve things between us. I'm really not. But suppose that we were to agree what the key results or parameters were and what these need to be for you to be happy with us, quite like we have at the moment. And suppose that we continue to report and update you on these in as much detail as you require? And suppose also that we agree what we want for this company, so that it plays a major part in the well-being of the corporation and in the well-being of everybody associated with us, like I mentioned last night? And suppose we shared and agreed our overall strategy and the projects that we believe will deliver on that strategy and then continue to update you on it, in a sufficiently but adequately detailed way? And suppose that I give you a very firm commitment that I'll keep you informed of any major developments or problems, so that you're not surprised by things when they happen? I mean ones that we genuinely feel we'll not be able to resolve? How would that be for a start? And, I repeat, I'm not suggesting that it will deal with all the issues between us, and we're both clear that the ultimate consequences of our working together is no longer compatible." Mike thanked Brendan quietly in his head for the gift of the Bear.

"Thanks for that, Mike, and I think there's a lot in what you say; it's a start at least." he laughed. "I have to say that I've been impressed by what I've heard and seen here and I also want to say that I've been impressed and heartened by your own attitude, openness and warmth. I mean that and Martha knows that I've been impressed. I hear all you have said and I'm happy with it, but I'm still not convinced that our two approaches are compatible.

I'm sorry to say that. Yes, there are some things that I have to think about but I see a fundamental difference in how we see managing and leading. I need not go over the same ground again, but

> "The glue that holds all relationships together - including the relationship between the leader and the led - is trust, and trust is based on integrity"
>
> **Brian Tracy**

to me it's all about control and I'm feeling that one has to have enough control. I don't feel that in this case, I'm sorry to say. I don't feel you are sufficiently in control and personally, *I* don't feel adequately in control."

"I understand that, Brad, even if I'm sorry to hear it. What I was hoping was that you would see that Albert, and Tom and others *are* very much in control of their areas and operations but it's a different kind of control and one that gets the best out of everybody. If either of them operated with the traditional approach to being in control, then they'd only enjoy the benefit of their own thinking, their own ideas, using their own heads. By giving ownership and trusting their people, they have the benefit of 20, 40, 100 minds, as I said yesterday, and double that of ears and eyes working for them. It's an enormous power that they're in touch with.

I say this with respect, Brad, but if you came here and simply gave us your instructions and told us what you want, and if we, out of fear or whatever, went along with them, diligently, obediently, then you too would lose the thinking of six or seven hundred people. You might feel you were in control, but look at the damage that version or kind of control would do to us!" You would get *what you want* but that would pale compared to *what you could get.*

"But, it's the responsibility of every manager and leader, surely, to identify what they want and, then, get it?", said Brad.

"If you mean "what they want" in terms of outcomes, or results, or a goal or vision – then I'm with you," said Mike. But if by what we want, we mean doing things *our* way then I see it differently. One of the biggest challenges I see for every manager is to realise that there's no automatic connection between being certain and being right. We can all be certain of many things and later discover we were wrong. This is true of all of life. There are people in my life that I believe are making mistakes. I feel certain of it. But, I might be wrong. And I have no right or ability to impose my view of what they should do on them. Even if it was right, it might not work for them. But when you couple these two – being certain and being right - with power, then you have a very dangerous cocktail because we have – like you have right now – the power to enforce what we think, our version of what's right and we do so confidently because we feel certain.

So right now, Brad, you have the ability, the power, to decide what should be done in this situation and how you handle and take that decision, I believe, is very important. In these two days, you've seen a different approach to managing, leading, and decision-making and I believe it's a better one and one that's working. But, at the moment, you don't and can't see that."

"Yes, you're right. So we're still in the same place. Still with this impasse. No further on!"

"I happen to think we are." Mike said smiling. "I think there's a way out, and a good one!"

"Pray, tell me!", Brad laughed.

"Well, there are a few possible ways you could resolve this or we could resolve it.

One is that you simply decide how things should be done and you impose that decision with all of the consequences that it involves, including firing me, or my resigning," Mike laughed.

"Alternatively, you could decide that pragmatically it's best to leave things as they are, that enforcing your way of thinking might be more trouble than it's worth and so leave well-enough or fairly well-enough alone. That's an option and you might think that it's the one that I prefer. But, in fact, I don't.

I think there's a third option, which is that we try to make this work while respecting both *your* wishes and *our* wishes and that we both cling to our respective positions and, at the same time, make a huge effort to listen, respect and meet the wishes of the other side. And we trust, in blind faith, in ourselves that we

> "Sometimes beautiful things come into our lives out of nowhere. We can't always understand them, but we have to trust in them. I know you want to question everything, but sometimes it pays to just have a little faith"
>
> **Lauren Kate, Torment**

will make this happen. I'm a great believer in moving from the past to the future, not in everything, of course, but in certain situations. It's only in the future that we can make things happen, new things, great things, irrespective of what happened in the past. I would love it if we both had the confidence to try this, to give it a chance, and to see what the future and life offers us."

"I think I understand, but what exactly do you mean?"

"Maybe I'm not entirely sure myself, Brad, but I wonder if, after these two days, there's a place, or a level where we both want the same thing. It's probably at a deeper level. But, if we went with that, I wonder if we could continue to work together to achieve that while continuing to listen to and respect each other just like we have been doing in these two days? I believe it'll work. And, if it doesn't, then we can revert to one of the other two options. What do you think Martha? Can you help us here?"

"I really like what you're saying, Mike, and I would like to try to make it work also. Who knows? I know it's a challenge for you Brad, and you may be going back with a different outcome from the one you had in mind, but I actually think it's a richer and better one. I really do. But, would you like a little chat with me on your own about this?"

"Thanks Martha and I appreciate that offer, but let me surprise you all by saying alright, let's give it a try, our best try and, as you say, Mike, let the *future* help us to find a really good answer. We have basic differences but why not let the future and concrete situations and realities decide what's the right thing to do in each situation and operate out of this searching and open and trusting way, like we've been doing, to be fair, during these last two days. I think we might be capable of finding an answer every time to anything that comes up. I do."

Mike and Martha were both equally taken aback at the jump that Brad had made, but they both quietly expressed their delight and thanks. "That's just great to hear, Brad," Mike said. "I'm truly grateful for that opportunity and I assure you I'll do my utmost to make it work for both of us and for everybody."

"I share your delight," Martha said, "and I too, will do my utmost to make it work. As both of you know, I admire many of the things you're doing here, Mike, even if I might not agree with all of them. One thing I forgot to ask about is this union or whatever it is that some people wanted to form here. I don't want this to scupper this agreement we're reaching but you know how problematic this would be for us in Human Resources and, indeed, for many in the corporation!"

"You can forget about any fears around that Martha. There's no union or anything like that here, nor will there be. And, the reason, very simply, is that people see what we're doing here and have complete trust in management and feel very included in the activity and welfare of the company. They want the best for the company here and it was that group that I mentioned earlier that could help us with our thinking on rewards and other issues."

"Ah, that's great to hear. I'm not surprised, to be honest, to hear that, but it will be a big help to Brad and to me in convincing people back home about what we've seen and heard and in bringing key people with us on some of these matters. That's great. Well done."

It was time to go to the airport, back to work, into the future – into the unknown.

When they left, Teresa wandered in to find out how it happened and how Mike was.

He gave her a brief description of what they had agreed and stressed that it was an agreement.

They also agreed that it would be important to bring everybody up to speed with what had happened.

Questions for reflection and action

1. Why are they differing over control? What control does Mike want, if any? Where do you agree you on this?
2. Do you agree with Brad that they are, after all, a business? Why, then, are Sally and Bernard going after these other things? Any implications for you and your company from this?
3. Is there a clash of loyalties here? To the local company or to the corporation? Ever been in that situation?
4. Do you think Mike's position is tenable? Do you understand Brad's position and responsibilities? Do you think it will work? On what will making it work depend?
5. How did the turn-around happen? What shift in the power base did Mike use? Does this have implications for you and the kind of power you use?

Chapter 30

You are Sitting on Gold

Celebrating the treasures all around us in work and life

After Teresa had left, Mike got up from his desk and stood and looked out his window at the entrance area that he had driven into so many months earlier. His mind jumped back to then rather than to the tumultuous meeting he had had with Brad and Martha. He reflected on how much had changed. Of course, they hadn't reached his goal of making it a truly special place to work and a place to which people enjoyed coming and in which they felt fulfilled, but they were well on their way. As he gazed into space, three operators, whom he didn't recognise, looked up at his window. They saw him and caught his eye.

All three gave thumbs up or thumbs down signs – questions! Mike smiled back at them and gave them a strong thumbs up sign. The three returned the thumbs up sign, punched the air and skipped away cheering. "What a miracle" Mike thought. "What a little sign of endorsement. Yes, much was changing and several of the workforce and operators had previously commented on this to him. Some were not sure it would continue and feared that management might revert to their old ways. Mike believed they would not and was determined to ensure that.

A considerable part of his confidence came from his own senior team who, he believed, had really got the message and had radically changed in their thinking and behaviour. They had shown this in the heat of battle in the meeting with Brad and Martha ... as challenging a meeting as one would ask for. And, they had changed, not only as individuals, but as a group, as a team. The level of honesty and

"In a time of deceit telling the truth is a revolutionary act"

George Orwell

trust and risk-taking sometimes surprised even him. What Sally was trying with the government, what Bernard was doing in community, what Teresa was proposing around rewards etc. He also believed that it would continue, because everybody saw it was such a better way to manage and, indeed, to live.

Results were better but, what was even more important, more and more people were really enjoying the satisfaction of doing a good job and of playing a really important part in the overall success of the organisation. Naturally, what was happening was not going unnoticed by the outside world as he had just experienced. He was determined to play his part and hoped that it would help Brad and the corporation to play theirs. His gamble or hope was that they would back off, trust more, interfere less and appreciate the improved overall performance they were achieving. It would be great, he thought, if they showed a really positive interest in the overall change or transformation happening in Mike's company. And – he dreamed – even took it on board for other companies in the corporation. Why not?

Before the team re-assembled, he made two phone calls, the first to book a table in Mark's restaurant and the second to let Joan know they were going out for dinner.

Flash forward

He found it hard to read the looks on the faces of the people as they came into the room. They were different. Some looked tired. They all looked as if they had been through something together. But they all seemed upbeat and optimistic.

He was about to say something when Terry led the group in going to him and giving him a big and warm hug. No one said anything. The spontaneous embrace said it all. Without knowing the detail of how the meeting with Brad and Martha had finished up, they had picked up that Mike had survived and was happy. Mike found it hard to keep back the tears and was not even sure what the tears were about. They all sat down, and the room was filled with a long, loud and heartfelt applause as they each looked at Mike. He was overcome. He felt so tired and he again fought the tears. Then he put an end to it by saying:

"Some of you know how the meeting with Brad and Martha ended and we can go through the detail of it another time. "I actually feel very good about the visit, what happened and what we achieved. I really do. I think it's all to play for and I think that we were honest with each other. I think we managed to bring about a fairly radical change in how Brad sees us and our company and I say "we" because I think we all did it. I truly admire all of your openness and courage and honesty over the past two days. There's no doubt in my mind that some big change took place in Brad and I'm not at all clear when or how that happened.

But, however it happened, I'm very happy with the outcome. It's not what I had in mind prior to the visit, if I had anything in my mind at all, but I think it's an excellent outcome. I can honestly say that I could not ask for more or better. We are alive and well and have the chance to make this work or to continue to make this work. I want to say just one thing to you all and to each and every one of you. Thank you." He paused, caught each person's eye and let the silence spread for a few moments.

Team performance

Everybody seemed relieved and some were more than relieved. All were astounded at what had transpired and how Brad had made such a radical change in such a short time.

"Do you think this is a post-mortem, Mike," Frank asked, "or a celebration? Did we win, or lose, or was it a draw?" He laughed.

"The way I see it, Frank," Mike answered, "is that we won and Brad and the corporation won as well. I honestly believe it was win–win. But

"The best way to predict the future is to invent it"

Alan Kay

whether I'm right or wrong in that will only be answered by what happens now, what we do and by how well we do it. The future and how we all handle it will decide what happens and if we can all be winners. We have some changes to make too and I especially have to change some specific matters. But there's nothing there that we can't deal with and deal with in a way that respects and preserves our integrity and the authentic goals we've set for ourselves. But, to do justice to your question, Frank, why don't we have a little celebration at our monthly meeting next week in Mark's restaurant? We could include him in our thanks, couldn't we? And I'm being absolutely honest in saying thanks to you all.

You all played a big part in this. Sally was brilliant in dealing with the enormous issue around our responsibilities to the government and to our country. I still can hardly believe that you at least got his agreement to consider and support your proposal on this, Sally.

I'm proud of you. Tom, you and your people were at the centre of much of this issue and I have to say that you and Albert and the others must have been brilliant, in whatever you said or however you handled things. Teresa did a great job in defending our decision around Heather and much of this was due to the fact that Martha could not identify or spot, one iota of disagreement, or jealousy, or rivalry or whatever in what we did, or any one of you did, around Heather's promotion. And you did good work with Martha on the whole rewards topic. And Terry, you did a great job in standing by our handling of the issue with KEY Services Limited. And Heather too. A really wonderful job.

> "We are made to persist. That's how we find out who we are"
>
> **Tobias Wolff**

I felt you were really in there batting for all of us and I, personally, felt great strength and support for all of us. A real team performance. You have no idea what part that played with Brad and Martha. But I can't help but feel that you, Frank, and you Natalie, and you Tony, and you, Bernard also played your part in how you were and in how you handled the various conversations over the past few days. Of course, I appreciate that very much, as I always appreciate your support and friendship. While I could thank you for how faithful you were to me and to what we all stand for, I want to thank you for something else.

I want to thank you for being faithful to this company and to every single person in it. And I want to thank you for being faithful to yourselves and to your own values and principles around our company and how you want it to be in itself and in this community. So many of you were very brave and honest during these two days. I'm sure some of you could have made friends in some high places if you'd supported existing views and prejudices at corporate level. I don't want to single anyone out but what you took on was gigantic, Sally, and there were times when I thought you were being foolish.

But you've worked very hard on this and you performed a Herculean task by getting Brad to take your proposal back to corporate level. As he said, it could put the corporation in a different league and create a whole new and much richer role for corporations like ours. We can give the lead on that, and Brad now sees that. The same holds true for your initiatives Bernard, and I only mention both of you because they would run counter to the narrow view that most people have of corporations. But I was proud of you all.

Some of you took big risks in possibly being seen to be defensive of us and our operation. I can honestly say that I was filled with admiration for what many of you did during these days. You were brilliant and what I loved most of all was your complete honesty at all times. Who knows what will happen? The game is still on. But one thing I know is that every one of you will grow and benefit from how you behaved. Again, thank you."

He paused. "I take it that we're all clear about where things stand generally and where things are with me, and to some extent, with all of us with the corporation? Are we?"

It was Teresa who spoke up. "Yes, I think so, Mike. It's as you have just said: the game is still on. I think we and this whole new departure in management style are being given a real chance to show it works and is the right way to go. And I don't mean that like in a yellow card or final warning kind of chance, but a real fighting chance. And we have that real chance because we made sense to Brad and Martha. They ended up, if not fully convinced, then relatively confident. Is that how it is or how people see it?"

"Yes, I think it is," Sally said, "I think Brad is going back in a very different place than where he was when he first arrived yesterday morning".

"And you could see he knows he has a job to do with some people back home. But he's no fool and he wouldn't take that on unless he was confident he could make it happen." Tony added. "And now we might be happy that he's a bear! If he were weak, we know he would achieve nothing. But this bear is pretty powerful."

They all agreed and laughed.

Transformation of people

"And that's what still puzzles me," Tom said, "what brought about that road to Damascus change in the man?"

"Well," Mike answered after a few seconds, "your 'road to Damascus' is not an inappropriate description or naming of what happened. There's no doubt a big change took place in Brad sometime today. You all saw that and have alluded to it."

"But, how did you make that happen?" Frank asked. "It was miraculous."

Several nodded in agreement.

Tony ventured: "I know you'll all think I'm off the wall in saying this, and some of you see me like that much of the time" he laughed. "We often talk about this in our little community group and we all believe in miracles. We believe with Einstein that we live in a world that's truly miraculous. By that we don't mean things happening against or contrary to the natural world, but that the natural or real world is quite a remarkable and miraculous place. Just look at nature and the daily miracles that happen there.

Or the eye and what the evolutionary process has come up with. Or 250,000 leaves on every tree of the millions of trees in the world and no two identical … or the six billion human faces, a very limited space to work with, and yet no two are the same.

Sorry for going on about this and I'm sure I'm losing or boring some of you, but my point is that when we behave and perform well as human beings, we tap into this miraculous power, you might call it, that's in everything and everybody, including Brad. And I believe you, Mike, did just that in these days. Anyway, enough from me."

"Miracles are not in contradiction to nature. They are only in contradiction with what we know of nature"

St. Augustine

Mike smiled. "I like all that, Tony, and it all makes sense to me. I would love to take the credit for some master move I made or powerful tactic that made this happen. I could boast that I knew this would happen and that it was all part of a great plan.

But that would be dishonest, just not true. I didn't know what would happen or how Brad would respond. I hoped that he would see for himself what was happening and be able to respond honestly to it. Which he did.

And the credit for that goes in large part to Brad. There is a basic goodness and honesty in that man that was touched or activated by what we all said and by how we related to him. It happened, but it might not have happened. I think our whole approach of being completely honest with him about everything is what made that happen. I think that we by our behaviour, honesty and concern for him actually enabled or facilitated him in responding as he did."

"But did you plan and, deep down, know that this would happen," Natalie asked.

"No, I didn't. I did not know that Brad would respond as he did. I hoped that he would. I hoped that if we made sense to him about what we were doing and why we were doing it and how it was good for us and for him and for the corporation and for everyone, that he would respond positively. But it was only a hope. It was not a plan. More like the compass in that I knew where I wanted to get to but just kept checking along the way where to go next. Maybe in some sense, I was relying on that power that Tony has spoken about."

> "Trust each other again and again. When the trust level gets high enough, people transcend apparent limits, discovering new and awesome abilities of which they were previously unaware"
>
> **David Armistead**

Trust unavoidably involves risk

"But was that not a huge risk?" Sally asked. "What if he hadn't responded as he did?"

"You're right. It was a huge risk and even for me alone it was a huge risk. But I just had to trust what we were doing, trust myself and trust him as well. There's no way around this. I think it's a fundamental part of life."

"Yes," Sally persisted, "but think of the enormous consequences had it not turned out as well as it did."

"I know but there was no other way. Maybe you might say that I could have handled things differently and made sure that he responded well. How might that have worked do you think?"

"Not very well," Bernard answered, "it would have been trying to manipulate and manage him, the things we normally do and that people see through and that don't work. We have talked about these many times. "

"And why do they not work, do you think?", asked Mike".

It was Frank who answered. "Because they see through it all, or most of it, and they don't trust what we're telling them and so then they doubt *everything*, including us."

"And, yes," Heather said, "they feel badly about what we're doing to them, they don't like it and it's this feeling, this mistrust that prevents them from doing what's right. In a sense, we block them from behaving in a good way, from doing what's right and best. I can see that very clearly now. It was great but yes, it was risky."

"I agree with you, Heather," Tom said, "but Mike as the manager here has a huge responsibility to us and to everyone who works here and depends on this place and you could say that he took a big risk with our lives and those of everyone who works here. It was very risky management or whatever you call it."

"And you're right and I took risks around my own family too, don't forget. But what was the risk that I took, Tom?"

"You took the risk of trusting that Brad would respond well by how you refused to try to persuade him, or put pressure on him or "manipulate" him - as Bernard called it - in any way."

"So, the risk I took was that I trusted him?"

"Yes, in a sense, that was it."

"And what else did I trust that enabled me to do that?" Mike asked the others.

"I think you trusted yourself or the merits of what we are doing here and that it makes sense." Teresa answered.

"I think that's exactly right. I trusted the validity and merit of what we're doing, that it's good and makes sense and then I trusted Brad that he would see that and respond."

> "A hero is someone who understands the responsibility that comes with his freedom"
>
> **Bob Dylan**

"Extraordinary" Terry commented.

"Yes it is" Tom agreed.

"But hold on now. Why is this any different from what we've been doing or trying to do here with our own people? We have spoken about this many times. Do you know now what I'm referring to?"

Bernard answered: "Is it the core model of the Person and the Situation you mean?"

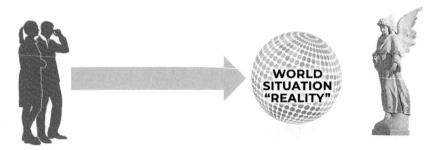

"It's exactly that. I painted a picture of our situation and how good and meaningful it is and I tried to help Brad see the truth, in the hope that he would respond well to it. I trusted him that he would see it, that he too would see the sense in the situation, the "angel in the stone" because it's there. In a sense this is exactly what we're all trying to do every day with our people, is it not? It's no different really. But tell me this, if he failed to respond well and to see the genuine merit in what we're doing, why might that have happened? Why would he have failed?"

"It might be," Tony answered, "because he believed he knew better and didn't really listen or need to."

"Or because he had his mind made up beforehand anyway and so nothing you said would have had any effect." Frank added.

"Very good," Mike said ... any other reason?

"He might have done so for ego reasons," Tom suggested, "and didn't want to give in or be second best or appear weak in front of us."

"Yes, and, a bit like Frank said, around having his mind made up, he could actually have decided with others in corporate management before he came, and, in fact, this might still be the case." Sally said.

"They're all great and, bringing it back to us, do you think that we could occasionally make the same mistake?"

"Only all the time." Tony answered, "I always know better than anyone else as you all know well."

"You're right," Tom came in, "it's a mistake I might make if I happened to have an ego. Luckily I don't" he said, laughing.

"And how often do we take decisions here and then stick to those decisions, no matter what we hear back?" Sally asked.

"And getting what he wanted and going home with the prize – maybe your head, Mike – might have been a huge achievement for him and boosted his chances of an even higher position in the corporation. There are people like that, believe me," Terry laughed.

"Ok, I don't want to flog this to death but in summary, we were clear and confident and enthusiastic about what we're doing and want to do. We shared that with Brad without any manipulation or dressing up or exaggeration, trusting what we're doing and trusting him, and it worked. He saw the value in it. I maintain that's what we always have to do and it will always work if we do it in that way and trust in that way. This is not to say that there will not be times when we must intervene and insist on something when we really believe it's right and when we have done the necessary work to make sure it is. But one last question.

> "Yes, your transformation will be hard. Yes, you will feel frightened, messed up and knocked down. Yes, you'll want to stop. Yes, it's the best work you'll ever do"
>
> **Robin Sharma**

Do you remember Tom accused me of taking too big a chance with people's lives and so of not being responsible? So, Tom, suppose I took your advice and, suppose I had an "in" to Art, the corporate CEO. Suppose he and I are friends going back a long way and I shared my predicament with him? And suppose he assures me and tells me not to worry and that he'll have a word in Brad's little ear and that there will be no problem. How about that? Should I – responsibly – make that call and have that chat with Art? Wouldn't that be a good way to live up to that responsibility you talked about, Tom?"

Tom laughed. "No, he said. It might backfire on you and Brad might find some other way to get you or get at you … eventually."

"Well, even if he wasn't as vindictive as Tom is or as Tom reckons Brad might be, I don't think you should make the call." Teresa, who had been silent, said. "And I say this, not just because you would be going behind Brad's back and using politics. I don't think it would be right. Yes, it would mean you get your own way, but that might not be the best thing either. Maybe what you or we want is not the best or only way to go and, if it weren't, then we would never know. Now we know or are much more confident that it is the right way to go. Do you know what I mean?"

It seemed they all did.

"I think that's great, Teresa, and very well put. If we always go after what's right and best and only and always do that rather than what *we* want, then we can never lose. By sharing it all with Brad, we were giving us all the very best chance of it being the right thing to do. You see this is one of the biggest problems there is – who or what are we faithful to? That is why I believe it was a great outcome, even better than if we had got our way on everything. Why might that be so?"

"Is it," Bernard asked, "that getting our way may not be the right thing and if that is all we want and go after, then we may never get to what is right and best? We have to go after something bigger – a greater good. This is what most organisations and institutions do. They only want their own welfare and their people are only faithful to the institution to which they belong no matter what it is doing. This is always very dangerous. There were many very good people in Hitler's Nazi party who were faithful to the party. To be completely loyal to any institution over everything or anything else is enormously dangerous and wrong. Does that make any sense toi anyone?"

"I hope it does," Mike replied, "it is hugely important, Bernard. More harm is done by people forsaking what is right and true to remain faithful to some group or institution than from anywhere else. Nearly all wars stem from this. The way we are going forward on this in this open and engaging and searching way with Brad, means that we will all go after what is right and best overall and not just what is good for them or for us. It is different but wonderful, I believe. Is everyone happy with that?"

They all were.

"I think it is very meaningful, at least for me," Tony said, "I have a lot to learn and practise here."

There were several mumbles of "You're not alone." around the room.

"You see, I believe there's one other reason why Brad might not have gone along with what I was saying! It's that he might justifiably and genuinely not have been convinced and not have seen it as being the right or best way to go and that for very good reasons … whatever those were. That's a possibility, a real possibility. And I have to be open to that possibility being true. And, for that reason, it would have been wrong for me to manipulate and gerrymander the process to prevent Brad reaching that conclusion, even if I believe it to be the right and best conclusion.

Now, that does take honesty and courage. In this case I didn't have that option. I don't know Art and, even if I did, there's no guarantee that he would agree to influencing Brad. After all, there was a risk and there will always be a risk when we rely on other people responding and doing what's the right thing.

But avoiding that risk is an even bigger one and a much more damaging one because it means that we'll try to 'manage' every situation to get the result or outcome that we want, irrespective of whether it's the right and best one or not. I believe this is a better way to ensuring we get the right result and I think it's the right way to relate to somebody like Brad. Does that make sense to you all?"

"It certainly does," Tom answered quickly and strongly, "and it's exactly what we have been trying to follow over the past months in looking for a better way to manage our people and the operation. Now we have a very clear and very powerful example of how challenging that is and how rewarding it is or can be.

Our challenge is to trust people and believe that if we give them the opportunity and the invitation to decide, then they will make better decisions and, as a result, we too will make better decisions. I think all of this brings home to us – at least to me – the huge change that's involved in relating in this way and the enormous courage it will take. As you have just demonstrated, Mike. It changes everything. Not just in work but in all of life and our lives."

> "Because to take away a man's freedom of choice, even his freedom to make the wrong choice, is to manipulate him as though he were a puppet and not a person"
>
> **Madeline L'Engle**

"Good. And thank you Tom. I think we've given this enough time and I hope it remains as a very strong example of the kind of managing and leading we want to use and the kind of managers and leaders and people we want to be."

There was no doubt that people felt they had had a special experience and one that they would never forget. They had learned more through the experience of the last few hours than they had through all of the training and talking and sharing and searching they had done previously. Now they *knew* that what they were doing was right and true and that nothing would move them from that conviction.

Back in the house of harmony restaurant

When the younger ones had got their drinks and Joan and Mike their wine, he told them that he wanted the meal as a celebration and to say thanks to them for their part in it.

Were you playing golf today, Daddy?" Rose asked, after they had sat down in the restaurant.

"Or," Harry asked, "have you won some new company prize?"

"No," Mike answered, "I just want to celebrate life, everything, including all of you, who have not only helped me wonderfully over the past few months, but are such a source of joy, inspiration and admiration for me.

"But why tonight?" Rose persisted.

"Because your father," Joan intervened, "has been trying to take his people to a new place, to what he calls his "promised land", over the past months, and I feel that he, at last, believes he's getting there. And I also believe this will be good for all of us."

"Is that why you mentioned to us some time ago that we might have to move to a different house and that other things might change as well?" Harry asked.

"Well I only said that it *could* happen but now it won't. But I remember what you both said and how it wouldn't matter at all once your father was alright and happy ... as well as having time to spend with you. Remember?"

They both clearly did.

> "You may say I'm a dreamer, but I'm not the only one. I hope someday you'll join us. And the world will live as one"
>
> **John Lennon**

"And what's this new place Daddy," Rose asked, this "promised land?"

So Mike explained to them that several months earlier it had dawned on him that people at work, while grateful to have a job, were not happy in their work and saw their job and the workplace as a burden and not as the place they really wanted to be. "And it wasn't really great for me either," he told them.

"And is that realistic?" Rose asked smiling. "I mean nobody likes work. Doesn't everyone look forward to weekends and holidays?"

"Yes, you're right, Rose" her father answered, "but work doesn't have to be like that. Work is supposed to be enjoyable and there are lots of people who enjoy their work like actors, musicians, creative people etcetera. It's not about work but about how we organise work and how we manage. Don't forget it was you two who taught me all this."

"What do you mean, "taught you all this"?" Rose asked.

"Have you any idea what I'm talking about, Harry?"

"I don't know. Was it about that chat we had about how Uncle Pat worked?"

"Yes, it was exactly that Harry. Remember how you gave me a hard time about it … and you Rose challenged me on why I could not just do like Uncle Pat did? What a grilling!" he laughed. And then they all laughed.

"That's only one of many ways that your mother has contributed to the transformation of the company in these months. And then he told them how he had been trying to transform completely how they managed and led the organisation and now people were truly enjoying their work, were committed to the success of the organisation as something of real importance for them, felt trusted to handle things in their own way, were taking much more ownership and accountability for things, operating with a new level of confidence and working really well together with respect and as a united team. All those things you brought up about how Uncle Pat and his people worked."

> "The future belongs to those who believe in the beauty of their dreams"
>
> **Eleanor Roosevelt**

"But why are you smirking, Rose?"

"I'm not smirking, I'm only wondering why you left it so long to do all this," she said jokingly.

Sitting on treasures

"Okay, okay, and you're right, Rose," Mike said. "I've asked myself that same question quite often. But better late than never. Did you ever hear about the beggar who for years sat on a box in the street asking for money? One day, a woman stopped and apologised that she had no money on her and, of course, the beggar continued to plead.

The passer-by, out of curiosity, asked the beggar what was inside the box he had been sitting on for so many years.

"I've no idea" the beggar answered. "I've never looked!"

"So why don't we have a look?" the woman suggested.

So they did, and they discovered that inside the box there was gold that had been lying there all along.

So, you're right, Rose, that I could have done this a long time ago and that I have been sitting on a treasure for many years, but it's not too late, and I'm very happy to have discovered the gold that was always present, if hidden, in the people and in the organisation. So, this is a moment for celebration and it's very good news, but not only for me and for the company and all who work in it, but also for you, Rose and for you Harry, to realise that there's always gold there to be found in life's situations even if it's hidden sometimes, and I hope that both of you, as well as Alex of course, will always believe this. All of you, all of us are sitting on treasure if we can only realise it.

New lifestyles, new lives

"And why is this so good for you, Mum, and for all of us as you said earlier?," Harry asked.

"Well, it's going to be good for you two and for Alex as well, because you're going to see more of your father. He's going to drop you to school when that's necessary and take you to football Harry, and you to your tennis, Rose."

"Oh that's great, Daddy, Are you going to retire from work? Or why will you do this now?"

And Mike told them that he and their mother had been talking about this for a long time and how so much of the weight of the house and family fell on her and now they were going to balance that a bit better. "I couldn't do it before now because I had to make sure my own bosses and people understood me and what I am after and now I think they do."

"So you'll have lots of more time now Mum, to meet up with your friends for coffees and chats. Sounds great."

"Well, yes it is, but it may not be like that. I have some news too and I haven't even spoken about this to your father. In the theatre group that I belong to, I have always done a lot of re-writing of plays and acts we put on. Just changes in direction that the director sees as necessary or that I spot to make the play easier for people to understand and more meaningful.

Today, he asked me if I would be willing to work as a screen writer for a film studio where he works. He really likes what I do and my previous experience as a journalist and writer is a big help. He was clear that I would be able to do most of the work from home so it wouldn't cause any inconvenience there. But, of course, I didn't tell him yes or no until I had spoken to your Dad about it and hopefully we all agree it, but it sounds interesting."

"Wow, it sure does," Harry blurted out, "why would you turn it down?"

For the third time in a few days, Mike felt tears in his eyes. He was overcome with joy and happiness for Joan. He composed himself and covered up his emotion.

"I agree Harry," Mike said, taking Joan's hand. "I think it's a super idea, Joan. I'm just delighted. I'm sure there are lots of details you have to work out but I can't say how happy I am with this." He looked at Joan and she saw his tears and squeezed his hand. Again he covered up. "What do you think, Rose?" he asked.

"I agree, but once it doesn't mean that you're away a lot from the house and us."

"No, that's an absolute must for me, Rose. That won't happen.

"I think it would be well, and proper, and obedient, and pure, to grasp your one necessity and not let it go, to dangle from it limp wherever it takes you"

Annie Dillard

Sorry for dumping this on you Mike, tonight. It's just that I didn't want to distract you prior to the meeting or take from the wonderful day you had and what you achieved. So, I decided to share it now as part of our celebration rather than waiting till we got home. And aren't you always talking about sharing things with people and involving them openly?," she laughed.

Mike laughed too. "I like that and thank you so much for being so unselfish in not wanting to steal my thunder. It doesn't do that and, in fact, it adds to it. What I'm thinking and feeling is that today opens up a whole new life and challenge for all of us. We don't know what will happen or how things will work out, but it will depend on how we handle things in the future. I look forward to that change and that challenge as I told Brad, my corporate boss today."

"I hope I'm not interrupting," said Mark, the restaurant owner, as he approached the table. "You all seem in great form, but also very solemn! "

"Ah Mark," Mike said, "here's someone who has helped me greatly to find my gold over the past few months and someone who a long time ago discovered that restaurants, and organisations, and people are full of treasure and we only have to discover that treasure and release it. Thanks for everything, Mark, and even for helping to ensure that even Alex enjoyed this little celebration."

"Well, I hope he grows up to be as successful as his father and that you're both proud of him."

"Whatever about being successful, I think Joan and I will be proud and happy if he's able to be himself, be authentic and do real justice to himself and to the world. That's why I think what we're trying to do is so important, Mark, as we've said to often, to create places of work, work environments, where people feel free and genuinely enjoy what they're doing. This to me is more important than the usual forms of recognised success. But what am I saying? You know all this. You taught me all this. And you were just great last night, Mark. You said all the right things, without my even having to brief you," he joked.

"I agree completely," Mark replied, "I've had so many offers of much more remunerative jobs from people of influence who come to the restaurant and see what we have. But, I've always said "no" because I'm so happy doing what we do here. And, it's not about just being in a comfort zone. You're never in a comfort zone in the restaurant business, and there's never a shortage of both challenges and opportunities. It's more about enjoying what we do and seeing people enjoy themselves when they come here.

This restaurant is so many things to so many people – a haven, a place to celebrate, like you're doing, a place to mend relationships, a place to philosophise, a place to be with friends, and for friends to kiss and make up, and a place to enjoy really good food and a place to just be. I find that very satisfying and I also enjoy the fact that everyone who works here does too. As we've said, Mike, having our employees feel part of something and allowing and enabling them to do a really good job is both rewarding and important. And, the more workplaces like this we have, the happier Alexes we will have in this world, I believe."

"Use your time wisely, so that when you look back towards the end of your days you will smile at a life well-lived. Let not your song remain unsung. Do not hold back from sharing your love with the world for fear of lack or thought of a rainy day. If Love calls you, answer"

Peter M. Parr

"Well said, Mark," Joan said, "I have to say I admire all you're both saying and doing. And I say this, not on behalf of just Alex but also on behalf of you, Rose, and you Harry. Like your father said, I don't care what you do in life or how successful you are. What I do care about is that you're happy and fulfilled in whatever you do and live really full and rich lives. Why don't you grab a glass, Mark, and we'll toast that. I'll pay for it this time" she said laughing, as I'm now, possibly, going to earn my own money" and she told Mark of her plans.

"Delighted to hear that, Joan. A whole new chapter in your life. Let's toast that … to Joan"

"And to Daddy," Rose toasted.

"To Uncle Pat, who knew it all," Harry added.

"To Mark and his leadership and his many faceted restaurant," Mike toasted.

"To a new future for work and workers everywhere," Joan proclaimed.

"To you all and to life and to the wonderful things we can make happen when we have the courage to trust others and be true to ourselves," Mark added solemnly.

The final nightcap

When they got home and the children had gone to bed, Mike suggested that they have a little nightcap to jointly celebrate the events of the day. Joan was delighted, partly because she felt guilty about dumping the new job offer and possible new career on Mike over dinner.

"I would love that, because I would love us to talk about this new venture I mentioned over dinner and, to some extent, dumped on you. But I think we should celebrate what was a really eventful day for you and there are some things that I would like to know more about."

Mike got them their little nightcaps and he went over the main points and outcomes from the day.

"One of the things that most pleases me about today was, in fact, the very positive change I hope it will make to our own home situation. Quite coincidentally, I believe that the new relationship I will have with Martha and with Brad, as well as the new way of working with my own team, will fit perfectly well with your situation which I find so exciting. And I know and I can see that you do too.

Maybe now we will find ourselves spending more time talking about *your* challenges and *your* writing and *your* films, rather than about my boring Quantum Logistics System topics," he laughed. "I know that I'll have much more time and freedom to dedicate to the home as well as to other things, because I'll be surrounded by a team of people sharing and taking full responsibility for things."

"Yes, I've heard you say that a few times, Mike, and that makes me very happy, not just for the children, and myself, but for you. And, you're right, I'm excited about this new challenge and, as I said to Martha, I believe it will not take from being a good mother, but will actually help me to be a better mother. She said that she heard somebody once say that a mother's greatest obligation to her children is to be the best person she can possibly be. I think this will help me to be a better person and a better mother, and, maybe, a better friend and partner to you as well."

"That makes me so happy to hear, Joan, it really does. Let's hope it all works well and, as I've said to my own team and to everybody, there's no guarantee that this will work. There's no written agreement or contract for how this will work with Brad. It's up to him and to us to make it work and I find that enormously exciting."

Yes Mike, I can see that and I know that you've been wondering about your whole role as chief executive of this company and the difference that you want to make. I hope you see and appreciate the enormous difference you've made, are making, and will make. Just look at the huge changes that every member of your team have made and the difference they're making. Tony, by all accounts, is a new man.

Teresa is in a completely new place around herself and her two children. I know how fairly agreeably surprised you were at Terry's loyalty to you and the local company. Frank has had a great year, both as a manager in the company and as the manager of his football team. The whole community talks about Bernard and how much they appreciate what he does and what the company are doing in the community. And what about Sally? What a challenge she took on and that from somebody who was initially very fearful.

You took a big risk with Heather and it seems you're getting well rewarded for that. You can see how Tom has changed and how well he uses his energy. And Natalie seems to be a much stronger person as well. Am I missing anybody? Isn't that all accurate? People, customers, "company". Oh, and my brother heading off for the weekend with one of your managers, I hear."

"What?" Mike asked.

"Haven't you noticed how helpful and attentive my brother has been to your H.R. manager of late?"

"Ah I see. I see. Wow! Now it all adds up. I get it. But, another surprise. Another miracle. What a day! What a life! What a world! I'm nearly afraid to end it!"

"You need not. It's only beginning Mike"

"You're right. It is so exciting. So full of life. And life-giving"

"I agree,' Joan said taking his hand and pulling him to his feet. 'Let's go. ¡Come on! It's not over yet!:

> "Is that what they call a vocation, what you do with joy as if you had fire in your heart, the devil in your body?"
>
> **Josephine Baker**

Questions for reflection and action

1. What changes was Mike celebrating? How many can you name?
2. Do you think this is realistic? And realistic for you?
3. Do you think you can take a similar journey and enjoy it?
4. Imagine if you answered "No", what this means … for you, for your organisation, for your life?
5. Why did Mike celebrate with his family? What had it got to do with them?
6. What treasures are you sitting on, in your company, in your life in general?
7. If you are standing looking out your window in a year or two's time, what will you be seeing and thinking?
8. Are you playing small or in what way might you be doing so?
9. Have you enjoyed this journey over the past while with us?
10. And the next part?

Bibliography

Adams, John D., *Transforming Work*, US: Miles River Press, 1984.

Agassi, Andre, *Open*, UK: Harper Collins, 2009.

Allende, Isabel, *The House of Spirits*, UK: Alfred A. Knopf, 1985.

Amado, Jorge, *Tent of Miracles*, UK: Alfred A. Knopf, 1971.

Andricopoulos, Yannis, *In Bed with Madness*, UK: Imprint Academic, 2008.

Annunzio, Susan Lucia, *Contagious Success*, US: Penguin, 2004.

Appleyard, Bryan, *Understanding the Present*, US: Doubleday, 1993.

Ariely, Dan, *The Upside of Irrationality*, UK: Harper Collins, 2011.

Assagioli, Roberto, *Psychosynthesis*, UK: Psychosynthesis Research Foundation, 1965.

Baker, Carolyn, *Navigating the Coming Chaos*, US. iUniverse, 2011

Ball, Alan, *American Beauty*, UK: FilmFour Books, 2000.

Bandler, Richard and Grinder, John, *The Structure of Magic*, US: Science and Behaviour Books, 1975.

Barbery, Muriel, *The Elegance of the Hedgehog*, UK: Gallic Books, 2008.

Barker, Joel Arthur, *Paradigms*, US: Harper Collins, 1992.

Barry, Brunonia, *The Lace Reader*, US: Harper Collins, 2006.

Bauby, Jean-Dominique, *The Diving Bell and the Butterfly*, UK: Fourth Estate, 1997.

Becker, Ernest, *Escape from Evil*, The Free Press, US, 1975

Bentley Hart, David, *The Beauty of the Infinite*, US, Wm B.Eerdmans Publishing Co., 2003

Berg, Art, *The Impossible Just Takes a Little Longer*, UK: Judy Piatkus, 2002.

Berger, John, *Hold Everything Dear*, UK: Verso, 2007.

Berger, Peter L., *The Homeless Mind*, UK: Penguin Books, 1973.

Berry, Thomas, *The Dream of the Earth*, US: Sierra Club Books, 1988.

Bohm, David, *Wholeness and the Implicate Order*, US: Routledge Classics, 2006.

Bonhoeffer, Dietrich, *Letters and Papers from Prison*, UK: Fontana Books, 1959.

Borges, Luis, *Fictions*, UK: Penguin Books, 1999.

Boyle, Nicholas, *Who Are We Now?* US: University of Notre Dame Press, 1998.

Boyne, John, *The Boy in the Striped Pyjamas*, UK: Random House, 2006.

Bregman, Rutger, *Human Kind*, UK, Bloomsbury, 2020

Capra, Fritjof, *Uncommon Wisdom*, UK: Century Hutchinson, 1988.

Cartwright, Justin, *The Song before It Is Sung*, UK: Bloomsbury Publishing, 2007.

Castaneda, Carlos, *A Separate Reality*, UK: Penguin Books, 1973.

Catford, Lorna and Ray, Michael, *The Path of the Everyday Hero*, US: Jeremy P. Tarcher, 1976.

Chabris, Christopher and Simons, Daniel, *The Invisible Gorilla*, US: Random House, 2010.

Chardin, Teilhard de, *The Phenomenon of Man*, UK: William Collins Sons, 1959.

Chopra, Deepak, *The Way of the Wizard*, UK: Rider, 1996.

Conrad, Joseph, *The Secret Agent*, UK: Penguin, 1994.

Covey, Stephen, *Principle-Centred Leadership*, US: Simon & Schuster, 1990.

Csikszentmihalyi, Mihaly, *Creativity*, US: Harper Collins, 1997.

Csikszentmihalyi, Mihaly, *Flow*, US: Harper Collins, 1990.

Davies, Robertson, *The Deptford Trilogy*, UK: Penguin Books, 1983.

Dawkins, Richard, *The Blind Watchmaker*, UK: Penguin Books, 1988.

De Geus, Arie, *The Living Company*, UK: Nicholas Brealey, 1999.

Delio, Ilia, *The Unbearable Wholeness of Being*, Orbis Books, US, 2013

Delio, Ilia, *Re-enchanting the Earth*, Orbis Books, US, 2020

De Mello, Anthony, *Awareness*, UK: Harper Collins, 1990.

De Mello, Anthony, *Wellsprings*, US: Doubleday, 1986.

De Pree, Max, *Leadership Is an Art*, US: Dell Publishing, 1989.

Deutsch, David, *The Fabric of Reality*, US: Penguin Books, 1998.

Diamond, Jared, *Guns, Germs and Steel*, UK: Vintage, 1998.

Dillard, Annie, *The Maytrees*, UK: Hesperus Press, 2007.

Dillard, Annie, *Pilgrim at Tinker Creek*, US: Harper Perennial, 1990.

Dillard, Annie, *Teaching a Stone to Talk*, US: Harper Perennial, 1982.

Donohue, John, *Anam Cara*, UK: Bantam Press, 1997.

Dostoyevsky, Fyodor, *The Brothers Karamazov*, UK: Penguin Books, 1958.

Douthwaite, Richard, *Short Circuit*, UK: Green Books, 1996.

Dyer, Wayne W., *Your Erroneous Zones*, UK: Sphere Books, 1977.

Eagleton, Terry, *The Meaning of Life*, US: Oxford University Press, 2007.

Eagleton, Terry, *After Theory*, UK: Penguin Books, 2004.

Eisenstein, , Charles, *Sacred Economics*, US, Evolver Editions, 2011

Eisenstein, Charles, *The More Beauitful World our Hearts Know Is Possible*, US, North Atlntic Books 2013

Eisenstein, Charles, *Coronaation*, US, Chelsea Green Publishing, US, 2022

Feehan, John, *The Singing Heart of the World*, Ireland, Columba Press, 2010

Feehan, John, *Every Bush Aflame*, Ireland, Veritas 2021

Ferguson, Marilyn, *The Aquarian Conspiracy*, US: Jeremy P. Tarcher, 1980.

Fisher, Roger and Ury, William, *Getting to Yes*, UK: Hutchinson & Co., 1983.

Frankl, Viktor E., *Man's Search for Meaning*, UK: Beacon Press, 1962.

Freire, Paulo, *Pedagogy of Hope*, US: The Continuum Publishing Company, 1997.

Fritz, Robert, *The Path of Least Resistance*, US: Ballantine Books, 1989.

Fromm, Erich, *To Have or to Be*, UK: Jonathan Cape, 1978.

Fromm, Erich, *The Fear of Freedom*, UK: Routledge & Kegan Paul, 1942.

Fukuyama, Francis, *Our Posthuman Future*, UK: Profile Books, 2002.

Fukuyama, Francis, *Trust*, UK: Hamish Hamilton, 1995.

Gaddis, William, *Agape Agape*, US: Viking Penguin, 2002.

Gallwey, Timothy, *The Inner Game of Work*, UK: Orion Business, 2000.

Garaudy, Roger, *The Alternative Future*, UK: Penguin Books, 1976.

Gardner, Howard, *Leading Minds*, US: Basic Books, 1996.

Gatlin, Jonathan, *Bill Gates: The Path to the Future*, US: Perennial Currents, 1999.

Gelb, Michael J. and Buzan, Tony, *Lessons from the Art of Juggling*, UK: Aurum Press, 1995

Gendlin, Eugene T., *Focusing*, UK: Random House, 2003.

Gendlin, Eugene T., *A Process Model*, U.S. Northwestern University, 2018

Gendlin, Eugene T., *Focusing-Oriented Psychotherapy*, US, The Guildford Press, 1996

Gibran, Kahlil, *The Prophet*, UK: William Heinemann, 1991.

Girard, Rene, *Things Hidden from the Foundation of the World*, UK, Bloomsbury 2016

Glasser, William, *Reality Therapy*, US: Perennial Library, 1990.

Gleick, James, *Chaos*, UK: Penguin Books, 1988.

Glover, Jonathan, *Humanity*, UK: Jonathan Cape, 1990.

Goldratt, Eliyahu and Cox, Jeff, *The Goal*, UK: Gower Publishing, 1989.

Gordon, William J., *Synectics*, US: Macmillan, 1961.

Grayling, A.C., *The Meaning of Things*, UK: Weidenfeld and Nicholson, 2001.

Greenberg, Gary, *Manufacturing Depression*, UK: Bloomsbury Publishing, 2011.

Greenberg, Joanne, *I Never Promised You a Rose Garden*, US: Signet, 1989.

Greene, Graham, *Brighton Rock*, UK: Penguin Books, 1943.

Grey, Mary, *The Wisdom of Fools*, UK: Society for Promoting Christian Knowledge, 1993.

Guenon, Rene, *The Crisis of the Modern World*, Sophia Perennis, U.S. 2001

Haley, Jay, *Uncommon Therapy*, US: W.W. Norton & Company, 1986.

Hamel, Gary, *The Future of Management*, US: Harvard Business School Publishing, 2007.

Hamel, Gary, *Leading the Revolution*, US: Harvard Business School Press, 2000.

Handy, Charles *The Hungry Spirit*, UK: Random House, 1997.

Handy, Charles, *Beyond Certainty*, UK: Arrow Books Limited, 1988.

Harris, Thomas A., *I'm OK – You're OK*, UK: Jonathan

Harvey, Andrew & Bernstein, Seymour, *Play Life more Beautifully*, Hay House 2016

Haughton, Rosemary, *The Passionate God*, UK: Darton, Longman & Todd, 1981.

Hawkins, David R., *Power Vs Force*, US: Hay House, 2002.

Hederman, Mark Patrick, *Kissing the Dark*, Ireland: Veritas Publications, 1999.

Herrigel, Eugen, *Zen in the Art of Archery*, US: Vintage Books, 1971.

Hickel, Jason, *Less is More*, UK, Penguin Random House, 2020

Hickel, Jason, *The Divide*, UK, Penguin Random House, 2017

Houlahan, Jack, *A Ghost in Daylight*, Ireland: Veritas Publications, 2006.

Huston, Tracy, *Inside Out*, US: Society for Organizational Learning, 2007.

Huxley, Aldous, *Brave New World*, UK: Vintage Books, 2004.

Illich, Ivan, *Shadow Work*, UK: Marion Boyars, 1981.

Ionesco, Eugéne, *'Rhinoceros'*, *'The Chairs'* and *'The Lesson'*, UK: Penguin Books, 1962.

Jacobs, Jane, *Dark Age Ahead*, US: Vintage Books, 2005.

Jaworski, Joseph, *Synchronicity*, US: Berrett-Koehler, 1996.

Jenkinson, Stephen, *Reckoning*, Canada, Iron God of Mercy Ltd., 2022

Kabat-Zinn, Jon, *Full Catastrophe Living*, UK: Judy Piatkus, 1996.

Kafka, Franz, *Metamorphosis and Other Stories*, UK: Penguin Books, 1961.

Kafka, Franz, *The Trial*, UK: Penguin, 1935.

Kahane, Adam, *Power and Love*, US, Adam Morris Kahane, 2010

Katie, Byron, *Loving What Is*, UK: Random House, 2002.

Kay, John, *Obliquity*, UK: Profile Books, 2011.

Keen, Sam, *The Passionate Life*, US: Harper & Row, 1983.

Keirsey, David and Bates, Marilyn, *Please Understand Me*, US: Prometheus Nemesis Book Company, 1978.

Kelman, James, *How Late it Was, How Late*, UK: Vintage, 1998.

Kenneally, Christy, *Life after Loss*, Ireland: Mercier Press, 1999.

Kimmage, Paul, *A Rough Ride*, UK: Yellow Jersey Press, 2007.

Klein, Naomi, *No Logo*, UK: Harper Collins, 2001.

Kohn, Alfie, *No Contest*, US: Houghton Mifflin, 1980.

Koonz, Claudia, *The Nazi Conscience*, US: Harvard University Press, 2003.

Kriegel, Robert J., *If it Ain't Broke…Break It*, US: Warner Books, 1992.

Kubler-Ross, Elisabeth, *On Life after Death*, US: Celestial Arts, 1991.

Kundera, Milan, *The Unbearable Lightness of Being*, US: Harper & Row, 1984.

Kushner, Harold S., *When Bad Things Happen to Good People*, US: Avon Books, 1981.

Laborde, Genie Z., *Influencing with Integrity*, US: Syntony Publishing, 1987.

Laing, R.D., *The Divided Self*, UK: Penguin Books, 1960.

Lambe, Wally, *I Know This Much Is True*, US: Harper Collins, 1999.

Latour, Bruno, *Down to Earth*, UK, Polity Press, 2018

Latour, Bruno, *After Lockdown*, UK, Polity Press, 2021

Lawrence, D.H., *Women in Love*, UK: Penguin Books Ltd, 1995.

Le Carré, John, *Absolute Friends*, UK: Hodder & Stoughton, 2004.

Le Carré, John, *The Constant Gardener*, UK: Hodder & Stoughton, 2001.

Le Carré, John, *Tinker Tailor Soldier Spy*, UK: Hodder & Stoughton, 1974.

Lehrer, Jonah, *How We Decide*, US: Houghton Mifflin Harcourt, 2009.

Liedloff, Jean, *The Continuum Concept*, UK: Penguin Books, 1986.

Llosa, Mario Vargas, *Conversation in the Cathedral*, UK: Faber & Faber, 1993.

Llosa, Mario Vargas, *The Time of the Hero*, UK: Picador, 1986.

Llosa, Mario Vargas, *Aunt Julia and the Scriptwriter*, UK: Faber & Faber, 1983.

Lorenz, Konrad, On *Aggression*, UK: Methuen, 1996.

Lovett, Brendan, *A Dragon Not for the Killing*, Philippines: Claretian Publications, 1998.

Lovett, Brendan, *It's Not Over Yet*, Philippines: Claretian Publications, 1990.

Lovett, Brendan, *Life Before Death*, Philippines: Claretian Publications, 1986.

MacArthur, Ellen, *Taking on the World*, UK: Penguin Group, 2003.

McCabe, Eugene, *Heaven Lies about Us*, UK: Jonathan Cape, 2005.

McEwan, Ian, *Saturday*, UK: Jonathan Cape, 2005.

MacMillan, Margaret, *Paris 1919*, US: Random House, 2002.

Maher, Barry, *No Lie*, US: Barry Maher & Associates, 2006.

Morgan, Gareth, *Images of Organization*, UK: Sage Publications, 1986.

Marquez, Gabriel Garcia, *Love in the Time of Cholera*, UK: Penguin Books, 1988.

Marquez, Gabriel Garcia, *No One Writes to the Colonel*, UK: Jonathan Cape, 1979.

Marquez, Gabriel Garcia, *One Hundred Years of Solitude*, UK: Penguin Books, 1972.

Martel, Yann, *The Life of Pi*, UK: Canongate Books, 2002.

Martinez, Mario E., *The Man from Autumn*, US: Llumina Press, 2005.

Maturana, Humberto R. and Varela, Francisco J., *The Tree of Knowledge*, US: Shambhala Publications, 1987.

Mayer S., Bernard, *Beyond Neutrality*, US: Josey Bass, 2004.

Mengestu, Dinaw, *Children of the Revolution*, UK: Jonathan Cape, 2007.

Minstry, Rohinton, *A Fine Balance*, UK: Faber & Faber, 1996.

Moore, Sebastian, *God Is a New Language*, UK: Darton, Longman & Todd, 1967.

Moriarty, John, *Dreamtime*, Ireland: The Lilliput Press, 1994.

Mountain Dreamer, Oriah, *The Invitation*, US, Harper Collins, 1999

Mumford, Lewis, *Technics and Human Development*, U.S. Harvest HBJ, 1966

Murdoch, Iris, *The Sovereignty of Good*, US: Routledge Classics, 2007.

Murray, Charles, *Human Diversity*, Twelve, U.S.2020

Naisbitt, John, *High Tech High Touch*, UK: Nicholas Brealey, 2001.

Neisser, Ulric and Winograd, Eugene, *Remembering Reconsidered*, US: Cambridge University Press, 1995.

Nolan, Vincent, *The Innovator's Handbook*, UK: Sphere Books, 1987.

Nolan, Vincent, *Open to Change*, UK: Password Publications, 1984.

Nouwen, Henri J.M., *Reaching Out*, UK: William Collins Sons & Co., 1976.

Okri, Ben, *Astonishing the Gods*, UK: Phoenix House, 1995.

Owen, Harrison, *Leadership Is*, US: Abbott Publishing, 1990.

Palmer, Helen, *The Enneagram in Love and Work*, US: Harper Collins, 1995.

Parks, Rosa, *My Story*, US: Penguin Group, 1999.

Phillips, Adam, *Going Sane*, UK: Penguin Books, 2006.

Phillips, Nicola, *Reality Hacking*, UK: Capstone Publishing, 1997.

Pirsig, Robert M., *Zen and the Art of Motorcycle Maintenance*, UK: The Godley Head, 1974.

Powell, John, *Through Seasons of the Heart*, UK: Fount Paperbacks, 1986.

Pressfield, Steven, *The Legend of Bagger Vance*, UK: Bantam Books, 2001.

Prince, George, *The Practice of Creativity*, US: Macmillan Publishing, 1970.

Putnam, Robert D., *Bowling Alone*, US: Simon & Schuster, 2000.

Riso, Don Richard, *Personality Types*, UK: The Aquarian Press, 1987.

Robinson, Marilyn, *Home*, UK: Virago Press, 2008.

Rome I, David, *Your Body Knows the Answer*, US, Shambhala Publications, 2014

Rozier, Gilles, *Love Without Resistance*, UK: Little, Brown, 2005.

Runciman, David, *Political Hypocrisy*, US: Princeton University Press, 2008.

Saint-Exupéry, Antoine de, *The Little Prince*, UK: Pan Books, 1982.

Saint-Exupery, Antone de, Wind, *Sand and Stars*, UK: Pan Books, 1975.

Saul, John Ralston, *Voltaire's Bastards*, UK: The Free Press, 1992.

Schlink, Bernhard, *Homecomings*, UK: Weidenfeld & Nicholson, 2008.

Schlink, Bernhard, *The Reader*, UK: Phoenix House, 1997.

Schneider, Keith, 'Uranium Miners Inherit Dispute's Sad Legacy', New York Times, 9 January 1990.

Schumacher, Christian, *God in Work*, UK: Lion Publishing, 1998.

Senge, Peter, *Presence*, US: Random House, 2004.

Senge, Peter, *The Dance of Change*, UK: Nicholas Brealey, 1999.

Sereny, Gitta, *Into that Darkness*, UK: Pimlico, 1974.

Serrat, Joan Manuel, *En Transito*, Spain: Estudios Eurosonic de Madrid, 1981.

Shah, Idries, *Wisdom of the Idiots*, UK: The Octagon Press, 1969.

Shaw, Patricia, *Changing Conversations in Organizations*, US: Routledge, 2002.

Shirky, Clay, *Cognitive Surplus*, UK: Penguin Books, 2010.

Solnit, Rebecca, *A Field Guide to Getting Lost Canongate Books*, UK, 2017

Stacey, Ralph D., *The Chaos Frontier*, UK: Butterworth-Heinemann Limited, 1993.

Stacey, Ralph D., *Strategic Management and Organisational Dynamics*, UK: Pearson Education, 1993.

Stacey, Ralph D., *Managing Chaos*, UK: Kogan Page Limited, 1992.

Steinbeck, John, *The Pearl*, UK: William Heinemann, 1948.

Steiner, George, *Grammars of Creation*, UK: Faber & Faber, 2001.

Steiner, Rudolph, *The Philosophy of Freedom*, Bravo Ebooks, UK, 1916

Storr, Anthony, *Music and the Mind*, UK: Harper Collins Publishers, 1997.

Storr, Anthony, *The Integrity of the Personality*, US: Ballantine Books, 1960.

Szabo, Magda, *The Door*, UK: Vintage, 2005.

Taleb, Nassim Nicholas, *The Black Swan*, UK: Penguin Books, 2007.

Tannen, Deborah, *You Just Don't Understand*, US: Ballantine Books, 1991.

Thompson, D'Arcy, *On Growth and Form*, US: Cambridge University Press, 1961.

Thouless, Robert, *Straight and Crooked Thinking*, UK: Hodder & Stoughton Ltd, 1930.

Tillich, Paul, *The Courage to Be*, US, Yale University Press, 2014

Toffler, Alvin, *Future Shock*, UK: The Bodley Head, 1971.

Tolle, Eckhart, *A New Earth*, UK: Penguin Group, 2005.

Tzu, Sun, *The Art of War*, US: Shambhala Publications, 1988.

Varoufakis, Yanis, *Adults in The Room*, UK, Penguin Random House, 2017

Wall, William, *The Map of Tenderness*, UK: Hodder & Stoughton, 2002.

Watts, Alan, *The Two Hands of God*, U.S. New World Library, 1963

Watzlawick, Paul, *Ultra Solutions*, US: W.W. Norton & Company, 1988.

Watzlawick, Paul, *The Situation Is Hopeless But Not Serious*, Canada: Penguin Books, 1983.

Watzlawick, Paul, *Pragmatics of Human Communication*, Canada: Penguin Books, 1967.

Weiser Cornell, Ann, *Presence*, US, Calluna Press, 2015

Weiser Cornell, Ann, *The Power of Focusing*, US, New Harbinger Publications 1996

Wells, H.G., *The Country of the Blind*, UK: Penguin Group, 2005.

Wheatley, Margaret J., *Finding Our Way*, US: Berrett-Koehler, 2007.

Wheatley, Margaret, *A Simpler Way*, US: Berrett-Koehler, 1996.

Wheatley, Margaret, *Leadership and the New Science*, US: Berrett-Koehler, 1992.

Wheen, Francis, *How Mumbo Jumbo Conquered the World*, UK: Harper Perennial, 2004.

Whitmore, John, *Coaching for Performance*, UK: Nicholas Brealey Publishing, 1992.

Williamson, Marianne, *A Return to Love: Reflections on the Principles of a 'Course in Miracles'*, US: Harper Collins, 1992.

Zander, Rosamund Stone and Zander, Benjamin, *The Art of Possibility: Transforming Professional and Personal Life*, US: Harward Business School Press, 2000.

Zizek, Slaoj, *Violence*, UK: Profile Books, 2008.

About the Author

Brian Smyth is a founding Partner and member of Maybe International, a dynamic organisation dedicated to helping individuals and organisations realise more of their possibilities.

Prior to Maybe International, Brian worked for 20 years with one of the world's leading international creativity consultancy companies, Synectics Corporation. Brian was tasked with designing management systems, programmes and tools in areas such as coaching, product development, culture change, performance management, and, of course, leadership. Some of the largest organisations in the world - Coca Cola, Unilever, Mars, BMW, BP Oil, Kraft, CRH, AIB, Codelco (in Chile) — benefited from systems, programmes and tools designed and led by Brian.

In addition to Synectics Brian's professional experience includes a stint as Managing Director of a General Motors plant in Dublin for five years and NASA in South America during a period of political turmoil (he witnessed the coup that overthrew the socialist government of Salvador Allende while at NASA).

Outside of work he has a strong interest in sport and has excelled in a variety of mentoring roles with many successful individuals and teams across a range of sports in Ireland and globally. He enjoys reading, gardening, 'golf', nature and, as he says, "the adventure of every day". He is passionate about the need and possibility for people in organisations and in general to be helped and encouraged to live meaningful and joyful lives. To this end he developed and supports a large suite of on-line leadership programmes to help managers move to a whole new paradigm of managing and leading. He is the author of two other books: *Managing to be Human* and *Your Beautiful Life: A Gift*.

He lives in County Meath in Ireland

Dear Readers,

Thank you for joining me on a journey through *The Courage to Be True: A story of one manager's journey to find a meaningful life*. I would love to hear about your thoughts and experiences, ideas and recollections, that were stimulated while you read. Why not leave a review on where you purchased the book, so other readers can consider your views, thoughts and impressions on Mike and his story.

Is what Mike did and achieved realistic and feasible? I have consistently said that all that is said is true and realistic. But the best and only way to find out is to try it. To help you do just that you will find a whole suite of online courses available at maybe.ie (QR code below) to help you deal with all the challenges and steps you will encounter on your journey.

Feel free to email me directly, through the address below. I am always happy to provide information to and answer questions from people interested in what I do.

Live a true and meaningful life,
Brian Smyth

Email: brian@maybe.ie

Teams and Teamworking Course

Collaborative versus Competitive Culture Course

Facilitative Leadership Course

Printed in Great Britain
by Amazon

22795870R00278